Y0-BRK-428

WITHDRAWN

FANCIES VERSUS FADS

BY

G. K. CHESTERTON

in Essay and General Literature Index

249750

ST. PAUL
PUBLIC LIBRARY

NEW YORK
DODD, MEAD AND COMPANY
1923

PR
929
C 52F

Copyright, 1923,
By DODD, MEAD AND COMPANY, Inc.

ST. PAUL
PUBLIC LIBRARY

PRINTED IN THE U. S. A. BY
The Quinn & Boden Company
BOOK MANUFACTURERS
RAHWAY   NEW JERSEY

INTRODUCTION

I HAVE strung these things together on a slight enough thread; but as the things themselves are slight, it is possible that the thread (and the metaphor) may manage to hang together. These notes range over very variegated topics and in many cases were made at very different times. They concern all sorts of things from lady barristers to cave-men, and from psycho-analysis to free verse. Yet they have this amount of unity in their wandering, that they all imply that it is only a more traditional spirit that is truly able to wander. The wild theorists of our time are quite unable to wander. When they talk of making new roads, they are only making new ruts. Each of them is necessarily imprisoned in his own curious cosmos; in other words, he is limited by the very largeness of his own generalization. The explanations of the Marxian must not go outside economics; and the student of Freud is forbidden to forget sex. To see only the fanciful side of these serious sects may seem a very frivolous pleasure—and I will not dispute that these are very frivolous criticisms. I only submit that this frivolity is the last lingering form of freedom.

INTRODUCTION

In short the note of these notes, so to speak, is that it is only from a normal standpoint that all the nonsense of the world takes on something of the wild interest of wonderland. I mean it is only in the mirror of a very moderate sense and sanity, which is all I have ever claimed to possess, that even insanities can appear as images clear enough to appeal to the imagination. After all, the ordinary orthodox person is he to whom the heresies can appear as fantasies. After all, it is we ordinary human and humdrum people who can enjoy eccentricity as a sort of elfland; while the eccentrics are too serious even to know that they are elves. When a man tells us that he disapproves of children being told fairy-tales, it is we who can perceive that he is himself a fairy. He himself has not the least idea of it. When he says he would discourage children from playing with tin soldiers, because it is militarism, it is we and not he who can enjoy in fancy the fantastic possibilities of his idea. It is we who suddenly think of children playing with little tin figures of philanthropists, rather round and with tin top-hats; the little tin gods of our commercial religion. It is we who develop his imaginative idea for him, by suggesting little leaden dolls of Conscientious Objectors in fixed attitudes of refined repugnance; or a whole regiment of tiny Quakers with little grey coats and white flags. He would never have thought of any of these substitutes for himself; his negation is purely negative. Or when an educational philosopher tells us that the child should have complete equality with the adult, he cannot really carry his idea any farther without our assistance. It will be from us and not from him that the natural suggestion will come; that the baby should take its turn and carry the mother, the moment the mother is tired of carrying the baby. He will not, when left to himself, call up the poetical picture of the child wheeling a double perambulator with the father and mother at each end. He has no motive to look for lively logical developments; for him the assimilation of parent and child is simply a platitude; and an inevitable part of his own rather platitudinous philosophy. It is we and not he who can behold the whole vista and vanishing perspective of his own opinions; and work out what he really means. It is only those who have ordinary views who have extraordinary visions.

There is indeed nothing very extraordinary about these visions, except the extraordinary people who have provoked some of them. They are only very sketchy sort of sketches of some of the strange things that may be found in the modern world. But however inadequate be the example, it is none the less true that this is the sound principle behind much better examples; and that, in those great things as in these small ones, sanity was the condition of satire. It is because Gulliver is a man of moderate stature that he can stray into the land of the giants and the land of the pygmies. It is Swift and not the professors of Laputa who sees the real romance of getting sunbeams out of cucumbers. It would be less than exact to call Swift a sunbeam in the house; but if he did not himself get much sunshine out of cucumbers, at least he let daylight into professors. It was not the mad Swift but the sane Swift who made that story so wild. The truth is more self-evident in men who were more sane. It is the good sense of Rabelais that makes him seem to grin like a gargoyle; and it is in a sense because Dickens was a Philistine that he saw the land so full of strange gods. These idle journalistic jottings have nothing in common with such standards of real literature, except the principle involved; but the principle is the right one.

But while these are frivolous essays, pretending only to touch on topics and theories they cannot exhaustively examine, I have added some that may not seem to fit so easily even into so slight a scheme. Nevertheless, they are in some sense connected with it. I have opened with an essay on rhyme, because it is a type of the sort of tradition which the anti-traditionalists now attack; and I have ended with one called " Milton and Merry England," because

INTRODUCTION

I feel that many may misunderstand my case against the new Puritans, if they have no notion of how I should attempt to meet the more accepted case in favour of the old Puritans. Both these articles appeared originally in the " London Mercury," and I desire to express my thanks to Mr. J. C. Squire for his kind permission to reprint them. But, in the latter case, I had the further feeling that I wished to express somewhere the historical sentiment that underlies the whole; the conviction that there did and does exist a more normal and national England, which we once inhabited and to which we may yet return; and which is not a Utopia but a home. I have therefore thought it worth while to write this line of introduction to show that such a scrap-book is not entirely scrappy; and that even to touch such things lightly we need something like a test. It is necessary to have in hand a truth to judge modern philosophies rapidly; and it is necessary to judge them very rapidly to judge them before they disappear.

CONTENTS

xi

CONTENTS

FANCIES VERSUS FADS

FANCIES VERSUS FADS

THE ROMANCE OF RHYME

THE poet in the comic opera, it will be remembered
(I hope), claimed for his æsthetic authority that
"Hey diddle diddle will rank as an idyll, if I pronounce it chaste." In face of a satire which still
survives the fashion it satirized, it may require some
moral courage seriously to pronounce it chaste, or
to suggest that the nursery rhyme in question has
really some of the qualities of an idyll. Of its
chastity, in the vulgar sense, there need be little
dispute, despite the scandal of the elopement of
the dish with the spoon, which would seem as free
from grossness as the loves of the triangles. And
though the incident of the cow may have something
of the moonstruck ecstasy of Endymion, that also
has a silvery coldness about it worthy of the wilder
aspects of Diana. The truth more seriously tenable
is that this nursery rhyme is a complete and compact
model of the nursery short story. The cow jumping over the moon fulfils to perfection the two es-

sentials of such a story for children. It makes an effect that is fantastic out of objects that are familiar; and it makes a picture that is at once incredible and unmistakable. But it is yet more tenable, and here more to the point, that this nursery rhyme is emphatically a rhyme. Both the lilt and the jingle are just right for their purpose, and are worth whole libraries of elaborate literary verse for children. And the best proof of its vitality is that the satirist himself has unconsciously echoed the jingle even in making the joke. The metre of that nineteenth-century satire is the metre of the nursery rhyme. "Hey diddle diddle, the cat and the fiddle" and "Hey diddle diddle will rank as an idyll" are obviously both dancing to the same ancient tune; and that by no means the tune the old cow died of, but the more exhilarating air to which she jumped over the moon.

The whole history of the thing called rhyme can be found between those two things: the simple pleasure of rhyming "diddle" to "fiddle," and the more sophisticated pleasure of rhyming "diddle" to "idyll." Now the fatal mistake about poetry, and more than half of the fatal mistake about humanity, consists in forgetting that we should have the first kind of pleasure as well as the second. It might be said that we should have the first pleasure as the basis of the second; or yet more truly, the first pleasure inside the second. The fatal metaphor of progress, which means leaving things behind us, has utterly obscured the real idea of growth, which means leaving things inside us. The heart of the tree remains the same, however many rings are added to it; and a man cannot leave his heart behind by running hard with his legs. In the core of all culture are the things that may be said, in every sense, to be learned by heart. In the innermost part of all poetry is the nursery rhyme, the nonsense that is too happy even to care about being nonsensical. It may lead on to the more elaborate nonsense of the Gilbertian line, or even the far less poetic nonsense of some of the Browningesque rhymes. But the true enjoyment of poetry is always in having the simple pleasure as well as the subtle pleasure. Indeed it is on this primary point that so many of our artistic and other reforms seem to go wrong. What is the matter with the modern world is that it is trying to get simplicity in everything except the soul. Where the soul really has simplicity is can be grateful for anything—even complexity. Many peasants have to be vegetarians, and their ordinary life is really a simple life. But the peasants do not despise a good dinner when they can get it; they wolf it down with enthusiasm, because they have not only the simple life but the simple spirit. And it is so with the modern modes of art which revert, very rightly, to what is " primitive."

But their moral mistake is that they try to combine the ruggedness that should belong to simplicity with a superciliousness that should only belong to satiety. The last Futurist draughtsmanship, for instance, evidently has the aim of drawing a tree as it might be drawn by a child of ten. I think the new artists would admit it; nor do I merely sneer at it. I am willing to admit, especially for the sake of argument, that there is a truth of philosophy and psychology in this attempt to attain the clarity even through the crudity of childhood. In this sense I can see what a man is driving at when he draws a tree merely as a stick with smaller sticks standing out of it. He may be trying to trace in black and white or grey a primeval and almost pre-natal illumination; that it is very remarkable that a stick should exist, and still more remarkable that a stick should stick up or stick out. He may be similarly enchanted with his own stick of charcoal or grey chalk; he may be enraptured, as a child is, with the mere fact that it makes a mark on the paper—a highly poetic fact in itself. But the child does not despise the real tree for being different from his drawing of the tree. He does not despise Uncle Humphrey because that talented amateur can really draw a tree. He does not think less of the real sticks because they are live sticks, and can grow and branch and curve in a way uncommon in walking sticks. Because he has a single eye he can enjoy a double pleasure. This distinction, which seems strangely neglected, may be traced again in the drama and most other domains of art. Reformers insist that the audiences of simpler ages were content with bare boards or rudimentary scenery if they could hear Sophocles or Shakespeare talking a language of the gods. They were very properly contented with plain boards. But they were not discontented with pageants. The people who appreciated Antony's oration as such would have appreciated Alladin's palace as such. They did not think gilding and spangles substitutes for poetry and philosophy, because they are not. But they did think gilding and spangles great and admirable gifts of God, because they are.

But the application of this distinction here is to the case of rhyme in poetry. And the application of it is that we should never be ashamed of enjoying a thing as a rhyme as well as enjoying it as a poem. And I think the modern poets who try to escape from the rhyming pleasure, in pursuit of a freer poetical pleasure, are making the same fundamentally fallacious attempt to combine simplicity with superiority. Such a poet is like a child who could take no pleasure in a tree because it looked like a tree, or a playgoer who could take no pleasure in the Forest of Arden because it looked like a forest. It is not impossible to find a sort of prig who professes that he could listen to literature in any scenery, but strongly objects to good scenery. And in poetical criticism and creation there has also appeared the prig who insists that any new poem must avoid the sort of melody that makes the beauty of any old song. Poets must put away childish things, including the child's pleasure in the mere sing-song of irrational rhyme. It may be hinted that when poets put away childish things they will put away poetry. But it may be well to say a word in further justification of rhyme as well as poetry, in the child as well as the poet. Now, the neglect of this nursery instinct would be a blunder, even if it were merely an animal instinct or an automatic instinct. If a rhyme were to a man merely what a bark is to a dog, or a crow to a cock, it would be clear that such natural things cannot be merely neglected. It is clear that a canine epic, about Argus instead of Ulysses, would have a beat ultimately consisting of barks. It is clear that a long poem like " Chantecler," written by a real cock, would be to the tune of Cock-a-doodle-doo. But in truth the nursery rhyme has a nobler origin; if it be ancestral it is not animal; its principle is a primary one, not only in the body but in the soul.

Milton prefaced " Paradise Lost " with a ponderous condemnation of rhyme. And perhaps the finest and even the most familiar line in the whole of " Paradise Lost " is really a glorification of rhyme.

6

THE ROMANCE OF RHYME

" Seasons return, but not to me return," is not only an echo that has all the ring of rhyme in its form, but it happens to contain nearly all the philosophy of rhyme in its spirit. The wonderful word " return " has, not only in its sound but in its sense, a hint of the whole secret of song. It is not merely that its very form is a fine example of a certain quality in English, somewhat similar to that which Mrs. Meynell admirably analysed in a former issue of this magazine in the case of words like " unforgiven." It is that it describes poetry itself, not only in a mechanical but a moral sense. Song is not only a recurrence, it is a return. It does not merely, like the child in the nursery, take pleasure in seeing the wheels go round. It also wishes to go back as well as round; to go back to the nursery where such pleasures are found. Or to vary the metaphor slightly, it does not merely rejoice in the rotation of a wheel on the road, as if it were a fixed wheel in the air. It is not only the wheel but the wagon that is returning. That labouring caravan is always travelling towards some camping-ground that it has lost and cannot find again. No lover of poetry needs to be told that all poems are full of that noise of returning wheels; and none more than the poems of Milton himself. The whole truth is obvious, not merely in the poem, but even in the two words of the title. All poems might be bound in one book under the title of " Paradise Lost." And the only object of writing " Paradise Lost " is to turn it, if only by a magic and momentary illusion, into " Paradise Regained."

It is in this deeper significance of return that we must seek for the peculiar power in the recurrence we call rhyme. It would be easy enough to reply to Milton's strictures on rhyme in the spirit of a sensible if superficial liberality by saying that it takes all sorts to make a world, and especially the world of the poets. It is evident enough that Milton might have been right to dispense with rhyme without being right to despise it. It is obvious that the peculiar dignity of his religious epic would have been weakened if it had been a rhymed epic, beginning :—

> Of man's first disobedience and the fruit
> Of that forbidden tree whose mortal root.

But it is equally obvious that Milton himself would not have tripped on the light fantastic toe with quite so much charm and cheerfulness in the lines :—

> But come thou Goddess fair and free
> In heaven yclept Euphrosyne

if the goddess had been yclept something else, as, for the sake of argument, Syrinx. Milton in his

more reasonable moods would have allowed rhyme in
theory a place in all poetry, as he allowed it in
practice in his own poetry. But he would certainly
have said at this time, and possibly at all times,
that he allowed it an inferior place, or at least a
secondary place. But is its place secondary; and
is it in any sense inferior?

The romance of rhyme does not consist merely
in the pleasure of a jingle, though this is a pleasure
of which no man should be ashamed. Certainly
most men take pleasure in it, whether or not they
are ashamed of it. We see it in the older fashion
of prolonging the chorus of a song with syllables
like " rumty tumty " or " tooral looral." We see
it in the similiar but later fashion of discussing
whether a truth is objective or subjective, or whether
a reform is constructive or destructive, or whether
an argument is deductive or inductive: all bearing
witness to a very natural love for those nursery
rhyme recurrences which make a sort of song without
words, or at least without any kind of intellectual
significance. But something much deeper is involved
in the love of rhyme as distinct from other poetic
forms, something which is perhaps too deep and
subtle to be described. The nearest approximation
to the truth I can think of is something like this: that
while all forms of genuine verse recur, there is in
rhyme a sense of return to exactly the same place.

All modes of song go forward and backward like the tides of the sea; but in the great sea of Homeric or Virgilian hexametres, the sea that carried the labouring ships of Ulysses and Œneas, the thunder of the breakers is rhythmic, but the margin of the foam is necessarily irregular and vague. In rhyme there is rather a sense of water poured safely into one familiar well, or (to use a nobler metaphor) of ale poured safely into one familiar flagon. The armies of Homer and Virgil advance and retreat over a vast country, and suggest vast and very profound sentiments about it, about whether it is their own country or only a strange country. But when the old nameless ballad boldly rhymes " the bonny ivy tree " to " my ain countree " the vision at once dwindles and sharpens to a very vivid image of a single soldier passing under the ivy that darkens his own door. Rhythm deals with similarity, but rhyme with identity. Now in the one word identity are involved perhaps the deepest and certainly the dearest human things. He who is homesick does not desire houses or even homes. He who is lovesick does not want to see all the women with whom he might have fallen in love. Only he who is sea-sick, perhaps, may be said to have a cosmopolitan craving for all lands or any kind of land. And this is probably why seasickness, like cosmopolitanism, has never yet been a high inspiration to song. Songs, especially the most poignant of them, generally refer to some absolute, to some positive place or person for whom no similarity is a substitute. In such a case all approximation is merely asymptotic. The prodigal returns to his father's house and not the house next door, unless he is still an imperfectly sober prodigal; the lover desires his lady and not her twin sister, except in old complications of romance; and even the spiritualist is generally looking for a ghost and not merely for ghosts. I think the intolerable torture of spiritualism must be a doubt about identity. Anyhow, it will generally be found that where this call for the identical has been uttered most ringingly and unmistakably in literature, it has been uttered in rhyme. Another purpose for which this pointed and definite form is very much fitted is the expression of dogma, as distinct from doubt or even opinion. This is why, with all allowance for a decline in the most classical effects of the classical tongue, the rhymed Latin of the mediæval hymns does express what it had to express in a very poignant poetical manner, as compared with the reverent agnosticism so nobly uttered in the rolling unrhymed metres of the ancients. For even if we regard the matter of the mediæval verses as a dream, it was at least a vivid dream, a dream full of faces, a dream of love and of lost things. And something of the same spirit runs in a vaguer way through proverbs and phrases

11

that are not exactly religious, but rather in a rude sense philosophical, but which all move with the burden of returning; things to be felt only in familiar fragments . . . *on revient toujours* . . . it's the old story—it's love that makes the world go round; and all roads lead to Rome: we might almost say that all roads lead to Rhyme.

Milton's revolt against rhyme must be read in the light of history. Milton is the Renascence frozen into a Puritan form; the beginning of a period which was in a sense classic, but was in a still more definite sense aristocratic. There the Classicist was the artistic aristocrat because the Calvinist was the spiritual aristocrat. The seventeenth century was intensely individualistic; it had both in the noble and the ignoble sense a respect for persons. It had no respect whatever for popular traditions; and it was in the midst of its purely logical and legal excitement that most of the popular traditions died. The Parliament appeared and the people disappeared. The arts were put under patrons, where they had once been under patron saints. The schools and colleges at once strengthened and narrowed the New Learning, making it something rather peculiar to one country and one class. A few men talked a great deal of good Latin, where all men had once talked a little bad Latin. But they talked even the good Latin so that no Latinist in the world could understand them. They confined all study of the classics to that of the most classical period, and grossly exaggerated the barbarity and barrenness of patriotic Greek or mediæval Latin. It is as if a man said that because the English translation of the Bible is perhaps the best English in the world, therefore Addison and Pater and Newman are not worth reading. We can imagine what men in such a mood would have said of the rude rhymed hexametres of the monks; and it is not unnatural that they should have felt a reaction against rhyme itself. For the history of rhyme is the history of something else, very vast and sometimes invisible, certainly somewhat indefinable, against which they were in aristocratic rebellion.

That thing is difficult to define in impartial modern terms. It might well be called Romance, and that even in a more technical sense, since it corresponds to the rise of the Romance languages as distinct from the Roman language. It might more truly be called Religion, for historically it was the gradual re-emergence of Europe through the Dark Ages, because it still had one religion, though no longer one rule. It was, in short, the creation of Christendom. It may be called Legend, for it is true that the most overpowering presence in it is that of omnipresent and powerful popular Legend; so that things that may never have happened, or, as some say,

could never have happened, are nevertheless rooted
in our racial memory like things that have happened
to ourselves. The whole Arthurian Cycle, for instance, seems something more real than reality. If
the faces in that darkness of the Dark Ages, Lancelot
and Arthur and Merlin and Modred, are indeed faces
in a dream, they are like faces in a real dream: a
dream in a bed and not a dream in a book. Sub-
consciously at least, I should be much less surprised
if Arthur was to come again than I should be if the
Superman were to come at all. Again, the thing
might be called Gossip: a noble name, having in
it the name of God and one of the most generous
and genial of the relations of men. For I suppose
there has seldom been a time when such a mass of
culture and good traditions of craft and song have
been handed down orally, by one universal buzz of
conversation, through centuries of ignorance down
to centuries of greater knowledge. Education must
have been an eternal *viva voce* examination; but
the men passed their examination. At least they
went out in such rude sense masters of art as to
create the Song of Roland and the round Roman
arches that carry the weight of so many Gothic
towers. Finally, of course, it can be called ignorance,
barbarism, black superstition, a reaction towards
obscurantism and old night; and such a vie is
eminently complete and satisfactory, only that it

leaves behind it a sort of weak wonder as to why the very youngest poets do still go on writing poems about the sword of Arthur and the horn of Roland.

All this was but the beginning of a process which has two great points of interest. The first is the way in which the mediæval movement did rebuild the old Roman civilization; the other was the way in which it did not. A strange interest attaches to the things which had never existed in the pagan culture and did appear in the Christian culture. I think it is true of most of them that they had a quality that can very approximately be described as popular, or perhaps as vulgar, as indeed we still talk of the languages which at that time liberated themselves from Latin as the vulgar tongues. And to many Classicists these things would appear to be vulgar in a more vulgar sense. They were vulgar in the sense of being vivid almost to excess, of making a very direct and unsophisticated appeal to the emotions. The first law of heraldry was to wear the heart upon the sleeve. Such mediævalism was the reverse of mere mysticism, in the sense of mere mystery; it might more truly be described as sensationalism. One of these things, for instance, was a hot and even an impatient love of colour. It learned to paint before it could draw, and could afford the twopence coloured long before it could manage the penny plain. It culminated at last, of course, in the energy and gaiety of the Gothic; but even the richness of Gothic rested on a certain psychological simplicity. We can contrast it with the classic by noting its popular passion for telling a story in stone. We may admit that a Doric portico is a poem, but no one would describe it as an anecdote. The time was to come when much of the imagery of the cathedrals was to be lost; but it would have mattered the less that it was defaced by its enemies if it had not been already neglected by its friends. It would have mattered less if the whole tide of taste among the rich had not turned against the old popular masterpieces. The Puritans defaced them, but the Cavaliers did not truly defend them. The Cavaliers were also aristocrats of the new classical culture, and used the word Gothic in the sense of barbaric. For the benefit of the Teutonists we may note in parenthesis that, if this phrase meant that Gothic was despised, it also meant that the Goths were despised. But when the Cavaliers came back, after the Puritan interregnum, they restored not in the style of Pugin but in the style of Wren. The very thing we call the Restoration, which was the restoration of King Charles, was also the restoration of St. Paul's. And it was a very modern restoration.

So far we might say that simple people do not like simple things. This is certainly true if we compare the classic with these highly coloured things of mediævalism, or all the vivid visions which first began to glow in the night of the Dark Ages. Now one of these things was the romantic expedient called rhyme. And even in this, if we compare the two, we shall see something of the same paradox by which the simple like complexities and the complex like simplicities. The ignorant like rich carvings and melodious and often ingenious rhymes. The learned like bare walls and blank verse. But in the case of rhyme it is peculiarly difficult to define the double and yet very definite truth. It is difficult to define the sense in which rhyme is artificial and the sense in which it is simple. In truth it is simple because it is artificial. It is an artifice of the kind enjoyed by children and other poetic people; it is a toy. As a technical accomplishment it stands at the same distance from the popular experience as the old popular sports. Like swimming, like dancing, like drawing the bow, anybody can do it, but nobody can do it without taking the trouble to do it; and only a few can do it very well. In a hundred ways it was akin to that simple and even humble energy that made all the lost glory of the guilds. Thus their rhyme was useful as well as ornamental. It was not merely a melody but also a mnemonic; just as their towers were not merely trophies but beacons and belfries. In another aspect rhyme is akin to rhetoric, but of a very positive and emphatic sort: the coincidence of sound giving the effect of saying, "It is certainly so." Shakespeare realized this when he rounded off a fierce or romantic scene with a rhymed couplet. I know that some critics do not like this, but I think there is a moment when a drama ought to become a melodrama. Then there is a much older effect of rhyme that can only be called mystical, which may seem the very opposite of the utilitarian, and almost equally remote from the rhetorical. Yet it shares with the former the tough texture of something not easily forgotten, and with the latter the touch of authority which is the aim of all oratory. The thing I mean may be found in the fact that so many of the old proverbial prophecies, from Merlin to Mother Shipton, were handed down in rhyme. It can be found in the very name of Thomas the Rhymer.

But the simplest way of putting this popular quality is in a single word: it is a song. Rhyme corresponds to a melody so simple that it goes straight like an arrow to the heart. It corresponds to a chorus so familiar and obvious that all men can join in it. I am not disturbed by the suggestion that such an arrow of song, when it hits the heart, may entirely miss the head. I am not concerned to deny that the chorus may sometimes be a drunken chorus, in which men have lost their heads to find their tongues. I am not defending but defining; I am trying to find words for a large but elusive distinction between certain things that are certainly poetry and certain other things which are also song. Of course it is only an accident that Horace opens his greatest series of odes by saying that he detests the profane populace and wishes to drive them from his temple of poetry. But it is the sort of accident that is almost an allegory. There is even a sense in which it has a practical side. When all is said, *could* a whole crowd of men sing the " Descende Cœlo," that noble ode, as a crowd can certainly sing the " Dies Irae," or for that matter " Down among the Dead Men "? Did Horace himself sing the Horatian odes in the sense in which Shakespeare could sing, or could hardly help singing, the Shakespearean songs. I do not know, having no kind of scholarship on these points. But I do not feel that it could have been at all the same thing; and my only purpose is to attempt a rude description of that thing. Rhyme is consonant to the particular kind of song that can be a popular song, whether pathetic or passionate or comic; and Milton is entitled to his true distinction; nobody is likely to sing " Paradise Lost " as if it were a song of that kind. I have tried to suggest my sympathy with rhyme, in terms true enough to be accepted by the other side as expressing their antipathy for it. I have admitted that rhyme is a toy and even a trick, of the sort that delights children. I have admitted that every rhyme is a nursery rhyme. What I will never admit is that anyone who is too big for the nursery is big enough for the Kingdom of God, though the God were only Apollo.

A good critic should be like God in the great saying of a Scottish mystic. George Macdonald said that God was easy to please and hard to satisfy. That paradox is the poise of all good artistic appreciation. Without the first part of the paradox appreciation perishes, because it loses the power to appreciate. Good criticism, I repeat, combines the subtle pleasure in a thing being done well with the simple pleasure in it being done at all. It combines the pleasure of the scientific engineer in seeing how the wheels work together to a logical end with the pleasure of the baby in seeing the wheels go round. It combines the pleasure of the artistic draughtsman in the fact that his lines of charcoal, light and apparently loose, fall exactly right and in a perfect relation with the pleasure of the child in the fact that the charcoal makes marks of any kind on the paper. And in the same fashion it combines the critic's pleasure in a poem with the child's pleasure in a rhyme. The historical point about this kind of poetry, the rhymed romantic kind, is that it rose out of the Dark Ages with the whole of this huge popular power behind it, the human love of a song, a riddle, a proverb, a pun or a nursery rhyme; the sing-song of innumerable children's games, the chorus of a thousand campfires and a thousand taverns. When poetry loses its link with all these people who are easily pleased it loses all its power of giving pleasure. When a poet looks down on a rhyme it is, I will not say as if he looked down on a daisy (which might seem possible to the more literal-minded), but rather as if he looked down on a lark because he had been up in a balloon. It is cutting away the very roots of poetry; it is revolting against nature because it is natural, against sunshine because it is bright, or mountains because they are high, or moonrise because it is mysterious. The freezing process began after the Reformation with a fastidious search for finer yet freer forms; to-day it has ended in formlessness.

But the joke of it is that even when it is formless it is still fastidious. The new anarchic artists are not ready to accept everything. They are not ready to accept anything except anarchy. Unless it observes the very latest conventions of unconventionality, they would rule out anything classic as coldly as any classic ever ruled out anything romantic. But the classic was a form; and there was even a time when it was a new form. The men who invented Sapphics did invent a new metre; the introduction of Elizabethan blank verse was a real revolution in literary form. But *vers libre*, or nine-tenths of it, is not a new metre any more than sleeping in a ditch is a new school of architecture. It is no more a revolution in literary form than eating meat raw is an innovation in cookery. It is not even original, because it is not creative; the artist does not invent anything, but only abolishes something. But the only point about it that is to my present purpose is expressed in the word " pride." It is not merely proud in the sense of being exultant, but proud in the sense of being disdainful. Such outlaws are more exclusive than aristocrats; and their anarchial arrogance goes far beyond the pride of Milton and the aristocrats of the New Learning. And this final refinement has completed the work which the saner aristocrats began, the work now most evident in the world: the separation of art from the people. I need not insist on the sensational and self-evident character of that separation. I need not recommend the modern poet to attempt to sing his *vers libres* in a public house. I need not even urge the young Imagist to read out a number of his disconnected Images to a public meeting. The thing is not only admitted but admired. The old artist remained proud in spite of his unpopularity; the new artist is proud because of his unpopularity; perhaps it is his chief ground for pride.

Dwelling as I do in the Dark Ages, or at latest along the mediæval fairy-tales, I am yet moved to remember something I once read in a modern fairy-tale. As it happens, I have already used the name of George Macdonald; and in the best of his books there is a description of how a young miner in the mountains could always drive away the subterranean goblins if he could remember and repeat any kind of rhyme. The impromptu rhymes were often doggerel, as was the dog-Latin of many monkish hexametres or the burden of many rude Border ballads. But I have a notion that they drove away the devils, blue devils of pessimism and black devils of pride. Anyhow Madame Montessori, who has apparently been deploring the educational effects of fairy-tales, would probably see in me a pitiable example of such early perversion, for that image which was one of my first impressions seems likely enough to be one of my last; and when the noise of many new and original musical instruments, with strange shapes and still stranger noises, has passed away like a procession, I shall hear in the succeeding silence only a rustle and scramble among the rocks and a boy singing on the mountain.

HAMLET AND THE PSYCHO-ANALYST

THIS morning, for a long stretch of hours before breakfast, and even as it were merging into breakfast, and almost overlapping breakfast, I was engaged in scientific researches in the great new department of psycho-analysis. Every journalist knows by this time that psycho-analysis largely depends on the study of dreams. But in order to study our dreams it is necessary to dream; and in order to dream it is necessary to sleep. So, while others threw away the golden hours in lighter and less learned occupations, while ignorant and superstitious peasants were already digging in their ignorant and superstitious kitchen-gardens, to produce their ignorant and superstitious beans and potatoes, while priests were performing their pious mummeries and poets composing lyrics on listening to the skylark—I myself was pioneering hundreds of years ahead of this benighted century; ruthlessly and progressively probing into all the various horrible nightmares, from which a happier future will take its oracles and its commandments. I will not describe my dreams in detail; I am not quite so ruthless a psychologist as all that. And

24

indeed it strikes me as possible that the new psychologist will be rather a bore at breakfast. My dream was something about wandering in some sort of catacombs under the Albert Hall, and it involved eating jumbles (a brown flexible cake now almost gone from us, like so many glories of England) and also arguing with a Theosophist. I cannot fit this in very well with Freud and his theory of suppressed impulses. For I swear I never in my life suppressed the impulse to eat a jumble or to argue with a Theosophist. And as for wandering about in the Albert Hall, nobody could ever have had an impulse to do that.

When I came down to breakfast I looked at the morning paper; not (as you humorously suggest) at the evening paper. I had not pursued my scientific studies quite so earnestly as that. I looked at the morning paper, as I say, and found it contained a good deal about Psycho-Analysis, indeed it explained almost everything about Psycho-Analysis except what it was. This was naturally a thing which newspapers would present in a rather fragmentary fashion; and I fitted the fragments together as best I could. Apparently the dreams were merely symbols; and apparently symbols of something very savage and horrible which remained a secret. This seems to me a highly unscientific use of the word symbol. A symbol is not a disguise but rather a display; the best expression of something that cannot otherwise be expressed. Eating a jumble may mean that I wished to bite off my father's nose (the mother-complex being strong on me); but it does not seem to show much symbolic talent. The Albert Hall may imply the murder of an uncle; but it hardly makes itself very clear. And we do not seem to be getting much nearer the truth by dreaming, if we hide things by night more completely than we repress them by day. Anyhow, the murdered uncle reminds me of Hamlet, of whom more anon; at the moment I am merely remarking that my newspaper was a little vague; and I was all the more relieved to open my "London Mercury" and find an article on the subject by so able and suggestive a writer as Mr. J. D. Beresford.

Mr. J. D. Beresford practically asked himself whether he should become a psycho-analyst or continue to be a novelist. It will readily be understood that he did not put it precisely in these words; he would probably put psycho-analysis higher, and very possibly his own fiction lower; for men of genius are often innocent enough of their own genuine originality. That is a form of the unconscious mind with which none of us will quarrel. But I have no desire to watch a man of genius tying himself in knots, and perhaps dying in agony, in the attempt to be conscious of his own unconsciousness.

I have seen too many unfortunate sceptics thus committing suicide by self-contradiction. Haeckel and his Determinists, in my youth, bullied us all about the urgent necessity of choosing a philosophy which would prove the impossibility of choosing anything. No doubt the new psychology will somehow enable us to know what we are doing, about all that we do without knowing it. These things come and go, and pass through their phases in order, from the time when they are as experimental as Freudism to the time when they are as exploded as Darwinism. But I never can understand men allowing things so visibly fugitive to hide things that are visibly permanent, like morals and religion and (what is in question here) the art of letters. *Ars longa, scientia brevis.*

Anyhow, as has been said, psycho-analysis depends in practice upon the interpretation of dreams. I do not know whether making masses of people, chiefly children, confess their dreams, would lead to a great output of literature; though it would certainly lead, if I know anything of human nature, to a glorious output of lies. There is something touching in the inhuman innocence of the psychologist, who is already talking of the scientific exactitude of results reached by the one particular sort of evidence that cannot conceivably be checked or tested in any way whatever. But, as Mr. Beresford

truly says, the general notion of finding signs in
dreams is as old as the world; but even the special
theory of it is older than many seem to suppose.
Indeed, it is not only old, but obvious; and was never
discovered, because it was always noticed. Long
before the present fashion I myself (who, heaven
knows, am no psychologist) remember saying that
as there is truth in all popular traditions, there is
truth in the popular saying that dreams go by the
rule of contraries. That is, that a man does often
think at night about the very things he does not
think by day. But the popular saying had in it a
certain virtue never found in the anti-popular
sciences of our day. Popular superstition has one
enormous element of sanity; it is never serious. We
talk of ages like the mediæval as the ages of faith;
but it would be quite as true a tribute to call them
the ages of doubt; of a healthy doubt, and even a
healthy derision. There was always something
more or less consciously grotesque about an old
ghost story. There was fun mixed with the fear;
and the yokels knew too much about turnips not
occasionally to think of turnip-ghosts. There is no
fun about psycho-analysis. One yokel would say,
"'Ar,' they do say dreams go by contraries." And
then the others would say, "Ar," and they would
all laugh in a deep internal fashion. But when
Mr. J. D. Beresford says that Freud's theory is

among scientific theories the most attractive for novelists, " it was a theory of sex, the all but universal theme of the novel," it is clear that our audience is slower and more solemn than the yokels. For nobody laughs at all. People seem to have lost the power of reacting to the humorous stimulus. When one milkmaid dreamed of a funeral, the other milkmaid said, " That means a wedding," and then they would both giggle. But when Mr. J. D. Beresford says that the theory " adumbrated the suggestion of a freer morality, by dwelling upon the physical and spiritual necessity for the liberation of impulse," the point seems somehow to be missed. Not a single giggle is heard in the deep and disappointing silence. It seems truly strange that when a modern and brilliant artist actually provides jokes far more truly humorous than the rude jests of the yokels and the milkmaids, the finer effort should meet with the feebler response. It is but an example of the unnatural solemnity, like an artificial vacuum, in which all these modern experiments are conducted. But no doubt if Freud had enjoyed the opportunity of explaining his ideas in an ancient ale-house, they would have met with more spontaneous applause.

I hope I do not seem unsympathetic with Mr. Beresford; for I not only admire his talent, but I am at this moment acting in strict obedience to his theories. I am—I say it proudly—acting as a disciple of Freud, who apparently forbids me to conceal any impulse, presumably including the impulse to laugh. I mean no disrespect to Mr. Beresford; but my first duty, of course, is to my own psychological inside. And goodness knows what damage might not be done to the most delicate workings of my own mental apparatus (as Mr. Arnold Bennett called it) if I were to subject it to the sudden and violent strain of not smiling at the scientific theory which is attractive because it is sexual, or of forcing my features into a frightful composure when I hear of the spiritual necessity for the liberation of impulse. I am not quite sure how far the liberation of impulse is to be carried out in practice by its exponents in theory; I do not know whether it is better to liberate the impulse to throw somebody else out of an express train in order to have the carriage to oneself all the way; or what may be the penalties for repressing the native instinct to shoot Mr. Lloyd George. But obviously the greater includes the less; and it would be very illogical if we were allowed to chuck out our fellow-traveller but not to chaff him; or if I were permitted to shoot at Mr. George but not to smile at Mr. Beresford. And though I am not so serious as he is, I assure him that in this I am quite as sincere as he is. In that sense I do seriously regret his seriousness; I do seriously think

30

such seriousness a very serious evil. For some healthy human impulses are really the better for the relief by words and gestures, and one of them is the universal human sense that there is something comic about the relations of the sexes. The impulse to laugh at the mention of morality as " free " or of sex science as " attractive " is one of the impulses which is already gratified by most people who have never heard of psycho-analysis and is only mortified by people like the psycho-analysts.

Mr. Beresford must therefore excuse me if, with a sincere desire to follow his serious argument seriously, I note at the beginning a certain normal element of comedy of which critics of his school seem to be rather unconscious. When he asks whether this theory of the Nemesis of suppression can serve the purposes of great literary work, it would seem natural at first to test it by the example of the greatest literary works. And, judged by this scientific test, it must be admitted that our literary classics would appear to fail. Lady Macbeth does not suffer as a sleep-walker because she has resisted the impulse to murder Duncan, but rather (by some curious trick of thought) because she has yielded to it. Hamlet's uncle is in a morbid frame of mind, not, as one would naturally expect, because he had thwarted his own development by leaving his own brother alive and in possession; but actually because he has triumphantly liberated himself from the morbid impulse to pour poison in his brother's ear. On the theory of psycho-analysis, as expounded, a man ought to be haunted by the ghosts of all the men he has not murdered. Even if they were limited to those he has felt a vague fancy for murdering, they might make a respectable crowd to follow at his heels. Yet Shakespeare certainly seems to represent Macbeth as haunted by Banquo, whom he removed at one blow from the light of the sun and from his own sub-consciousness. Hell ought to mean the regret for lost opportunities for crime; the insupportable thought of houses still standing unburned or unburgled, or of wealthy uncles still walking about alive with their projecting watchchains. Yet Dante certainly seemed to represent it as concerned exclusively with things done and done with, and not as merely the morbidly congested imagination of a thief who had not thieved and a murderer who had not murdered. In short, it is only too apparent that the poets and sages of the past knew very little of psycho-analysis, and whether or no Mr. Beresford can achieve great literary effects with it, they managed to achieve their literary effects without it. This is but a preliminary point, and I touch the more serious problem in a few minutes, if the fashion has not changed before then. For the moment I only take the test

of literary experience, and of how independent of
such theories have been the real masterpieces of man.
Men are still excited over the poetic parts of poets
like Shakespeare and Dante; if they go to sleep it is
over the scientific parts. It is over some system of
the spheres which Dante thought the very latest
astronomy, or some argument about the humours of
the body which Shakespeare thought the very latest
physiology. I appeal to Mr. Beresford's indestructi-
ble sense of humanity and his still undestroyed sense
of humour. What would have become of the work
of Dickens if it had been rewritten to illustrate the
thesis of Darwin? What even of the work of Mr.
Kipling if modified to meet the theories of Mr. Kidd?
Believe me, the proportions are as I have said. Art
is long, but science is fleeting; and Mr. Beresford's
sub-consciousness, though stout and brave, is in
danger of being not so much a muffled drum as a
drum which somebody silences for ever; by knock-
ing a hole in it, only to find nothing inside.

But there is one incidental moral in the matter
that seems to me topical and rather arresting. It
concerns the idea of punishment.

The psycho-analysts continue to buzz in a mysterious manner round the problem of Hamlet. They
are especially interested in the things of which
Hamlet was unconscious, not to mention the things
of which Shakespeare was unconscious. It is in vain

for old-fashioned rationalists like myself to point out that this is like dissecting the brain of Puck or revealing the real private life of Punch and Judy. The discussion no longer revolves round whether Hamlet is mad, but whether everybody is mad, especially the experts investigating the madness. And the curious thing about this process is that even when the critics are really subtle enough to see subtle things, they are never simple enough to see self-evident things. A really fine critic is reported as arguing that in Hamlet the consciousness willed one thing and the sub-consciousness another. Apparently the conscious Hamlet had unreservedly embraced and even welcomed the obligation of vengeance, but the shock (we are told) had rendered the whole subject painful, and started a strange and secret aversion to the scheme. It did not seem to occur to the writers that there might possibly be something slightly painful, at the best, in cutting the throat of your own uncle and the husband of your own mother. There might certainly be an aversion from the act; but I do not quite see why it should be an unconscious aversion. It seems just possible that a man might be quite conscious of not liking such a job. Where he differed from the modern morality was that he believed in the possibility of disliking it and yet doing it.

But to follow the argument of these critics, one

would think that murdering the head of one's
family was a sort of family festivity or family joke;
a gay and innocent indulgence into which the young
prince would naturally have thrown himself with
thoughtless exuberance, were it not for the dark and
secretive thoughts that had given him an unaccount-
able distaste for it. Suppose it were borne in upon
one of these modern middle-class critics, of my own
rank and routine of life (possibly through his confidence in the messages at a Spiritualist séance) that
it was his business to go home to Brompton or
Surbiton and stick the carving-knife into Uncle
William, who had poisoned somebody and was beyond the reach of the law. It is possible that the
critic's first thought would be that it was a happy
way of spending a half-holiday; and that only in
the critic's sub-consciousness the suspicion would stir
that there was something unhappy about the whole
business. But it seems also possible that the regret
might not be confined to his sub-consciousness, but
might swim almost to the surface of his consciousness.
In plain words, this sort of criticism has lost the last
rags of common sense. Hamlet requires no such sub-
conscious explanation, for he explains himself, and
was perhaps rather too fond of doing so. He was a
man to whom duty had come in a very dreadful and
repulsive form, and to a man not fitted for that
form of duty. There was a conflict, but he was

conscious of it from beginning to end. He was not an unconscious person; but a far too conscious one.

Strangely enough, this theory of sub-conscious repulsion in the dramatic character is itself an example of sub-conscious repulsion in the modern critic. It is the critic who has a sort of subliminal prejudice which makes him avoid something, that seems very simple to others. The thing which he secretly and obscurely avoids, from the start, is the very simple fact of the morality in which Shakespeare did believe, as distinct from all the crude psychology in which he almost certainly did not believe. Shakespeare certainly did believe in the struggle between duty and inclination. The critic instinctively avoids the admission that Hamlet's was a struggle between duty and inclination; and tries to substitute a struggle between consciousness and sub-consciousness. He gives Hamlet a complex to avoid giving him a conscience. But he is actually forced to talk as if it was a man's natural inclination to kill an uncle, because he does not want to admit that it might be his duty to kill him. He is really driven to talking as if some dark and secretive monomania alone prevented us all from killing our uncles. He is driven to this because he will not even take seriously the simple and, if you will, primitive morality upon which the tragedy is built. For that morality involves three moral propositions, from which the whole of the morbid modern subconsciousness does really recoil as from an ugly jar of pain. These principles are: first, that it may be our main business to do the right thing, even when we detest doing it; second, that the right thing may involve punishing some person, especially some powerful person; third, that the just process of punishment may take the form of fighting and killing. The modern critic is prejudiced against the first principle and calls it asceticism; he is prejudiced against the second principle and calls it vindictiveness; he is prejudiced against the third and generally calls it militarism. That it actually might be the duty of a young man to risk his own life, much against his own inclination, by drawing a sword and killing a tyrant, that is an idea instinctively avoided by this particular mood of modern times. That is why tyrants have such a good time in modern times. And in order to avoid this plain and obvious meaning, of war as a duty and peace as a temptation, the critic has to turn the whole play upside down, and seek its meaning in modern notions so remote as to be in this connexion meaningless. He has to make William Shakespeare of Stratford one of the pupils of Professor Freud. He has to make him a champion of psycho-analysis, which is like making him a champion of vaccination. He has to fit Hamlet's soul somehow into the classifications of Freud and Jung; which is just as if he had

37

to fit Hamlet's father into the classifications of Sir Oliver Lodge and Sir Arthur Conan Doyle. He has to interpret the whole thing by a new morality that Shakespeare had never heard of, because he has an intense internal dislike of the old morality that Shakespeare could not help hearing of. And that morality, which some of us believe to be based on a much more realistic psychology, is that punishment as punishment is a perfectly healthy process, not merely because it is reform, but also because it is expiation. What the modern world means by proposing to substitute pity for punishment is really very simple. It is that the modern world dare not punish those who are punishable, but only those who are pitiable. It would never touch anyone so important as King Claudius—or Kaiser William.

Now this truth is highly topical just now. The point about Hamlet was that he wavered, very excusably, in something that had to be done; and this is the point quite apart from whether we ourselves would have done it. That was pointed out long ago by Browning in " The Statue and the Bust." He argued that even if the motive for acting was bad, the motive for not acting was worse. And an action or inaction is judged by its real motive, not by whether somebody else might have done the same thing from a better motive. Whether or no the tyrannicide of Hamlet was a duty, it was accepted as

a duty and it was shirked as a duty. And that is
precisely true of a tyrannicide like that for which
everybody clamoured at the conclusion of the Great
War. It may have been right or wrong to punish the
Kaiser; it was certainly no more right to punish the
German generals and admirals for their atrocities.
But even if it was wrong, it was not abandoned because it was wrong. It was abandoned because it was
troublesome. It was abandoned for all those motives
—weakness and mutability of mood which we associate with the name of Hamlet. It might be
glory or ignominy to shed the blood of imperial enemies, but it is certainly ignominy to shout for what
you dare not shed; " to fall a-cursing like a common
drab, a scullion." Granted that we had no better
motives than we had then or have now, it would certainly have been more dignified if we had fatted all
the region-kites with this slave's offal. The motive
is the only moral test. A saint might provide us with
a higher motive for forgiving the War-Lords who
butchered Fryatt and Edith Cavell. But we have not
forgiven the War-Lords. We have simply forgotten
the War. We have not pardoned like Christ; we
have only procrastinated like Hamlet. Our highest
motive has been laziness; our commonest motive has
been money. In this respect indeed I must apologize
to the charming and chivalrous Prince of Denmark
for comparing him, even on a single point, with the

princes of finance and the professional politicians of our time. At least Hamlet did not spare Claudius solely because he hoped to get money out of him for the salaries of the Players, or meant to do a deal with him about wine supplied to Elsinore or debts contracted at Wittenburg. Still less was Hamlet acting entirely in the interests of Shylock, an inhabitant of the distant city of Venice. Doubtless Hamlet was sent to England in order that he might develop further these higher motives for peace and pardon. " 'Twill not be noticed in him there; there the men are as mad as he."

It is therefore very natural that men should be trying to dissolve the moral problem of Hamlet into the unmoral elements of consciousness and unconsciousness. The sort of duty that Hamlet shirked is exactly the sort of duty that we are all shirking; that of dethroning justice and vindicating truth. Many are now in a mood to deny that it is a duty because it is a danger. This applies, of course, not only to international but internal and especially industrial matters. Capitalism was allowed to grow into a towering tyranny in England because the English were always putting off their popular revolution, just as the Prince of Denmark put off his palace revolution. They lectured the French about their love of bloody revolutions, exactly as they are now lecturing the French about their love

of bloody wars. But the patience which suffered
England to be turned into a plutocracy was not the
patience of the saints; it was that patience which
paralyzed the noble prince of the tragedy; *accidia*
and the great refusal. In any case, the vital point
is that by refusing to punish the powerful we soon
lost the very idea of punishment; and turned our
police into a mere persecution of the poor.

THE MEANING OF MOCK TURKEY

HAVING lately taken part in a pageant of Nursery Rhymes, in the character of Old King Cole, I meditated not so much on the glorious past of the great kingdom of Colchester, as on the more doubtful future of Nursery Rhymes. The Modern Movements cannot produce a nursery rhyme; it is one of the many such things they cannot even be conceived as doing. But if they cannot create the nursery rhyme, will they destroy it? The new poets have already abolished rhyme; and presumably the new educationalists will soon abolish nurseries. Or if they do not destroy, will they reform; which is worse? Nursery rhymes are a positive network of notions and allusions of which the enlightened disapprove. To take only my own allotted rhyme as an example, some might think the very mention of a king a piece of reactionary royalism, inconsistent with that democratic self-determination we all enjoy under some five Controllers and a committee of the Cabinet. Perhaps in the amended version he will be called President Cole. Probably he will be confused with Mr. G. D. H. Cole, the first President of the Guild Socialistic

Republic. With the greatest admiration for Mr. Cole, I cannot quite picture him as so festive a figure; and I incline to think that the same influences will probably eliminate the festivity. It is said that America, having already abolished the bowl, is now attempting to abolish the pipe. After that it might very reasonably go on to abolish the fiddlers; for music can be far more maddening than wine. Tolstoy, the only consistent prophet of the Simple Life, did really go on to denounce music as a mere drug. Anyhow, it is quite intolerable that the innocent minds of children should be poisoned with the idea of anybody calling for his pipe and his bowl. There will have to be some other version, such as: " He called for his milk and he called for his lozenge," or whatever form of bodily pleasure is still permitted to mankind. This particular verse will evidently have to be altered a great deal; it is founded on so antiquated a philosophy, that I fear even the alteration will not be easy or complete. I am not sure, for instance, that there is not a memory of animism and spiritism in the very word " soul," used in calling the monarch a merry old soul. It would seem that some other simple phrase, such as " a merry old organism," might be used with advantage. Indeed it would save more advantages than one; for if the reader will say the amended line in a flowing and lyrical manner, he cannot but observe that the experiment has burst

43

the fetters of formal metre, and achieved one of these larger and lovelier melodies that we associate with *vers libre*.

It is needless to note the numberless other examples of nursery rhymes to which the same criticism applies. Some of the other cases are even more shocking to the true scientific spirit. For instance, in the typically old-world rhyme of " Girls and boys come out to play," there appear the truly appalling words: " Leave your supper and leave your sleep." As the great medical reformer of our day observed, in a striking and immortal phrase, " All Eugenists are agreed upon the importance of sleep." The case of supper may be more complex and controversial. If the supper were a really hygienic and wholesome supper, it might not be so difficult to leave it. But it is obvious that the whole vision which the rhyme calls up is utterly incompatible with a wise educational supervision. It is a wild vision of children playing in the streets by moonlight, for all the world as if they were fairies. Moonlight, like music, is credited with a power of upsetting the reason; and it is at least obvious that the indulgence is both unseasonable and unreasonable. No scientific reformer desires hasty and destructive action; for his reform is founded on that evolution which has produced the anthropoid from the amœba, a process which none have ever stigmatized as hasty. But when the eugenist recalls the reckless and romantic love affairs encouraged by such moonlight, he will have to consider seriously the problem of abolishing the moon.

But indeed I have much more sympathy with the simplicity of the baby who cries for the moon than with the sort of simplicity that dismisses the moon as all moonshine. And indeed I think that these two antagonistic types of simplicity are perhaps the pivotal terms of the present transition. It is a new thing called the Simple Life against an older thing which may be called the Simple Soul; possibly exemplified, so far as nursery rhymes are concerned, by the incident of Simple Simon. I prefer the old Simple Simon, who, though ignorant of the economic theory of exchange, had at least a positive and poetic enthusiasm for pies. I think him far wiser than the new Simple Simon, who simplifies his existence by means of a perverse and pedantic antipathy to pies. It is unnecessary to add that this philosophy of pies is applicable with peculiar force to mince-pies; and thus to the whole of the Christmas tradition which descended from the first carols to the imaginative world of Dickens. The morality of that tradition is much too simple and obvious to be understood to-day. Awful as it may seem to many modern people, it means no less than that Simple Simon should have his pies, even in the absence of his pennies.

But the philosophy of the two Simple Simons is plain enough. The former is an expansion of simplicity towards complexity; Simon, conscious that he cannot himself make pies, approaches them with an ardour not unmixed with awe. But the latter is a reaction of complexity towards simplicity; in other words the other Simon refuses pies for various reasons, often including the fact that he has eaten too many of them. Most of the Simple Life as we see it to-day is, of course, a thing having this character of the surfeit or satiety of Simon, when he has become less simple and certainly less greedy. This reaction may take two diverse forms; it may send Simon searching for more and more expensive and extravagant confectionery, or it may reduce him to nibbling at some new kind of nut biscuit. For it may be noted, in passing, that it probably will not reduce him to eating dry bread. The Simple Life never accepts anything that is simple in the sense of self-evident and familiar. The thing must be uncommonly simple; it must not be simply common. Its philosophy must be something higher than the ordinary breakfast table, and something drier than dry bread. The usual process, as I have observed it in vegetarian and other summaries, seems in one sense indeed to be simple enough. The pie-man produces what looks like the same sort of pie, or is supposed to look like it; only it has thinner crust outside and

nothing at all inside. Then instead of asking Simple
Simon for a penny he asks him for a pound, or possibly a guinea or a five-pound note. And what is
strangest of all, the customer is often so singularly
Simple a Simon that he pays for it. For that is
perhaps the final and most marked difference between
Simon of the Simple Spirit and Simon of the Simple
Life. It is the fact that the ardent and appreciative
Simon was not in possession of a penny. The more
refined and exalted Simon is generally in possession
of far too many pennies. He is often very rich and
needs to be; for the drier and thinner and emptier
are the pies, the more he is charged for them. But
this alone will reveal another side of the same paradox; and if it be possible to spend a lot of money on
the Simple Life, it is also possible to make a great
deal of money out of it. There are several self-
advertisers doing very well out of the new self-denial.
But wealth is always at one end of it or the other;
and that is the great difference between the two
Simons. Perhaps it is the difference between Simon
Peter and Simon Magus.

I have before me a little pamphlet in which the
most precise directions are given for a Mock Turkey,
for a vegetarian mince-pie, and for a cautious and
hygienic Christmas pudding. I have never quite
understood why it should be a part of the Simple
Life to have anything so deceptive and almost con-

spiratorial as an imitation turkey. The coarse and comic alderman may be expected, in his festive ribaldry, to mock a turtle; but surely a lean and earnest humanitarian ought not to mock a turkey. Nor do I understand the theory of the imitation in its relation to the ideal. Surely one who thinks meat eating mere cannibalism ought not to arrange vegetables so as to look like an animal. It is as if a converted cannibal in the Sandwich Islands were to arrange joints of meat in the shape of a missionary. The missionaries would surely regard the proceedings of their convert with something less than approval, and perhaps with something akin to alarm. But the consistency of these concessions I will leave on one side, because I am not here concerned with the concessions but with the creed itself. And I am concerned with the creed not merely as affecting its practice in diet or cookery but its general theory. For the compilers of the little book before me are great on philosophy and ethics. There are whole pages about brotherhood and fellowship and happiness and healing. In short, as the writer observes, we have " also some Mental Helps, as set forth in the flood of Psychology Literature to-day—but raised to a higher plane." It may be a little risky to set a thing forth in a flood, or a little difficult to raise a flood to a higher plane; but there is behind these rather vague expressions a very real modern intelligence and point of view, common to considerable numbers of cultivated people, and well worthy of some further study.

Under the title of "How to Think" there are twenty-four rules of which the first few are: "Empty Your Mind," "Think of the Best Things," "Appreciate," "Analyze," "Prepare Physically," "Prepare Mentally," and so on. I have met some earnest students of this school, who had apparently entered on this course, but at the time of our meeting had only graduated so far as the fulfilment of the first rule. It was more obvious, on the whole, that they had succeeded in the preliminary process of emptying the mind than that they had as yet thought of the best things, or analyzed or appreciated anything in particular. But there were others, I willingly admit, who had really thought of certain things in a genuinely thoughtful fashion, though whether they were really the best things might involve a difference of opinion between us. Still, so far as they are concerned, it is a school of thought, and therefore worth thinking about. Having been able to this extent to appreciate, I will now attempt to analyze. I have attempted to discover in my own mind where the difference between us really lies, apart from all these superficial jests and journalistic points; to ask myself why it is exactly that their ideal vegetarian differs so much from my ideal Christian. And the result of the concentrated contemplation of their

ideal is, I confess, a somewhat impatient forward
plunge in the progress of their initiation. I am
strongly disposed to "Prepare Physically" for a
conflict with the ideal vegetarian, with the only hope
of hitting him on the nose. In one of Mr. P. G.
Wodehouse's stories the vegetarian rebukes his
enemy for threatening to skin him, by reminding him
that man should only think beautiful thoughts; to
which the enemy gives the unanswerable answer:
"Skinning you is a beautiful thought." In the same
way I am quite prepared to think of the best things;
but I think hitting the ideal vegetarian on the nose
would be one of the best things in the world. This
may be an extreme example; but it involves a much
more serious principle. What such philosophers
often forget is that among the best things in the
world are the very things which their placid uni-
versalism forbids; and that there is nothing better
or more beautiful than a noble hatred. I do not profess to feel it for them; but they themselves do not
seem to feel it for anything.

But as my new idealistic instructor tells me to
analyze, I will attempt to analyze. In the ordinary
way it would perhaps be enough to say that I do
not like his ideals, and that I prefer my own, as I
should say I did not like the taste of nut cutlet so
much as the taste of veal cutlet. But just as it is
possible to resolve the food into formulas about pro-

teids, so it is partly possible to resolve the religious
preference into formulas about principles. The most
we can hope to do is to find out which of these principles are the first principles. And in this connexion
I should like to speak a little more seriously, and
even a little more respectfully, of the formulas about
emptying the mind. I do not deny that it is sometimes a good thing to empty the mind of the mere
accumulation of secondary and tertiary impressions.
If what is meant is something which a friend of mine
once called " a mental spring clean," then I can see
what it means. But the most drastic spring clean in
a house does not generally wash away the house. It
does not tear down the roof like a cobweb, or pluck up
the walls like weeds. And the true formula is not so
much to empty the mind as to discover that we cannot
empty the mind, by emptying it as much as we can.
In other words we always came back to certain fundamentals which are convictions, because we can
hardly even conceive their contraries. But it is the
paradox of human language that though these truths
are in a manner past all parallel, hard and clear, yet
any attempt to talk about them always has the
appearance of being hazy and elusive.

Now this antagonism, when thus analyzed, seems
to me to arise from one ultimate thing at the back
of the minds of these men; that they believe in taking
the body seriously. The body is a sort of pagan god,

ST. PAUL
PUBLIC LIBRARY

though the pagans are more often stoics than epicureans. To begin with, it is itself a beginning. The body, if not the creator of the soul in Heaven, is regarded as the practical producer of it on earth. In this their materialism is the very foundation of their asceticism. They wish us to consume clean fruit and clear water that our minds may be clear or our lives clean. The body is a sort of magical factory where these things go in as vegetables and come out as virtues. Thus digestion has the first sign of a deity; that of being an origin. It has the next sign of a deity; that if it is satisfied other things do not matter, or at any rate other things follow in their place. And so, they would say, the services of the body should be serious and not grotesque; and its smallest hints should be taken as terrible warnings. Art has a place in it because the body must be draped like an altar; and science is paraded in it because the service must be in Latin or Greek or some hieratic tongue. I quite understand these things surrounding a god or an altar; but I do not happen to worship at that altar or to believe in that god. I do not think the body ought to be taken seriously; I think it is far safer and saner when it is taken comically and even coarsely. And I think that when the body is given a holiday, as it is in a great feast, I think it should be set free not merely for wisdom but for folly, not merely to dance but to turn head over

ST. PAUL
PUBLIC LIBRARY

heels. In short, when it is really allowed to exaggerate its own pleasures, it ought also to exaggerate its own absurdity. The body has its own rank, and its own rights, and its own place under government; but the body is not the king but rather the Court Jester. And the human and historical importance of the old jests and buffooneries of Christmas, however vulgar or stale or trivial they appear, is that in them the popular instinct always resisted this pagan solemnity about sensual things. A man was meant to feel rather a goose when he was eating goose; and to realize that he is such stuff as stuffing is made of. That is why anyone who has in these things the touch of the comic will also have the taste for the conservative; he will be unwilling to alter what that popular instinct has made in its own absurd image. He will be doubtful about a Christmas pudding moulded in the shape of the Pyramid or the Parthenon, or anything that is not as round and ridiculous as the world. And when Mr. Pickwick, as round and ridiculous as any Christmas pudding or any world worth living in, stood straddling and smiling under the mistletoe he disinfected that vegetable of its ancient and almost vegetarian sadness and heathenism, of the blood of Baldur and the human sacrifice of the Druids.

SHAKESPEARE AND THE
LEGAL LADY

I wonder how long liberated woman will endure the
invidious ban which excludes her from being a hangman. Or rather, to speak with more exactitude, a
hangwoman. The very fact that there seems something vaguely unfamiliar and awkward about the
word, is but a proof of the ages of sex oppression
that have accustomed us to this sex privilege. The
ambition would not perhaps have been understood
by the prudish and sentimental heroines of Fanny
Burney and Jane Austen. But it is now agreed that
the farther we go beyond these faded proprieties the
better; and I really do not see how we could go
farther. There are always torturers of course; who
will probably return under some scientific name.
Obscurantists may use the old argument, that woman
has never risen to the first rank in this or other arts;
that Jack Ketch was not Jemima Ketch, and that the
headsman was called Samson and not Delilah. And
they will be overwhelmed with the old retort: that
until we have hundreds of healthy women happily engaged in this healthful occupation, it will be impos-

sible to judge whether they can rise above the average or no. Tearful sentimentalists may feel something unpleasing, something faintly repugnant, about the new feminine trade. But, as the indignant police-woman said the other day, when a magistrate excluded some of her sex and service from revolting revelations, " crime is a disease," and must be studied scientifically, however hideous it may be. Death also is a disease; and frequently a fatal one. Experiments must be made in it; and it must be inflicted in any form, however hideous, in a cool and scientific manner.

It is not true, of course, that crime is a disease. It is criminology that is a disease. But the suggestion about the painful duties of a policewoman leads naturally to my deduction about the painful duties of a hangwoman. And I make it in the faint hope of waking up some of the feminists, that they may at least be moved to wonder what they are doing, and to attempt to find out. What they are not doing is obvious enough. They are not asking themselves two perfectly plain questions; first, whether they want anybody to be a hangman; and second, whether they want everybody to be a hangman. They simply assume, with panting impetuosity, that we want everybody to be everything, criminologists, constables, barristers, executioners, torturers. It never seems to occur to them that some of us doubt

55

the beauty and blessedness of these things, and are rather glad to limit them like other necessary evils. And this applies especially to the doubtful though defensible case of the advocate.

There is one phrase perpetually repeated and now practically stereotyped, which to my mind concentrates and sums up all the very worst qualities in the very worst journalism; all its paralysis of thought, all its monotony of chatter, all its sham culture and shoddy picturesqueness, all its perpetual readiness to cover any vulgarity of the present with any sentimentalism about the past. There is one phrase that does measure to how low an ebb the mind of my unfortunate profession can sink. It is the habit of perpetually calling any of the new lady barristers "Portia."

First of all, of course, it is quite clear that the journalist does not know who Portia was. If he has ever heard of the story of the "Merchant of Venice," he has managed to miss the only point of the story. Suppose a man had been so instructed in the story of "As You Like It" that he remained under the impression that Rosalind merely was a boy, and was the brother of Celia. We should say that the plot of the comedy had reached his mind in a rather confused form. Suppose a man had seen a whole performance of the play of "Twelfth Night" without discovering the fact that the page called Cesario was really a girl called Viola. We should say that he had succeeded in seeing the play without exactly seeing the point. But there is exactly the same blind stupidity in calling a barrister Portia; or even in calling Portia a barrister. It misses in exactly the same sense the whole meaning of the scene. Portia is no more a barrister than Rosalind is a boy. She is no more the learned jurist whom Shylock congratulates than Viola is the adventurous page whom Olivia loves. The whole point of her position is that she is a heroic and magnanimous fraud. She has not taken up the legal profession, or any profession; she has not sought that public duty, or any public duty. Her action, from first to last, is wholly and entirely private. Her motives are not professional but private. Her ideal is not public but private. She acts as much on personal grounds in the Trial Scene as she does in the Casket Scene. She acts in order to save a friend, and especially a friend of the husband whom she loves. Anything less like the attitude of an advocate, for good or evil, could not be conceived. She seeks individually to save an individual; and in order to do so is ready to *break* all the existing laws of the profession and the public tribunal; to assume lawlessly powers she has not got, to intrude where she would never be legally admitted, to pretend to be somebody else, to dress up as a man; to do what is actually a crime against the law. This is not what is now called the attitude of a public woman; it is certainly not the attitude of a lady lawyer, any more than of any other kind of lawyer. But it is emphatically the attitude of a private woman; that much more ancient and much more powerful thing.

Suppose that Portia had really become an advocate, merely by advocating the cause of Antonio against Shylock. The first thing that follows is that, as like as not, she would be briefed in the next case to advocate the cause of Shylock against Antonio. She would, in the ordinary way of business, have to help Shylock to punish with ruin the private extravagances of Gratiano. She would have to assist Shylock to distrain on poor Launcelot Gobbo and sell up all his miserable sticks. She might well be employed by him to ruin the happiness of Lorenzo and Jessica, by urging some obsolete parental power or some technical flaw in the marriage service. Shylock evidently had a great admiration for her forensic talents; and indeed that sort of lucid and detached admission of the talents of a successful opponent is a very Jewish characteristic. There seems no reason why he should not have employed her regularly, whenever he wanted some one to recover ruthless interest, to ruin needy households, to drive towards theft or suicide the souls of desperate men. But there seems every reason to doubt whether the Portia whom Shakespeare describes for us is likely to have taken on the job.

Anyhow, that is the job; and I am not here arguing that it is not a necessary job; or that it is always an indefensible job. Many honourable men have made an arguable case for the advocate who has to support Shylock, and men much worse than Shylock. But that is the job; and to cover up its ugly realities with a loose literary quotation that really refers to the exact opposite, is one of those crawling and cowardly evasions and verbal fictions which make all this sort of servile journalism so useless for every worthy or working purpose. If we wish to consider whether a lady should be a barrister, we should consider sanely and clearly what a barrister is and what a lady is; and then come to our conclusion according to what we considered worthy or worthless in the traditions of the two things. But the spirit of advertisement, which tries to associate soap with sunlight or grapenuts with grapes, calls to its rescue an old romance of Venice and tries to cover up a practical problem in the robes of a romantic heroine of the stage. This is the sort of confusion that really leads to corruption. In one sense it would matter very little that the legal profession was formally open to women, for it is only a very exceptional sort of woman who would see herself as a vision of beauty in the character of Mr. Sergeant Buzfuz. And most girls are more likely to be stage-struck, and want to be the real Portia on the stage, rather than law-struck and want to be the very reverse of Portia in a law court. For that matter, it would make relatively little difference if formal permission were given to a woman to be a hangman or a torturer. Very few women would have a taste for it; and very few men would have a taste for the women who had a taste for it. But advertisement, by its use of the vulgar picturesque, can hide the realities of this professional problem, as it can hide the realities of tinned meats and patent medicines. It can conceal the fact that the hangman exists to hang, and that the torturer exists to torture. Similarly it can conceal the fact that the Buzfuz barrister exists to bully. It can hide from the innocent female aspirants outside even the perils and potential abuses that would be admitted by the honest male advocate inside. And that is part of a very much larger problem, which extends beyond this particular profession to a great many other professions; and not least to the lowest and most lucrative of all modern professions: that of professional politics.

I wonder how many people are still duped by the story of the extension of the franchise. I wonder how many Radicals have been a little mystified, in remarking how many Tories and reactionaries have helped in the extension of the franchise. The truth is that calling in crowds of new voters will very often be to the interest, not only of Tories, but of really tyrannical Tories. It will often be in the interest of the guilty to appeal to the innocent; if they are innocent in the matter of other people's conduct as well as of their own. The tyrant calls in those he has not wronged, to defend him against those he has wronged. He is not afraid of the new and ignorant masses who know too little; he is afraid of the older and nearer nucleus of those who know too much. And there is nothing that would please the professional politician more than to flood the constituencies with innocent negroes or remote Chinamen, who might possibly admire him more, because they knew him less. I should not wonder if the Party System had been saved three or four times at the point of extinction, by the introduction of new voters who had never had time to discover why it deserved to be extinguished. The last of these rescues by an inrush of dupes was the enfranchisement of women.

What is true of the political is equally true of the professional ambition. Much of the mere imitation of masculine tricks and trades is indeed trivial enough; it is a mere masquerade. The greatest of Roman satirists noted that in his day the more fast of the fashionable ladies liked to fight as gladiators in the amphitheatre. In that one statement he pinned and killed, like moths on a cork, a host of women prophets and women pioneers and large-minded liberators of their sex in modern England and America. But besides these more showy she-gladiators there are also multitudes of worthy and sincere women who take the new (or rather old) professions seriously. The only disadvantage is that in many of those professions they can only continue to be serious by ceasing to be sincere. But the simplicity with which they first set out is an enormous support to old and complex and corrupt institutions. No modest person setting out to learn an elaborate science can be expected to start with the assumption that it is not worth learning. The young lady will naturally begin to learn Law as gravely as she begins to learn Greek. It is not in that mood that she will conceive independent doubts about the ultimate relations of Law and Justice. Just as the Suffragettes are already complaining that the realism of industrial revolution interferes with their new hobby of voting, so the lady lawyers are quite likely to complain that the realism of legal reformers interferes with their new hobby of legalism. We are suffering in every department from the same cross-purposes that can be seen in the case of any vulgar patent medicine. In Law and Medicine, we have the thing advertised in the public press instead of analyzed by the public authority. What we want is not the journalistic Portia but the theatrical Portia, who is also the real Portia. We do not want the woman who will enter the law court with the solemn sense of a lasting vocation. We want a Portia; a woman who will enter it as lightly, and leave it as gladly as she did.

The same thing is true of a fact nobler than any fiction; the story, so often quoted, of the woman who won back mediæval France. Joan of Arc was a soldier; but she was not a normal soldier. If she had been, she would have been vowed, not to the war for France, but to any war with Flanders, Spain or the Italian cities to which her feudal lord might lead her. If she were a modern conscript, she would be bound to obey orders not always coming from St. Michael. But the point is here that merely making all women soldiers, under either system, could do nothing at all except whitewash and ratify feudalism or conscription. And both feudalism and conscription are much more magnanimous things than our modern system of police and prisons.

In fact there are few sillier implications than that in the phrase that what is sauce for the goose is sauce for the gander. A cook who really rules a kitchen on that principle would wait patiently for milk from the bull, because he got it from the cow. It is neither a perceptible fact nor a first principle that the sexes must not specialize; and if one sex must specialize in adopting dubious occupations, we ought to be very glad that the other sex specializes in abstaining from them. That is how the balance of criticism in the Commonwealth is maintained; as by a sort of government and opposition. In this, as in other things, the new régime is that everybody shall join the government. The government of the moment will be monstrously strengthened; for everybody will be a tyrant and everybody will be a slave. The detached criticism of official fashions will disappear; and none was ever so detached as the deadly criticism that came from women. When all women wear uniforms, all women will wear gags; for a gag is part of every uniform in the world.

ON BEING AN OLD BEAN

I was looking at some press cuttings that had pursued me down to a remote cottage beside a river of Norfolk; and as it happened, those that caught my eye were mostly not from the vulgar monopolist press, but from all sorts of quieter and even more studious publications. But what struck me as curious about the collection as a whole was the selection, among half a hundred things that were hardly worth saying, of the things that were considered worth repeating. There seemed to be a most disproportionate importance attached to a trivial phrase I had used about the alleged indecorum of a gentleman calling his father an old bean. I had been asked to join in a discussion in the " Morning Post," touching the alleged disrespect of youth towards age, and I had done so; chiefly because I have a respect for the " Morning Post " for its courage about political corruption and cosmopolitan conspiracies, in spite of deep disagreement on other very vital things. And I said what I should have thought was so true as to be trite. I said that it makes life narrower and not broader to lose the special note of piety or respect for the past still living; and that to call an old man

65

an old bean is merely to lose all intelligent sense of the significance of an old man. Since then, to my great entertainment, I seem to have figured in various papers as a sort of ferocious heavy father, come out on my own account to curse the numerous young sprigs who have called me an old bean. But this is an error. I should be the last to deny that I am heavy, but I am not fatherly; nor am I ferocious, at any rate I am not ferocious about this. Individually I regard the question with a detachment verging on indifference. I cannot imagine anybody except an aged and very lean vegetarian positively dancing with joy at being called an old bean; and I am not a very lean vegetarian. But still less can I imagine anyone regarding the accusation with horror or resentment; the sins and crimes blackening the career of a bean must be comparatively few; its character must be simple and free from complexity, and its manner of life innocent. A philosophic rationalist wrote to me the other day to say that my grubbing in the grossest superstitions of the past reminded him of " an old sow pig rooting in the refuse of the kitchen heap," and expressed a hope that I should be dragged from this occupation and made to resume " the cap and bells of yore." That is something like a vigorous and vivid comparison; though my Feminist friends may be distressed at my being compared to a sow as well as a pig; and though I am not quite clear myself about how the animal would get on when he had resumed the cap and bells of yore. But it would certainly be a pity, when it was possible to find this image in the kitchen heap, to be content with one from the kitchen garden. It would indeed be a lost opportunity to work yourself up to the furious pitch of calling your enemy a beast, and then only call him a bean.

From the extracts I saw, it would seem that certain ladies were especially lively in their protest against my antiquated prejudices; and rioted in quite a bean-feast of old beans. The form the argument generally takes is to ask why parents and children should not be friends, or, as they often put it (I deeply regret to say), pals. Neither term seems to me to convey a sufficiently distinctive meaning; and I take it that the best term for what they really mean is that they should be comrades. Now comradeship is a very real and splendid thing; but this is simply the cant of comradeship. A boy does not take his mother with him when he goes bird-nesting; and his affection for his mother is of another kind unconnected with the idea of her climbing a tree. Three men do not generally take an aged and beloved aunt with them as part of their luggage on a walking tour; and if they did, it would not be so much disrespectful to age as unjust to youth. For this confusion between two valuable but varied things, like most of

such modern confusions, is quite as liable to obscurantist as to mutinous abuse; and is as easy to turn
into tyranny as into licence. If a boy's aunts are his
comrades, why should he need any comrades except
his aunts? If his father and mother are perfect and
consummate pals, why should he fool away his time
with more ignorant, immature and insufficient pals?
As in a good many other modern things, the end of
the old parental dignity would be the beginning of a
new parental tyranny. I would rather the boy loved
his father as his father than feared him as a Franken-
stein giant of a superior and supercilious friend,
armed in that unequal friendship with all the weapons
of psychology and psycho-analysis. If he loves him
as a father he loves him as an older man; and if we
are to abolish all differences of tone towards those
older than ourselves, we must presumably do the
same to those younger than ourselves. All healthy
people, for instance, feel an instinctive and almost
impersonal affection for a baby. Is a baby a com-
rade? Is he to climb the tree and go on the walking
tour; or are we on his account to abolish all trees
and tours? Are the grandfather aged ninety, the
son aged thirty, and the grandson aged three, all to
set out together on their travels, with the same knap-
sacks and knickerbockers? I have read somewhere
that in one of the Ten or Twelve or Two Hundred

Types of Filial Piety reverenced by the Chinese, one was an elderly sage and statesman, who dressed up as a child of four and danced before his yet more elderly parents, to delight them with the romantic illusion that they were still quite young. This in itself could not but attract remark; but this in itself I am prepared to defend. It was an exceptional and even extraordinary festivity, like the reversals of the Saturnalia; and I wish we could have seen some vigorous old gentleman like Lord Halsbury or the Archbishop of Canterbury performing a similar act of piety. But in the Utopia of comradeship now commended to us, old and young are expected normally to think alike, feel alike and talk alike; and may therefore normally and permanently be supposed to dress alike. Whether the parents dress as children or the children as parents, it is clear that they must all dress as pals, whatever be the ceremonial dress of that rank. I imagine it as something in tweeds, with rather a loud check.

As I considered these things I looked across the kitchen garden of the cottage, and the association of peas and beans brought the fancy back to the foolish figure of speech with which the discussion began. There is a proverb, which is like most of our popular sayings, a country proverb, about things that are as like as two peas. There is something

significant in the fact that this is as near as the
rural imagination could get to a mere mechanical
monotony. For as a matter of fact it is highly improbable that any two peas are exactly alike. A
survey of the whole world of peas, with all their
forms and uses, would probably reveal every sort of
significance between the sweet peas of sentiment and
the dried peas of asceticism. Modern machinery has
gone far beyond such rude rural attempts at dull-
ness. Things are not as like as two peas in the sense
that they are as like as two pins. But the flippant
phrase under discussion does really imply that
they are as like as two beans. It is really part of the
low and levelling philosophy that assimilates all
things too much to each other. It does not mean that
we see any fanciful significance in the use of the term,
as in a country proverb. It is not that we see an old
gentleman with fine curling white hair and say to
him poetically, " Permit me, venerable cauliflower, to
inquire after your health." It is not that we address
an old farmer with a deep and rich complexion, saying, " I trust, most admirable of beetroots, that you
are as well as you look." When we say, " How are
you, old bean," the error is not so much that we say
something rude, but that we may say nothing because
we mean nothing.

As I happened to meet at that moment a girl
belonging to the family of the cottage, I showed her

the cutting, and asked her opinion upon the great progressive problem of calling your father an old bean. At which she laughed derisively, and merely said, " As if anybody would! "

THE FEAR OF THE FILM

Long lists are being given of particular cases in which children have suffered in spirits or health from alleged horrors of the kinema. One child is said to have had a fit after seeing a film; another to have been sleepless with some fixed idea taken from a film; another to have killed his father with a carving-knife through having seen a knife used in a film. This may possibly have occurred; though if it did, anybody of common sense would prefer to have details about that particular child, rather than about that particular picture. But what is supposed to be the practical moral of it, in any case? Is it that the young should never see a story with a knife in it? Are they to be brought up in complete ignorance of " The Merchant of Venice " because Shylock flourishes a knife for a highly disagreeable purpose? Are they never to hear of Macbeth, lest it should slowly dawn upon their trembling intelligence that it is a dagger that they see before them? It would be more practical to propose that a child should never see a real carving-knife, and still more practical that he should never see a real father. All that may come; the era of preventive and prophetic science has only begun.

We must not be impatient. But when we come to the cases of morbid panic after some particular exhibition, there is yet more reason to clear the mind of cant. It is perfectly true that a child will have the horrors after seeing some particular detail. It is quite equally true that nobody can possibly predict what that detail will be. It certainly need not be anything so obvious as a murder or even a knife. I should have thought anybody who knew anything about children, or for that matter anybody who had been a child, would know that these nightmares are quite incalculable. The hint of horror may come by any chance in any connexion. If the kinema exhibited nothing but views of country vicarages or vegetarian restaurants, the ugly fancy is as likely to be stimulated by these things as by anything else. It is like seeing a face in the carpet; it makes no difference that it is the carpet at the vicarage.

I will give two examples from my own most personal circle; I could give hundreds from hearsay. I know a child who screamed steadily for hours if he had been taken past the Albert Memorial. This was not a precocious precision or excellence in his taste in architecture. Nor was it a premature protest against all that gimcrack German culture which nearly entangled us in the downfall of the barbaric tyranny. It was the fear of something which he himself described with lurid simplicity as " The Cow with

73

the India-rubber Tongue." It sounds rather a good title for a creepy short story. At the base of the Albert Memorial (I may explain for those who have never enjoyed that monument) are four groups of statuary representing Europe, Asia, Africa, and America. America especially is very overwhelming; borne onward on a snorting bison who plunges forward in a fury of western progress, and is surrounded with Red Indians, Mexicans, and all sorts of pioneers, O pioneers, armed to the teeth. The child passed this transatlantic tornado with complete coolness and indifference. Europe however is seated on a bull so mild as to look like a cow; the tip of its tongue is showing and happened to be discoloured by weather; suggesting, I suppose, a living thing coming out of the dead marble. Now nobody could possibly foretell that a weather-stain would occur in that particular place, and fill that particular child with that particular fancy. Nobody is likely to propose meeting it by forbidding graven images, like the Moslems and the Jews. Nobody has said (as yet) that it is bad morals to make a picture of a cow. Nobody has even pleaded that it is bad manners for a cow to put its tongue out. These things are utterly beyond calculation; they are also beyond counting, for they occur all over the place, not only to morbid children but to any children. I knew this particular child very well, being a rather older child myself at the time. He certainly was not congenitally timid or feeble-minded; for he risked going to prison to expose the Marconi Scandal and died fighting in the Great War.

Here is another example out of scores. A little girl, now a very normal and cheerful young lady, had an insomnia of insane terror entirely arising from the lyric of "Little Bo-Peep." After an inquisition like that of the confessor or the psycho-analyst, it was found that the word "bleating" had some obscure connexion in her mind with the word "bleeding." There was thus perhaps an added horror in the phrase "heard"; in hearing rather than seeing the flowing of blood. Nobody could possibly provide against that sort of mistake. Nobody could prevent the little girl from hearing about sheep, any more than the little boy from hearing about cows. We might abolish all nursery rhymes; and as they are happy and popular and used with universal success, it is very likely that we shall. But the whole point of the mistake about that phrase is that it might have been a mistake about any phrase. We cannot foresee all the fancies that might arise, not only out of what we say, but of what we do not say. We cannot avoid promising a child a caramel lest he should think we say cannibal, or conceal the very word "hill" lest it should sound like "hell."

All the catalogues and calculations offered us by

the party of caution in this controversy are therefore quite worthless. It is perfectly true that examples can be given of a child being frightened of this, that or the other. But we can never be certain of his being frightened of the same thing twice. It is not on the negative side, by making lists of vetoes, that the danger can be avoided; it can never indeed be entirely avoided. We can only fortify the child on the positive side by giving him health and humour and a trust in God; not omitting (what will much mystify the moderns) an intelligent appreciation of the idea of authority, which is only the other side of confidence, and which alone can suddenly and summarily cast out such devils. But we may be sure that most modern people will not look at it in this way. They will think it more scientific to attempt to calculate the incalculable. So soon as they have realized that it is not so simple as it looks, they will try to map it out, however complicated it may be. When they discover that the terrible detail need not be a knife, but might just as well be a fork, they will only say there is a fork complex as well as a knife complex. And that increasing complexity of complexes is the net in which liberty will be taken.

Instead of seeing in the odd cases of the cow's tongue or the bleating sheep the peril of their past generalizations, they will see them only as starting

points for new generalizations. They will get yet
another theory out of it. And they will begin acting
on the theory long before they have done thinking
about it. They will start out with some new and
crude conception that sculpture has made children
scream or that nursery rhymes have made children
sleepless; and the thing will be a clause in a programme of reform before it has begun to be a conclusion in a serious study of psychology. That is the
practical problem about modern liberty which the
critics will not see; of which eugenics is one example
and all this amateur child-psychology is another. So
long as an old morality was in black and white like
a chess-board, even a man who wanted more of it
made white was certain that no more of it would be
made black. Now he is never certain what vices may
not be released, but neither is he certain what virtues
may be forbidden. Even if he did not think it wrong
to run away with a married woman, he knew that his
neighbours only thought it wrong because the woman
was married. They did not think it wrong to run
away with a red-haired woman, or a left-handed
woman, or a woman subject to headaches. But when
we let loose a thousand eugenical speculations, all
adopted before they are verified and acted on even
before they are adopted, he is just as likely as not
to find himself separated from the woman for those

or any other reasons. Similarly there was something
to be said for restrictions, even rather puritanical
and provincial restrictions, upon what children
should read or see, so long as they fenced in certain
fixed departments like sex or sensational tortures.
But when we begin to speculate on whether other
sensations may not stimulate as dangerously as sex,
those other sensations may be as closely controlled
as sex. When, let us say, we hear that the eye and
brain are weakened by the rapid turning of wheels
as well as by the most revolting torturing of men, we
have come into a world in which cart-wheels and
steam-engines may become as obscene as racks and
thumbscrews. In short, so long as we *combine* ceaseless and often reckless scientific speculation with
rapid and often random social reform, the result
must inevitably be not anarchy but ever-increasing
tyranny. There must be a ceaseless and almost mechanical multiplication of things forbidden. The
resolution to cure all the ills that flesh is heir to,
combined with the guesswork about all possible ills
that flesh and nerve and brain-cell may be heir to—
these two things conducted simultaneously must inevitably spread a sort of panic of prohibition. Scientific imagination and social reform between them
will quite logically and almost legitimately have
made us slaves. This seems to me a very clear, a
very fair and a very simple point of public criticism;

and I am much mystified about why so many publicists cannot even see what it is, but take refuge in charges of anarchism, which firstly are not true, and secondly have nothing to do with it.

WINGS AND THE HOUSEMAID

AMONG the numberless fictitious things that I have fortunately never written, there was a little story about a logical maiden lady engaging apartments in which she was not allowed to keep a cat or dog, who, nevertheless, stipulated for permission to keep a bird, and who eventually walked round to her new lodgings accompanied by an ostrich. There was a moral to the fable, connected with that exaggeration of small concessions, in which, for instance, the Germans indulged about espionage, or the Jews about interest. But this faded fancy returned to my mind in another fashion when a very humane lady suggested the other day that every domestic servant, including the butler, I presume, should be described as " a home-bird." Unless the lady is mis-reported, which is likely enough, she wanted servants called home-birds because they keep the home-fires burning, which, as many will be ready to point out, is hardly the particular form in which the domesticity of the nest commonly expresses itself. But I am not at all disposed to deride the lady's real meaning, still less her real motives, which referred to a real movement of social conscience and sentiment, however wrongly ex-

pressed. She was troubled about the implied insolence of calling servants servants and apparently
even of talking about "maids" or "the cook."
Therefore she evolved the ornithological substitute;
about which, of course, it would be easy to evolve a
whole aviary of allegorical parodies. It would be
easy to ask whether a private secretary is to be called
a secretary bird, or, perhaps, the telephone girl a
humming-bird; but it will be enough to say generally
of the proposal, in its present verbal form, that one
has only to submit it to any living and human housemaid in order to find that particular home-bird developing rapidly into a mocking-bird. Nevertheless,
as I have said, we should not merely dismiss any
social doubts thus suggested, or any impulse towards
a warmer respect for work generally grossly under-
valued. Too many people, of the more snobbish
social strata, have treated their servants as home-
birds; as owls, for instance, who can be up all night,
or as vultures, who can eat the refuse fit for the
dustbin. I would not throw cold water on any indignation on this score; but I note it as typical of
the time that the indignation should fail on the side
of intelligence. For it is the mark of our time, above
almost everything else, that it goes by associations
and not by arguments; that is why it has a hundred
arts and no philosophy.

Thus, for instance, the lady in question lumps together a number of terms that have no logical connexion at all. There is at least a meaning in objecting to one person calling another a servant. As I shall suggest in a moment, there is not much sense in changing the name when you do not change the thing; and there is a great deal of nonsense in denying the status of the servant at the moment when you are making it more servile. Still, anybody can see how the term might be held to hurt human dignity; but the other terms mentioned cannot hurt human dignity at all. I cannot conceive why it should insult a cook to call her a cook, any more than it insults a cashier to call him a cashier; to say nothing of the fact that dealing with cookery is far nobler than dealing with cash. And the third title certainly tells entirely the other way. The word "maid" is not only a noble old English word, with no note of social distinction; for a mediæval king might have praised his daughter as "a good maid." It is a word loaded with magnificent memories, in history, literature, and religion. Joan the Maid suggests a little more than Joan the maidservant; and, as it says in Mr. Belloc's stirring little poem:—

> By God who made the Master Maids,
> I know not whence she came;
> But the sword she bore to save the soul
> Went up like an altar flame.

WINGS AND THE HOUSEMAID

It is needless here to trace the idea back to its splendid sources; or to explain how the word maid has been the highest earthly title, not only on earth but in Heaven. "Mother and maiden was never none but she." Here at least modern humanitarian criticism has gone curiously astray, even for its own purposes; any servant may well be satisfied with the dignity of being called the maid, just as any workman may be rightly honoured by the accident which calls him the man. For in a modern industrial dispute, as reported in the papers, I always feel there is a final verdict and sentence in the very statement of the case of Masters *versus* Men.

The true objection lies much farther back. It begins with the simple fact that the home-bird is not in her own home. When that particular sparrow stokes the fire, as above described, it is not her own fireside; when we happen to meet a canary carrying a coal scuttle, the canary is not generally a coal-owner. In short, wherever we find pelicans, penguins, or flamingoes keeping the home-fires burning, they may all be earnestly wishing that they could fly away to their homes. Now a moderate amount of this temporary and vicarious domesticity is a natural enough accident in social relations, so long as it does not obscure and obstruct more individual and direct domesticity. In short, there is no particular harm in the maid being a housemaid in some one else's house, if she normally has a chance of being a housewife in her own. As I shall suggest in a moment, this is what was really implied in certain older institutions to which the wisest are now looking back. But in any case it is odd that the home-bird should thus plume itself at this moment; for the trend of the time is certainly not towards any domesticity, direct or indirect. The birds have long been netted or caged, by cold, fear and hunger, into larger and more terrorist systems. The happy home-birds are keeping the factory fires burning. The only legal and industrial tendency seems to be to shut up more and more of the women, those strange wild fowl, in those colossal cages of iron. Nor is the change one of mere æsthetic atmosphere; we know now that it is one of economic fact and may soon be one of legal definition. In a word, it is queer that we should suddenly grow sensitive about calling people servants when we are in the act of making them slaves. Indeed, in many concrete cases we may already be said to be making them convicts. The true moral meaning of much that is called the improvement of prisons is not that we are turning prisoners into a better sort of people, but rather that we are treating a better sort of people as prisoners. The broad arrow is broadened in so liberal a fashion as to cover those who would once have been counted respectable;

and there is a sense in which the broad arrow, becoming broader, is bound to become blunter. The prison becomes utilitarian as well as disciplinary, as the factory becomes disciplinary as well as utilitarian. The two become simply and substantially the same; for they have to treat the same sort of impecunious people in the same sort of impersonal way. People may differ about the definition of that common condition or status. Some may eagerly salute persons involved as home-birds; others may prefer to describe them as jail-birds.

For the rest, if anybody wants to strike the central stream of moderate sanity in the servant problem, I recommend him first to read with a close attention or preferably to sing in a loud voice, the song called " Sally in Our Alley." In that great and gloriously English lyric, the poet does not disguise the accidental discomforts of the great system of apprenticeship which was part of the glory of the Guilds. He even exhibits his Christian prejudices by comparing his master to a Turk. He actually entertains, as every reflective social reformer must, the hypothetical alternative of the Servile State, and considers the relative advantages of a slave that rows a galley. But the point is that what makes him refuse and endure is hope, the sure and certain hope of a glorious emancipation; not the hopeless hope of a chance in a scramble, with a general recommendation to get on or get out, but a charter of knowledge and honour, that " when his seven long years are past," a door shall open to him, which our age has shut on the great multitude of mankind.

THE SLAVERY OF FREE VERSE

THE truth most needed to-day is that the end is never the right end. The beginning is the right end at which to begin. The modern man has to read everything backwards; as when he reads journalism first and history afterwards—if at all. He is like a blind man exploring an elephant, and condemned to begin at the very tip of its tail. But he is still more unlucky; for when he has a first principle, it is generally the very last principle that he ought to have. He starts, as it were, with one infallible dogma about the elephant; that its tail is its trunk. He works the wrong way round on principle; and tries to fit all the practical facts to his principle. Because the elephant has no eyes in its tail-end, he calls it a blind elephant; and expatiates on its ignorance, superstition, and need of compulsory education. Because it has no tusks at its tail-end, he says that tusks are a fantastic flourish attributed to a fabulous creature, an ivory chimera that must have come through the ivory gate. Because it does not as a rule pick up things with its tail, he dismisses the magical story that it can pick up things with its trunk. He probably says it is plainly a piece of anthropomorphism to suppose that an elephant can pack its trunk. The result is that he becomes as pallid and worried as a pessimist; the world to him is not only an elephant, but a white elephant. He does not know what to do with it, and cannot be persuaded of the perfectly simple explanation; which is that he has not made the smallest real attempt to make head or tail of the animal. He will not begin at the right end; because he happens to have come first on the wrong end.

But in nothing do I feel this modern trick, of trusting to a fag-end rather than a first principle, more than in the modern treatment of poetry. With this or that particular metrical form, or unmetrical form, or unmetrical formlessness, I might be content or not, as it achieves some particular effect or not. But the whole general tendency, regarded as an emancipation, seems to me more or less of an enslavement. It seems founded on one sub-conscious idea; that talk is freer than verse; and that verse, therefore, should claim the freedom of talk. But talk, especially in our time, is not free at all. It is tripped up by trivialities, tamed by conventions, loaded with dead words, thwarted by a thousand meaningless things. It does not liberate the soul so much, when a man can say, " You always look so nice," as when he can say, " But your eternal summer shall not fade." The first is an awkward and constrained sentence ending with the weakest word ever used, or rather misused, by man. The second is like the gesture of a giant or the sweeping flight of an archangel; it has the very rush of liberty. I do not despise the man who says the first, because he *means* the second; and what he means is more important than what he says. I have always done my best to emphasize the inner dignity of these daily things, in spite of their dull externals; but I do not think it an improvement that the inner spirit itself should grow more external and more dull. It is thought right to discourage numbers of prosaic people trying to be poetical; but I think it much more of a bore to watch numbers of poetical people trying to be prosaic. In short, it is another case of tail-foremost philosophy; instead of watering the laurel hedge of the cockney villa, we bride the cockney to brick in the plant of Apollo.

I have always had the fancy that if a man were really free, he would talk in rhythm and even in rhyme. His most hurried post card would be a sonnet; and his most hasty wires like harp-strings. He would breathe a song into the telephone; a song which would be a lyric or an epic, according to the time involved in awaiting the call; or in his inevitable altercation with the telephone girl, the duel would be also a duet. He would express his preference among the dishes at dinner in short impromptu poems, combining the more mystical gratitude of grace with a certain epigrammatic terseness, more convenient for domestic good feeling. If Mr. Yeats can say, in exquisite verse, the exact number of bean-rows he would like on his plantation, why not the number of beans he would like on his plate? If he can issue a rhymed request to pro·· cure the honey-bee, why not pass the honey? Misunderstandings might arise at first with the richer and more fantastic poets; and Francis Thompson might have asked several times for " the gold skins of undelirious wine " before anybody understood that he wanted the grapes. Nevertheless, I will maintain that his magnificent phrase would be a far more real expression of God's most glorious gift of the vine, than if he had simply said in a peremptory manner " grapes "; especially if the culture of compulsory education had carefully taught him to pronounce it as if it were " gripes." And if a man could ask for a potato in the form of a poem, the poem would not be merely a more romantic but a much more realistic rendering of a potato. For a potato is a poem; it is even an ascending scale of poems; beginning at the root, in subterranean grotesques in the Gothic manner, with humps like the deformities of a goblin and eyes like a beast of Revelation, and rising up through the green shades of the earth to a crown that has the shape of stars and the hue of Heaven.

But the truth behind all this is that expressed in that very ancient mystical notion, the music of the spheres. It is the idea that, at the back of everything, existence begins with a harmony and not a chaos; and, therefore, when we really spread our wings and find a wider freedom, we find it in something more continuous and recurrent, and not in something more fragmentary and crude. Freedom is fullness, especially fullness of life; and a full vessel is more rounded and complete than an empty one, and not less so. To vary Browning's phrase, we find in prose the broken arcs, in poetry the perfect round. Prose is not the freedom of poetry; rather prose in the fragments of poetry. Prose, at least in the prosaic sense, is poetry interrupted, held up and cut off from its course; the chariot of Phœbus stopped by a block in the Strand. But when it begins to move again at all, I think we shall find certain old-fashioned things move with it, such as repetition and even measure, rhythm and even rhyme. We shall discover with horror that the wheels of the chariot go round and round; and even that the horses of the chariot have the usual number of feet.

Anyhow, the right way to encourage the cortège

is not to put the cart before the horse. It is not to make poetry more poetical by ignoring what distinguishes it from prose. There may be many new ways of making the chariot move again; but I confess that most of the modern theorists seem to me to be lecturing on a new theory of its mechanics, while it is standing still. If a wizard before my very eyes works a miracle with a rope, a boy and a mango plant, I am only theoretically interested in the question of a sceptic, who asks why it should not be done with a garden hose, a maiden aunt and a monkey-tree. Why not, indeed, if he can do it? If a saint performs a miracle to-morrow, by turning a stone into a fish, I shall be the less concerned at being asked, in the abstract, why a man should not also turn a camp-stool into a cockatoo; but let him do it, and not merely explain how it can be done. It is certain that words such as " birds " and " sweet," which are as plain as " fish " or " stone," can be combined in such a miracle as " Bare ruined quires where late the sweet birds sang." So far as I can follow my own feelings, the metre and fall of the feet, even the rhyme and place in the sonnet, have a great deal to do with producing such an effect. I do not say there is no other way of producing such an effect. I only ask, not without longing, where else in this wide and weary time is it produced? I know I cannot pro-

THE SLAVERY OF FREE VERSE

duce it; and I do not in fact feel it when I hear
vers libres. I know not where is that Promethean
heat; and, even to express my ignorance, I am glad
to find better words than my own.

PROHIBITION AND THE PRESS

An organ of the Nonconformist Conscience, while commenting very kindly on my recent remarks about America, naturally went on to criticize, though equally kind, my remarks about Prohibition. Now, so far as I am concerned, the problem is not so much Prohibition with a large P as prohibition with a small one. I mean, I am interested not so much in liquor as in liberty. I want to know on what principle the prohibitionists are proceeding in this case, and how they think it applies to any other case. And I cannot for the life of me make out. They might be expected to argue that there is something peculiar in principle about the position of liquor, and make that the basis for attacking liquor. But in point of fact they do not attack liquor; they do quite simply attack liberty. I mean that they are satisfied with saying about this liberty what can obviously be said about any liberty—that it can be, and is, abominably abused. If that had been a final objection to any form of freedom, there never would have been any form of freedom. And there most notably would never have been the particular forms of freedom which are most sacred to the Nonconformist Conscience. The Nonconformists have demanded liberty to secede, though they knew it led to an anarchy of sects and spiteful controversies. They had demanded the licence to print, though they knew it involved the licence to print twenty falsehoods to one truth. I suppose there is nothing in history of which the modern Puritan would be more innocently proud than the thing called the Liberty of the Press, which arose out of the pamphleteering of the seventeenth century, and especially the great pamphlet of Milton. Yet everything that Milton says, about allowing controversy in spite of its dangers, could be applied word for word to the case of allowing drinking in spite of its dangers. Is not the virtue that shuts itself up in a temperance hotel a fugitive and cloistered virtue? Is not the morality that dare not have wine on the table, or in the town, emphatically one that dares not sally out to meet its enemy? All Milton's arguments for freedom are arguments for beer; and, of course, Milton himself would certainly have applied them to beer. The highly successful brewer to whom he was Latin secretary—a gentleman of the name of Williams, otherwise Cromwell—would hardly have been pleased with him if he had not applied them to beer.

For instance the critic whom I am here venturing to criticize says that people differ about Prohibition according to their knowledge or ignorance of the dreadful state of the slums, the ravages of alcoholism in our industrial cities, and all the rest of it. Whether or no this be a good argument against the public-house, there is no doubt that I could easily turn it against the public press. I could insist that I am a common Cockney Fleet Street journalist who has done nightly work for daily papers and fed off nocturnal potato-stalls; whereas he is probably a cultivated Congregationalist minister writing in a library of theological works. I might say that I know better than he does, or than most people do, the cynicism and the vulgarity and the vices of journalism. But, as a matter of fact, the vices of journalism have by this time become as evident to the people who read journals as to the people who write them. All responsible people are complaining of the power and condition of the press, and no people more than these earnest and ethical Nonconformists. It is they who complain most bitterly that a Jingo press can manufacture war. It is they who declare most indignantly that a sensational press is undermining morality. They often, to my mind, unduly confuse matters of morality with matters of taste. They often, to my mind, denounce as mere Jingoism what is simply the deeply democratic and popular character of patriotism. But nobody will deny that to a large extent they are legitimately and logically alarmed about the abuses and absurdities of the newspapers. But they have not yet used this as an argument for a veto upon all newspapers. Why in the world should they use the parallel evils as an argument for a veto on all public-houses?

For my part I do feel very strongly about the frivolity and irresponsibility of the press. It seems impossible to exaggerate the evil that can be done by a corrupt and unscrupulous press. If drink directly ruins the family, it only indirectly ruins the nation. But bad journalism does directly ruin the nation, considered as a nation; it acts on the corporate national will and sways the common national decision. It may force a decision in a few hours that will be an incurable calamity for hundreds of years. It may drive a whole civilization to defeat, to slavery, to bankruptcy, to universal famine. Even at this moment there are prominent papers wildly urging us to war—not with our foes but with our friends. There are some journalists so wicked as to want war, almost for its own sake; there are more journalists so weak-minded as to work for war without even wanting it. Let us give one example out of fifty of the sort of phrases that flash by us when we turn over the papers. A headline in enormous letters announces that the French are " scuttling " out of the disputed areas in the Near East. The phrase about scuttling, and the policy of scuttle, has been familiar and firmly established in English journalism as meaning a cow-

ardly and servile surrender, admitting abject defeat.
And the suggestion is that the French, being notoriously a nation of cowards, having that tendency to
panic produced by a habit of dancing and a diet of
frogs, can vividly be pictured as scampering with
screams of terror from the sight of a Turk with a
drawn sabre. This is the way our newspapers improve our relations with our Allies. Only the newspaper men seem to have got a little mixed in their
eagerness to expatiate on the wide field of French
vileness and ignominy. Only a little while ago the
same papers were telling us that the French were
furious filibusters, forcing war in every corner of the
world. We were told that it was France which was
militaristic and aggressive, and all her rivals were
made to scuttle. We were told that it was the
Frenchman and not the Turk who was the terrible
person holding the drawn sabre. In plain words,
these journalists are resolved to show that whatever
the French do is wrong. If they advance, they are
arrogant; if they retreat, they are cowardly. If
they keep an army beyond the Rhine, they are pursuing a policy of militarism; if they withdraw an
army from somewhere else, they are pursuing a policy
of scuttle. Where M. Poincaré is ready to fight, he
is a fire-eater who cares for nothing but fighting;
where he is not ready to fight, he is a poltroon who
is always notoriously too timid to fight. The careful

98

selection of language of this sort, for a given period, might quite possibly land us in a European war—a war in which we should be certainly on the wrong side, and almost certainly on the losing side.

Suppose I come forward with this great reform of the Prohibition of the Press. Suppose I suggest that the police should forcibly shut up all the newspaper-offices, as the other reformers wish to shut up all the public-houses. What answer will the Puritan moralists make to me, or on what principle do they distinguish between the one reform and the other? There is no kind of doubt about the harm that journalism does; and their own line of argument precludes them from appealing merely to the good that it does. As a matter of fact, far better poems have been written in taverns than are ever likely to appear in daily papers. And, from Pantagruel to Pickwick, this form of festivity has a roll of literary glory to its credit which is never likely to be found in the back files of any newspaper that I know of. But the Puritans do not discuss the healthier tradition of wine; they consider their argument sufficiently supported by the unhealthy effects of gin and bad beer in the slums. And if we adopt that principle of judging by the worst, then the worst effects of the press are far wider than the worst effects of the public-house. What exactly is the principle by which they distinguish between lawful and unlawful liberty, or mixed and unmixed licence? I have a rough-and-ready test, which may be right or wrong, but which I can at least state; but where has their test been stated? I say that the simplest form of freedom is that which distinguishes the free man from the slave —the ownership of his own body and his own bodily activities. That there is a risk in allowing him this ownership is obvious, and has always been obvious. The risk is not confined to the question of drink, but covers the whole question of health. But surely the other forms of freedom, such as freedom to print, are very much more indirect and disputable. A newspaper may be made the instrument of the vilest sort of swindling or starving of a whole people. Why are we to grant the remote right, and deny the intimate right? Moreover, a newspaper is a new thing; if our fathers had the right to it, they never knew it. Fermented liquor is as old as civilization, or older. But what I have asked for again and again is simply the principle of the Prohibitionists: and I am asking still.

THE MERCY OF MR. ARNOLD BENNETT

Mr. Arnold Bennett recently wrote one of his humorous and humane *causeries*, pleading very properly for social imagination and the better understanding of our fellows. He carried it, however, to the point of affirming, as some fatalists do, that we should never judge anybody in the sense of condemning anybody, in connexion with his moral conduct. Some time ago the same distinguished writer showed that his mercy and magnanimity were indeed on a heroic scale by reviewing a book of mine, and even saying many kind things about it. But to these he added a doubt about whether true intelligence could be consistent with the acceptance of any dogma. In truth there are only two kinds of people; those who accept dogmas and know it, and those who accept dogmas and don't know it. My only advantage over the gifted novelist lies in my belonging to the former class. I suspect that his unconsciousness of his dogmas extends to an unconsciousness of what he means by a dogma. If it means merely the popular idea of being dogmatic, it might be suggested that

101

saying that all dogmatism is unintelligent is itself somewhat dogmatic. And something of what is true of his veto on dogma is also true of his veto on condemnation; which is really a veto on vetoes.

Mr. Arnold Bennett does not darken the question with the dreary metaphysics of determinism; he is far too bright and adroit a journalist for that. But he does make a simple appeal to charity, and even Christianity, basing on it the idea that we should not judge people at all, or even blame them at all. Like everybody else who argues thus, he imagines himself to be pleading for mercy and humanity. Like everybody else who argues thus, he is doing the direct contrary. This particular notion of not judging people really means hanging them without trial. It would really substitute for judgment not mercy but something much more like murder. For the logical process through which the discussion passes is always the same; I have seen it in a hundred debates about fate and free-will. First somebody says, like Mr. Bennett: "Let us be kinder to our brethren, and not blame them for faults we cannot judge." Then some casual common-sense person says: "Do you really mean you would let anybody pick your pocket or cut your throat without protest?" Then the first man always answers as Mr. Bennett does: "Oh, no; I would punish him to protect myself and protect society; but I would not *blame* him, because I would not venture to judge him." The philosopher seems to have forgotten that he set out with the idea of being kinder to the cut-throat and the pick-pocket. His sense of humour should suggest to him that the pick-pocket might possibly prefer to be blamed, rather than go to penal servitude for the protection of society.

Now of course Mr. Bennett is quite right in the most mystical and therefore the most deeply moral sense. We do not know what God knows about the merits of a man. Nor do we know what God knows about the needs of a community. A man who poisons his little niece for money may have mysterious motives and excuses we cannot understand. And so he may serve mysterious social purposes we cannot follow. We are not infallible when we think we are punishing criminals; but neither are we infallible when we think we are protecting society. Our inevitable ignorance seems to me to cut both ways. But even in our ignorance one thing is vividly clear. Mr. Bennett's solution is not the more merciful, but the less merciful of the two. To say that we may punish people, but not blame them, is to say that we have a right to be cruel to them, but not a right to be kind to them.

For after all, blame is itself a compliment. It is a compliment because it is an appeal; and an appeal to a man as a creative artist making his soul. To say

103

to a man, " rascal " or " villain " in ordinary society
may seem abrupt; but it is also elliptical. It is an
abbreviation of a sublime spiritual apostrophe for
which there may be no time in our busy social life.
When you meet a millionaire, the cornerer of many
markets, out at dinner in Mayfair, and greet him (as
is your custom) with the exclamation " Scoundrel! "
you are merely shortening for convenience some such
expression as: " How can you, having the divine
spirit of man that might be higher than the angels,
drag it down so far as to be a scoundrel? " When
you are introduced at a garden party to a Cabinet
Minister who takes tips on Government contracts,
and when you say to him in the ordinary way
" Scamp! " you are merely using the last word of a
long moral disquisition; which is in effect, " How
pathetic is the spiritual spectacle of this Cabinet
Minister, who being from the first made glorious by
the image of God, condescends so far to lesser ambitions as to allow them to turn him into a scamp."
It is a mere taking of the tail of a sentence to stand
for the rest; like saying 'bus for omnibus. It is
even more like the case of that seventeenth century
Puritan whose name was something like " If-Jesus-
Christ-Had-Not-Died-For-Thee-Thou-Hadst-Been-
Damned, Higgins "; but who was, for popular convenience, referred to as " Damned Higgins." But it
is obvious, anyhow, that when we call a man a

coward, we are in so doing asking him how he can be a coward when he could be a hero. When we rebuke a man for being a sinner, we imply that he has the powers of a saint.

But punishing him for the protection of society involves no regard for him at all. It involves no limit of proportion in the punishment at all. There are some limits to what ordinary men are likely to say that an ordinary man deserves. But there are no limits to what the danger of the community may be supposed to demand. We would not, even if we could, boil the millionaire in oil or skin the poor little politician alive; for we do not think a man deserves to be skinned alive for taking commissions on contracts. But it is by no means so certain that the skinning him alive might not protect the community. Corruption can destroy communities; and torture can deter men. At any rate the thing is not so self-evidently useless as it is self-evidently unjust and vindictive. We refrain from such fantastic punishments, largely because we *do* have some notion of making the punishment fit the crime, and not merely fit the community. If the State were the sole consideration, it may be inferred a priori that people might be much more cruel. And in fact, where the State was the sole consideration, it was found in experience that they were much more cruel. They were much more cruel precisely because they were freed from all responsibilities about the innocence or guilt of the individual. I believe that in heathen Rome, the model of a merely civic and secular loyalty, it was a common practice to torture the slaves of any household subjected to legal enquiry. If you had remonstrated, because no crime had been proved against the slaves, the State would had answered in the modern manner: " We are not punishing the crime; we are protecting the community."

Now that example is relevant just now in more ways than one. Of course I do not mean that this was the motive of all historical cruelties, or that some did not spring from quite an opposite motive. But it was the motive of such tyranny in the heathen world; and in this, as in other things, the modern world has largely become a heathen world. And modern tyranny can find its prototype in the torturing of heathen slaves in two fundamental respects. First, that the modern world has returned to the test of the heathen world, that of considering service to the state and not justice to the individual. And second, that the modern world, like the heathen world, is here inflicting it chiefly on subordinate and submerged classes of society; on slaves or those who are almost slaves.

For the heathen state is a Servile State. And no one has more of this view of the state than the State

Socialists. The official Labour Politician would be the first to say in theory that punishment must not be a moral recompense, but merely a social regulation. And he would be the first to say in practice that it is the poor and ignorant who must be regulated. Doubtless it is one thing to be regulated and another to be tortured. But when once the principle is admitted broadly, the progress towards torture may proceed pretty briskly. In the psychological sphere, it is already as bad as it has ever been. It may come as a surprise to the humanitarian to learn it; but it is none the less true, that a mother may undergo moral torture in the last degree, when her children are taken from her by brute force. And that incident has become so common in the policing of the poor nowadays as hardly to call for notice. And that example is particularly relevant to the present argument. Nobody could pretend that the affectionate mother of a rather backward child *deserves* to be punished by having all the happiness taken out of her life. But anybody can pretend that the act is needed for the happiness of the community. Nobody will say it was so wicked of her to love her baby that she deserves to lose it. But it is always easy to say that some remote social purpose will be served by taking it away. Thus the elimination of punishment means the extension of tyranny. Men would not do things so oppressive so long as they were vindictive. It is only when punishment is purged of vengeance that it can be as villainous as that.

For that matter, it would be easy to find examples much nearer than this one to the torturing of the Roman slaves. There is a very close parallel in the Third Degree, as applied by the police to the criminal class on suspicion, especially in America; for the criminal class is a submerged class like the slaves; and it is but an experiment on the nerves in one way instead of another, like a preference for the rack rather than the thumbscrew. But the point is that it is applied to the criminal type without any proof that it is in this case criminal; and the thing is justified not by the criminality of the individual but by the needs of the State. The police would answer exactly as the pagans answered: "We are not punishing the crime; we are protecting the community."

This tyranny is spreading. And there is no hope for liberty or democracy until we all demand again, with a tongue of thunder, the right to be blamed. We shall never feel like free men until we assert again our sacred claim to be punished. The denunciation of a man for what he chose to do is itself the confession that he chose to do it; and it is beneath his dignity to admit that he could have done nothing else. The only alternative theory is that we can do nothing but what we do, and our rulers can do anything whatever to restrain us. Compared with that, it would be better that roaring mobs should rise all over England, uproariously demanding to be hanged.

A DEFENCE OF DRAMATIC UNITIES

Injustice is done to the old classical rules of artistic criticism, because we do not treat them as artistic criticism. We first turn them into police regulations, and then complain of them for being so. But I suspect, with the submission proper to ignorance, that the art canons of Aristotle and others were much more generally artistic, in the sense of atmospheric. We allow a romantic critic to be as dogmatic as Ruskin, and still feel that he is not really being so despotic as Boileau. If a modern, like Maeterlinck, says that all drama is in an open door at the end of an empty passage, we do not take it literally, like a notice requiring an extra exit in case of fire. But if an ancient, like Horace, says that all drama demands a closed door, which shall hide Medea while she murders her children, then we do receive it as something rigid and formal, like the order to close the shutters on Zeppelin nights. Now how far the classical critics took their rules absolutely I do not know. But I am substantially sure that there is a true instinct at the back of them, whatever exceptions be allowed at the edges. The unities of time and place, that is the idea of keeping figures and events within the frame of a few hours or a few yards, is naturally decided as a specially artificial affront to the intellect. But I am sure it is an especially true suggestion to the imagination. It is exactly in the artistic atmosphere, where rules and reasons are so hard to define, that this unification would be most easy to defend. This limitation to a few scenes and actors really has something in it that pleases the imagination and not the reason. There are instances in which it may be broken boldly: there are types of art to which it does not apply at all. But wherever it can be satisfied, something not superficial but rather subconscious is satisfied. Something re-visits us that is the strange soul of single places; the shadow of haunting ghosts or of household gods. Like all such things, it is indescribable when it is successful: it is easier to describe the disregard of it as unsuccessful. Thus Stevenson's masterpiece, "The Master of Ballantrae," always seems to me to fall into two parts, the finer which revolves round Durisdeer and the inferior which rambles through India and America. The slender and sinister figure in black, standing on the shore or vanishing from the shrubbery, does really seem to have come from the ends of the earth. In the chapters of travel he only serves to show that, for a boy's adventure tale, a good villain makes a bad hero. And even about

Hamlet I am so heretical as to be almost classical; I doubt whether the exile in England does not rather dwarf than dignify the prisoner of Denmark. I am not sure that he got anything out of the pirates he could not have got out of the players. And I am very sure indeed that this figure in black, like the other, produces a true though intangible effect of tragedy when, and because, we see him against the great grey background of the house of his fathers. In a word it is what Mr. J. B. Yeats, the poet's stimulating parent, calls in his excellent book of essays " the drama of the home." The drama is domestic, and is dramatic because it is domestic.

We might say that superior literature is centripetal, while inferior literature is centrifugal. But oddly enough, the same truth may be found by studying inferior as well as superior literature. What is true of a Shakespearean play is equally true of a shilling shocker. The shocker is at its worst when it wanders and escapes through new scenes and new characters. The shocker is at its best when it shocks by something familiar; a figure or fact that is already known though not understood. A good detective story also can keep the classic unities; or otherwise play the game. I for one devour detective stories; I am delighted when the dagger of the curate is found to be the final clue to the death of the vicar. But there is a point of honour for the author; he may conceal the curate's crime, but he must not conceal the curate. I feel I am cheated when the last chapter hints for the first time that the vicar had a curate. I am annoyed when a curate, who is a total stranger to me, is produced from a cupboard or a box in a style at once abrupt and belated. I am annoyed most of all when the new curate is only the tool of a terrible secret society ramifying from Moscow or Thibet. These cosmopolitan complications are the dull and not the dramatic element in the ingenious tales of Mr. Oppenheim or Mr. Le Queux. They entirely spoil the fine domesticity of a good murder. It is unsportsmanlike to call spies from the end of the earth, as it is to call spirits from the vasty deep, in a story that does not imply them from the start. And this because the supply is infinite; and the infinite, as Coventry Patmore well said, is generally alien to art. Everybody knows that the universe contains enough spies or enough spectres to kill the most healthy and vigorous vicar. The drama of detection is in discovering how he can be killed decently and economically, within the classic unities of time and place.

In short the good mystery story should narrow its circles like an eagle about to swoop. The spiral should curve inwards and not outwards. And this inward movement is in true poetic mysteries as well as mere police mystifications. It will be assumed that I am joking if I say there is a serious social meaning in this novel-reader's notion of keeping a crime in the family. It must seem mere nonsense to find a moral in this fancy, about washing gory linen at home. It will naturally be asked whether I have idealized the home merely as a good place for assassinations. I have not; any more than I have idealized the Church as a thing in which the curates can kill the vicars. Nevertheless the thing, like many things, is symbolic though it is not serious. And the objection to it implies a subtle misunderstanding, in many minds, of the whole case for the home as I have sometimes had occasion to urge it. When we defend the family we do not mean it is always a peaceful family; when we maintain the thesis of marriage we do not mean that it is always a happy marriage. We mean that it is the theatre of the spiritual drama, the place where things happen, especially the things that matter. It is not so much the place where a man kills his wife as the place where he can take the equally sensational step of not killing his wife. There is truth in the cynicism that calls marriage a trial; but even the cynic will admit that a trial may end in an acquittal. And the reason that the family has this central and crucial character is the same reason that makes it in politics the only prop of liberty. The family is the test of freedom; because the family is the only thing that the free man makes for himself and by himself. Other institutions must largely be made for him by strangers, whether the institutions be despotic or democratic. There is no other way of organizing mankind which can give this power and dignity, not only to mankind but to men. If anybody likes to put it so, we cannot really make all men democrats unless we make all men despots. That is to say, the co-operation of the commonwealth will be a mere automatic unanimity like that of insects, unless the citizen has some province of purely voluntary action; unless he is so far not only a citizen but a king. In the world of ethics this is called liberty; in the world of economics it is called property, and in the world of æsthetics, necessarily so much more dim and indefinable, it is darkly adumbrated in the old dramatic unities of place or time. It must indeed be a mistake in any case to treat such artistic rules as rigidly as if they were moral rules. It was an error if they ever were so treated; it may well be a question whether they were ever meant to be so treated. But when critics have suggested that these classical canons were a mere superficial varnish, it may safely be said that it is the critics who are superficial. Modern artists would have been wiser if they had developed sympathetically some of the Aristotelian æsthetics, as mediæval philosophers developed sympathetically the Aristolian logic and ethics. For a more subtle study of the unities of time and place, for example, as outlined for the Greek drama, might have led us towards what is perhaps the last secret of all legend and literature. It might have suggested why poets, pagan or not, returned perpetually to the idea of happiness as a place for humanity as a person. It might suggest why the world is always seeking for absolutes that are not abstractions; why fairyland was always a land, and even the Superman was almost a man.

THE BOREDOM OF BUTTER-
FLIES

THERE is one thing which critics perhaps tend to
forget when they complain that Mr. H. G. Wells no
longer concerns himself with telling a story. It is
that nobody else could interest and excite us so much
without telling a story. It is possible to read one of
his recent novels almost without knowing the story
at all. It is possible to dip into it as into a book of
essays, and pick up opinions here and there. But all
the essays are brilliant essays, and all the opinions
are striking opinions. It does not much matter who
holds the opinions; it is possible that the author does
not hold them at all, and pretty certain that he will
not hold them long. But nobody else could make
such splendid stuff out of the very refuse of his
rejected opinions. Seen from this side, even what
is called his failure must be recognized as a remarkable success. The personal story may fade
away, but it is something of an achievement to be
still interesting after becoming impersonal; like the
achievement of the Cheshire cat who could grin
when he was no longer there. Moreover, these
impersonal and even irresponsible opinions of Mr.

Wells, though never conclusive, are always suggestive; each is a good starting-point for thought, if only for the thought that refutes it. In short, the critics of Mr. Wells rather exaggerate the danger of his story running to speculation, as if it were merely running to seed. Anyhow, they ought to remember that there are two meanings in running to seed; and one of them is connected with seed-time.

I have, however, a particular reason for mentioning the matter here. I confess there is more than one of Mr. Wells's recent novels that I have both read and not read. I am never quite sure that I have read all Shakespeare or all Boswell's Johnson; because I have so long had the habit of opening them anywhere. So I have opened the works of Mr. Wells anywhere, and had great fun out of the essays that would have seemed only long parentheses in the story. But, on getting to rather closer grips with the last of his stories, " The Secret Places of the Heart," I think I have caught a glimpse of a difficulty in this sort of narrative which is something deeper than mere digression. In a story like " Pickwick " or " Tristram Shandy " digression is never disappointment. But in this case, differing as I do from the merely hostile critics, I cannot dispel the atmosphere of disappointment. The story seems inconclusive in a sense beyond anything merely inconsistent; and I fancy I can guess why.

A pedantic logician may perhaps imagine that a thing can only be inconclusive at the conclusion. But I will boldly claim the liberty in language of saying that this sort of thing is inconclusive from the start. It begins inconclusive, and in that sense begins dull. The hero begins by telling the doctor about a mutable flux of flirtation, about his own experiments as a philanderer, always flitting like a butterfly from flower to flower. Now, it is highly probable that the diary of a butterfly would be very dull, even if it were only the diary of a day. His round need be no more really amusing than a postman's, since he has no serious spiritual interest in any of his places of call. Now, by starting his hero as a philosopher and also philanderer, and taking seriously his philosophy of philandering, the author as good as tells us, to start with, that his hero will not have any serious adventures at all. At the beginning of the story, he practically tells us that there will be no story. The story of a fickle man is not a story at all; because there is no strain or resistance in it. Somebody talked about tales with a twist; and it is certain that all tales are tales with a tug.

All the most subtle truths of literature are to be found in legend. There is no better test of the truth of serious fiction than the simple truths to be found in a fairy tale or an old ballad. Now, in the whole of folk-lore there is no such thing as free love.

There is such a thing as false love. There is also another thing, which the old ballads always talk of as true love. But the story always turns on the keeping of a bond or the breaking of it; and this quite apart from orthodox morality in the matter of the marriage bond. The love may be in the strict sense sinful, but it is never anarchical. There was quite as little freedom for Lancelot as for Arthur; quite as little mere philandering in the philosophy of Tristram as in the philosophy of Galahad. It may have been unlawful love, but it certainly was not lawless love. In the old ballads there is the triumph of true love, as in "The Bailiff's Daughter of Islington"; or the tragedy of true love, as in "Helen of Kirkconnel Lea"; or the tragedy of false love, as in the ballad of "Oh, waly, waly up the bank." But there is neither triumph nor tragedy in the idea of *avowedly* transient love; and no literature will ever be made out of it, except the very lightest literature of satire. And even the satire must be a satire on fickleness, and therefore involve an indirect ideal of fidelity. But you cannot make any enduring literature out of love *conscious* that it will not endure. Even if this mutability were working as morality, it would still be unworkable as art.

The decadents used to say that things like the marriage vow might be very convenient for commonplace public purposes, but had no place in the world of beauty and imagination. The truth is exactly the other way. The truth is that if marriage had not existed it would have been necessary for artists to invent it. The truth is that if constancy had never been needed as a social requirement, it would still have been created out of cloud and air as a poetical requirement. If ever monogamy is abandoned in practice, it will linger in legend and in literature. When society is haunted by the butterfly flitting from flower to flower, poetry will still be describing the desire of the moth for the star; and it will be a fixed star. Literature must always revolve round loyalties; for a rudimentary psychological reason, which is simply the nature of narrative. You cannot tell a *story* without the idea of pursuing a purpose and sticking to a point. You cannot tell a story without the idea of the Quest, the idea of the Vow; even if it be only the idea of the Wager.

Perhaps the most modern equivalent to the man who makes a vow is the man who makes a bet. But he must not hedge on a bet; still less must he welsh, or do a bolt when he has made a bet. Even if the story ends with his doing so, the dramatic emotion depends on our realizing the dishonesty of his doing so. That is, the drama depends on the keeping or breaking of a bond, if it be only a bet. A man wandering about a race-course, making bets that nobody took seriously, would be merely a bore. And so the hero wandering through a novel, making vows of love that nobody took seriously, is merely a bore. The point here is not so much that morally it cannot be a creditable story, but that artistically it cannot be a story at all. Art is born when the temporary touches the eternal; the shock of beauty is when the irresistible force hits the immovable post.

Thus in the last novel of Mr. Wells, what is inconclusive in the second part is largely due to what is convincing in the first part. By the time that the hero meets his new heroine on Salisbury Plain, he has seriously convinced us that there is nothing heroic about him, and that nothing heroic will happen to him; at any rate in that department. He disenchants the enchantment beforehand, and warns the reader against even a momentary illusion. When once a man looks forward as well as backward to disillusionment, no romance can be made of him.

Profligacy may be made romantic, precisely because it implies some betrayal or breaking of a law. But polygamy is not in the least romantic. Polygamy is dull to the point of respectability. When a man looks forward to a number of wives as he does to a number of cigarettes, you can no more make a book out of them than out of the bills from his tobacconist. Anything having the character of a Turkish harem has also something of the character of a Turkey carpet. It is not a portrait, or even a picture, but a pattern. We may at the moment be looking at one highly coloured and even flamboyant figure in the carpet; but we know that on every side, in front as well as behind, the image is repeated without purpose and without finality.

THE TERROR OF A TOY

IT would be too high and hopeful a compliment to
say that the world is becoming absolutely babyish.
For its chief weak-mindedness is an inability to appreciate the intelligence of babies. On every side we
hear whispers and warnings that would have
appeared half-witted to the Wise Men of Gotham.
Only this Christmas I was told in a toy-shop that
not so many bows and arrows were being made for
little boys; because they were considered dangerous.
It might in some circumstances be dangerous to have
a little bow. It is always dangerous to have a little
boy. But no other society, claiming to be sane, would
have dreamed of supposing that you could abolish all
bows unless you could abolish all boys. With the
merits of the latter reform I will not deal here
There is a great deal to be said for such a course;
and perhaps we shall soon have an opportunity of
considering it. For the modern mind seems quite in-
capable of distinguishing between the means and the
end, between the organ and the disease, between the
use and the abuse; and would doubtless break the
boy along with the bow, as it empties out the baby
with the bath.

But let us, by way of a little study in this mournful state of things, consider this case of the dangerous toy. Now the first and most self-evident truth is that, of all the things a child sees and touches, the most dangerous toy is about the least dangerous thing. There is hardly a single domestic utensil that is not much more dangerous than a little bow and arrow. He can burn himself in the fire, he can boil himself in the bath, he can cut his throat with the carving-knife, he can scald himself with the kettle, he can choke himself with anything small enough, he can break his neck off anything high enough. He moves all day long amid a murderous machinery, as capable of killing and maiming as the wheels of the most frightful factory. He plays all day in a house fitted up with engines of torture like the Spanish Inquisition. And while he thus dances in the shadow of death, he is to be saved from all the perils of possessing a piece of string, tied to a bent bough or twig. When he is a little boy it generally takes him some time even to learn how to hold the bow. When he does hold it, he is delighted if the arrow flutters for a few yards like a feather or an autumn leaf. But even if he grows a little older and more skilful, and has yet not learned to despise arrows in favour of aeroplanes, the amount of damage he could conceivably do with his little arrows would be about one hundredth part of the damage that he could always in any case have done by simply picking up a stone in the garden.

Now you do not keep a little boy from throwing stones by preventing him from ever seeing stones. You do not do it by locking up all the stones in the Geological Museum, and only issuing tickets of admission to adults. You do not do it by trying to pick up all the pebbles on the beach, for fear he should practise throwing them into the sea. You do not even adopt so obvious and even pressing a social reform as forbidding roads to be made of anything but asphalt, or directing that all gardens shall be made on clay and none on gravel. You neglect all these great opportunities opening before you; you neglect all these inspiring vistas of social science and enlightenment. When you want to prevent a child from throwing stones, you fall back on the stalest and most sentimental and even most superstitious methods. You do it by trying to preserve some reasonable authority and influence over the child. You trust to your private relation with the boy, and not to your public relation with the stone. And what is true of the natural missile is just as true, of course, of the artificial missile; especially as it is a very much more ineffectual and therefore innocuous missile. A man could be really killed, like St. Stephen, with the stones in the road. I doubt if he could be really killed, like St. Sebastian, with the arrows in the toyshop. But anyhow the very plain principle is the same. If you can teach a child not to throw a stone, you can teach him when to shoot an arrow; if you cannot teach him anything, he will always have something to throw. If he can be persuaded not to smash the Archdeacon's hat with a heavy flint, it will probably be possible to dissuade him from transfixing that head-dress with a toy arrow. If his training deters him from heaving half a brick at the postman, it will probably also warn him against constantly loosening shafts of death against the policeman. But the notion that the child depends upon particular implements, labelled dangerous, in order to be a danger to himself and other people, is a notion so nonsensical that it is hard to see how any human mind can entertain it for a moment. The truth is that all sorts of faddism, both official and theoretical, have broken down the natural authority of the domestic institution, especially among the poor; and the faddists are now casting about desperately for a substitute for the thing they have themselves destroyed. The normal thing is for the parents to prevent a boy from doing more than a reasonable amount of damage with his bow and arrow; and for the rest, to leave him to a reasonable enjoyment of them. Officialism cannot thus follow the life of the individual boy, as can the individual guardian. You cannot appoint a particular policeman for each boy, to pursue him when he climbs trees or falls into ponds. So the modern spirit has descended to the indescribable mental degradation of trying to abolish the abuse of things by abolishing the things themselves; which is as if it were to abolish ponds or abolish trees. Perhaps it will have a try at that before long. Thus we have all heard of savages who try a tomahawk for murder, or burn a wooden club for the damage it has done to society. To such intellectual levels may the world return.

There are indeed yet lower levels. There is a story from America about a little boy who gave up his toy cannon to assist the disarmament of the world. I do not know if it is true, but on the whole I prefer to think so; for it is perhaps more tolerable to imagine one small monster who could do such a thing than many more mature monsters who could invent or admire it. There were some doubtless who neither invented nor admired. It is one of the peculiarities of the Americans that they combine a power of producing what they satirize as " sob-stuff " with a parallel power of satirizing it. And of the two American tall stories, it is sometimes hard to say which is the story and which the satire. But it seems clear that some people did really repeat this story in a reverential spirit. And it marks, as I have said, another stage of cerebral decay. You can (with luck) break a window with a toy arrow; but you can hardly bombard a town with a toy gun. If people object to the mere model of a cannon, they must equally object to the picture of a cannon, and so to every picture in the world that depicts a sword or a spear. There would be a splendid clearance of all the great art-galleries of the world. But it would be nothing to the destruction of all the great libraries of the world, if we logically extended the principle to all the literary masterpieces that admit the glory of arms. When this progress had gone on for a century or two, it might begin to dawn on people that there was something wrong with their moral principle. What is wrong with their moral principle is that it is immoral. Arms, like every other adventure or art of man, have two sides according as they are invoked for the infliction or the defiance of wrong. They have also an element of real poetry and an element of realistic and therefore repulsive prose. The child's symbolic sword and bow are simply the poetry without the prose; the good without the evil. The toy sword is the abstraction and emanation of the heroic, apart from all its horrible accidents. It is the soul of the sword, that will never be stained with blood.

FALSE THEORY AND THE THEATRE

A THEATRICAL manager recently insisted on introducing Chinese labour into the theatrical profession. He insisted on having real Chinamen to take the parts of Chinese servants; and some actors seem to have resented it—as I think, very reasonably. A distinguished actress, who is clever enough to know better, defended it on the ground that nothing must interfere with the perfection of a work of art. I dispute the moral thesis in any case; and Nero would no doubt have urged it in defence of having real deaths in the amphitheatre. I do not admit in any case that the artist can be entirely indifferent to hunger and unemployment, any more than to lions or boiling oil. But, as a matter of fact, there is no need to raise the moral question, because the case is equally strong in relation to the artistic question. I do not think that a Chinese character being represented by a Chinese actor is the finishing touch to the perfection of a work of art. I think it is the last and lowest phase of the vulgarity that is called realism. It is in the same style and taste as the triumphs on which, I believe, some actor-managers

130

have prided themselves: the triumphs of having real silver for goblets or real jewels for crowns. That is not the spirit of a perfect artist, but rather of a purse-proud parvenu. The perfect artist would be he who could put on a crown of gilt wire or tinsel and make us feel he was a king.

Moreover, if the principle is to be extended from properties to persons, it is not easy to see where the principle can stop. If we are to insist on real Asiatics to act "Chu Chin Chow," why not insist on real Venetians to act "The Merchant of Venice"? We did experiment recently and I believe very successfully, in having the Jew acted by a real Jew. But I hardly think we should like to make it a rule that nobody must be allowed to act Shylock unless he can prove his racial right to call upon his father Abraham. Must the characters of Macbeth and Macduff only be represented by men with names like Macpherson and Macnab? Must the Prince of Denmark always be in private life a Dane? Must we import a crowd of Greeks before we are allowed to act "Troilus and Cressida," or a mob of real Egyptians to form the background of "Antony and Cleopatra"? Will it be necessary to kidnap an African gentleman out of Africa, by the methods of the slave trade, and force him into acting Othello? It was rather foolishly suggested at one time that our allies in Japan might be offended at the fantastic satire of " The Mikado." As a matter of fact, the satire of " The Mikado " is not at all directed against Japanese things, but exclusively against English things. But I certainly think there might be some little ill-feeling in Japan if gangs of Japanese coolies were shipped across two continents merely in order to act in it. If once this singular rule be recognized, a dramatist will certainly be rather shy of introducing Zulus or Red Indians into his dramas, owing to the difficulty in securing appropriate dramatic talent. He will hesitate before making his hero an Eskimo. He will abandon his intention of seeking his heroine in the Sandwich Islands. If he were to insist on introducing real cannibals, it seems possible that they might insist on introducing real cannibalism. This would be quite in the spirit of Nero and all the art critics of the Roman realism of the amphi-theatre. But surely it would be putting almost too perfect a finishing touch to the perfection of a work of art. That kind of finishing touch is a little too finishing.

The irony grew more intense when the newspapers that had insisted on Chinamen because they could not help being Chinamen began to praise them with admiration and astonishment because they looked Chinese. This opens up a speculation so complex and contradictory that I do not propose to follow it, for I am interested here not in the particular incident but in the general idea. It will be a sufficient statement of the fundamental fact of all the arts if I say simply that I do not believe in the resemblance. I do not believe that a Chinaman does look like a Chinaman. That is, I do not believe that any China- man will necessarily look like *the* Chinaman—the Chinaman in the imagination of the artist and the interest of the crowd. We all know the fable of the man who imitated a pig, and his rival who was hooted by the crowd because he could only produce what was (in fact) the squeak of a real pig. The crowd was perfectly right. The crowd was a crowd of very penetrating and philosophical art critics. They had come there not to hear an ordinary pig, which they could hear by poking in any ordinary pig-sty. They had come to hear how the voice of the pig affects the immortal mind and spirit of man; what sort of satire he would make of it; what sort of fun he can get out of it; what sort of exaggeration he feels to be an exaggeration of its essence, and not of its accidents. In other words, they had come to hear a squeak, but the sort of squeak which expresses what a man thinks of a pig—not the vastly inferior squeak which only expresses what a pig thinks of a man. I have myself a poetical enthusiasm for pigs, and the para- dise of my fancy is one where the pigs have wings. But it is only men, especially wise men, who discuss whether pigs can fly; we have no particular proof that pigs ever discuss it. Therefore the actor who imitated the quadruped may well have put into his squeak something of the pathetic cry of one longing for the wings of the dove. The quadruped himself might express no such sentiment; he might appear, and generally does appear, singularly unconscious of his own lack of feathers. But the same principle is true of things more dignified than the most dignified porker, though clad in the most superb plumage. If a vision of a stately Arab has risen in the imagination of an author who is an artist, he will be wise if he confides it to an actor who is also an artist. He will be much wiser to confide it to an actor than to an Arab. The actor, being a fellow-countryman and a fellow-artist, may bring out what the author thinks the Arab stands for; whereas the real Arab might be a particular individual who at that particular moment refused to stand for anything of the sort, or for anything at all. The principle is a general one; and I mean no disrespect to China in the porcine parallel, or in the figurative association of pigs and pig-tails.

But, as a matter of fact, the argument is especially apt in the case of China. For I fear that China is chiefly interesting to most of us as the other end of the world. It is valued as something far-off, and therefore fantastical, like a kingdom in the clouds of sunrise. It is not the very real virtues of the Chinese tradition—its stoicism, its sense of honour, its ancient peasant cults—that most people want to put into a play. It is the ordinary romantic feeling about something remote and extravagant, like the Martians or the Man in the Moon. It is perfectly reasonable to have that romantic feeling in moderation, like other amusements. But it is not reasonable to expect the remote person to feel remote from himself, or the man at the other end of the world not to feel it as this end. We must not ask the outlandish Oriental to feel outlandish, or a Chinaman to be astonished at being Chinese. If, therefore, the literary artist has the legitimate literary purpose of expressing the mysterious and alien atmosphere which China implies to him, he will probably do it much better with the aid of an actor who is not Chinese. Of course, I am not criticizing the particular details of the particular performance, of which I know little or nothing. I do not know the circumstances; and under the circumstances, for all I know, the experiment may have been very necessary or very successful. I merely protest against a theory of dramatic truth, urged in defence of the dramatic experiment, which seems to me calculated to falsify the whole art of the drama. It is founded on exactly the same fallacy as that of the infant in Stevenson's nursery rhyme, who thought that the Japanese children must suffer from home-sickness through being always abroad in Japan.

This brings us very near to an old and rather threadbare theatrical controversy, about whether staging should be simple or elaborate. I do not mean to begin that argument all over again. What is really wanted is not so much the simple stage-manager as the simple spectator. In a very real sense, what is wanted is the simple critic, who would be in truth the most subtle critic. The healthy human instincts in these things are at least as much spoiled by sophistication in the stalls as by elaboration on the stage. A really simple mind would enjoy a simple scene—and also a gorgeous scene. A popular instinct, to be found in all folk-lore, would know well enough when the one or the other was appropriate. But what is involved here is not the whole of that sophistication, but only one particular sophistry, and against that sophistry we may well pause to protest. It is the critical fallacy of cutting off a real donkey's head to put it on Bottom the Weaver; when the head is symbolical, and in that case more appropriate to the critic than to the actor.

THE SECRET SOCIETY OF MANKIND

WITH that fantastic love of paradox which gives pain to so many critics, I once suggested that there may be some truth in the notion of the brotherhood of men. This was naturally a subject for severe criticism from the modern or modernist standpoint; and I remember that the cleverest refutation of it occurred in a book which was called " We Moderns." It was written by a Mr. Edward Moore, and very well written too; indeed the author did himself some injustice in insisting on his own modernity; for he was not so very modern after all, but really quite lucid and coherent. But I will venture to take his remark as a text here because it concerns a matter on which most moderns darken council in a highly incoherent manner. It concerns the nature of the unity of men; which I did certainly state in its more defiant form as the equality of man. And I said that this norm or meeting-place of mankind can be found in the two extremes of the comic and the tragic. I said that no individual tragedy could be so tragic as having to die; and all men have equally to die. I said that nothing can be funnier than having two legs; and all men can join equally in the joke.

The critic in question was terribly severe on this remark. I believe that the words of his condemnation ran as follows: " Well, in this passage, there is an error so plain, it is almost inconceivable that a responsible thinker could have put it forward even in jest. For it is clear that the tragic and comic elements of which Mr. Chesterton speaks make not only mankind, but *all life*, equal. Everything that lives must die; and therefore it is, in Mr. Chesterton's sense, tragic. Everything that lives has shape; and therefore it is, in Mr. Chesterton's sense, comic. His premises lead to the equality not of mankind, but of all that lives; whether it be leviathan or butterfly, oak or violet, worm or eagle. . . . Would that he had said this! Then we who affirm inequality would be the first to echo him." I do not feel it hard to show that where Mr. Moore thinks equality wrong is exactly where it is right; and I will begin with mortality; premising that the same is true (for those who believe it) of immortality. Both are absolutes: a man cannot be somewhat mortal; nor can he be rather immortal.

To begin with, it must be understood that having an equality in being black or white is not even the same as being equally black or white. It is generally fair to take a familiar illustration; and I will take the ordinary expression about being all in the same boat. Mr. Moore and I and all men are not only all in the same boat, but have a very real equality implied in that fact. Nevertheless, since there is a word " inner " as well as a word " in," there is a sense in which some of us might be more in the boat than others. My fellow passengers might have stowed me at the bottom of the boat and sat on top of me, moved by a natural distaste for my sitting on top of them. I have noticed that I am often thus packed in a preliminary fashion into the back seats or basic parts of cabs, cars, or boats; there being evidently a feeling that I am the stuff of which the foundations of an edifice are made rather than its toppling minarets or tapering spires. Meanwhile Mr. Moore might be surveying the world from the masthead, if there were one, or leaning out over the prow with the forward gestures of a leader of men, or even sitting by preference on the edge of the boat with his feet paddling in the water, to indicate the utmost possible aristocratic detachment from us and our concerns. Nevertheless, in the large and ultimate matters which are the whole meaning of the phrase " all in the same boat," we should be all equally in the same boat. We should be all equally dependent upon the reassuring fact that a boat can float. If it did not float but sink, each one of us would have lost his one and only boat at the same decisive time and in the same disconcerting manner. If the King of the Cannibal Islands, upon whose principal island we might suffer the inconvenience of being wrecked, were to exclaim in a loud voice, "I will eat every single man who has arrived by that identical boat and no other," we should all be eaten, and we should all be equally eaten. For being eaten, considered as a tragedy, is not a matter of degree.

Now there is a fault in every analogy; but the fault in my analogy is not a fault in my argument; it is the chief fault in Mr. Moore's argument. It may be said that even in a shipwreck men are not equal, for some of us might be so strong that we could swim to the shore, or some of us might be so tough that the island king would repent of his rash vow after the first bite. But it is precisely here that I have again, as delicately as possible, to draw the reader's attention to the modest and little-known institution called death. We are all in a boat which will certainly drown us all, and drown us equally, the strongest with the weakest; we sail to the land of an ogre, *edax rerum*, who devours all without distinction. And the meaning in the phrase about being all in the same boat is, not that there are no degrees among the people in a boat, but that all those degrees are nothing compared with the stupendous fact that the boat goes home or goes down. And it is when I come to the particular criticism on my remarks about

" the fact of having to die " that I feel most confident that I was right and that Mr. Moore is wrong.

It will be noted that I spoke of the fact of having to die, not of the fact of dying. The brotherhood of men, being a spiritual thing, is not concerned merely with the truth that all men will die, but with the truth that all men know it. It is true, as Mr. Moore says, that everything will die, " whether it be leviathan or butterfly, oak or violet, worm or eagle " ; but exactly what, at the very start, we do not know is whether they know it. Can Mr. Moore draw forth leviathan with a hook, and extract his hopes and fears about the heavenly harpooner? Can he worm its philosophy out of a worm, or get the caterpillar to talk about the faint possibility of a butterfly? The caterpillar on the leaf may repeat to Blake his mother's grief; but it does not repeat to anybody its own grief about its own mother. Can he know whether oaks confront their fate with hearts of oak, as the phrase is used in a sailor's song? He cannot; and this is the whole point about human brotherhood, the point the vegetarians cannot see. This is why a harpooner is not an assassin; this is why eating whale's blubber, though not attractive to the fancy, is not repulsive to the conscience. We do not know what a whale thinks of death; still less what the other whales think of his being killed and eaten. He may be a pessimistic whale, and be perpetually wishing that this too, too solid blubber would melt, thaw and resolve itself into a dew. He may be a fanatical whale, and feel frantically certain of passing instantly into a polar paradise of whales, ruled by the sacred whale who swallowed Jonah. But we can elicit no sign or gesture from him suggestive of such reflections; and the working common sense of the thing is that no creatures outside man seem to have any sense of death at all. Mr. Moore has therefore chosen a strangely unlucky point upon which to challenge the true egalitarian doctrine. Almost the most arresting and even startling stamp of the solidarity and sameness of mankind is precisely this fact, not only of death, but of the shadow of death. We do know of any man whatever what we do not know of any other thing whatever, that his death is what we call a tragedy. From the fact that it is a tragedy flow all the forms and tests by which we say it is a murder or an execution, a martyrdom or a suicide. They all depend on an echo or vibration, not only in the soul of man, but in the souls of all men.

Oddly enough, Mr. Moore has made exactly the same mistake about the comic as about the tragic. It is true, I think, that almost everything which has a shape is humorous; but it is not true that everything which has a shape has a sense of humour.

142

The whale may be laughable, but it is not the whale who laughs; the image indeed is almost alarming. And the instant the question is raised, we collide with another colossal fact, dwarfing all human differentiations; the fact that man is the only creature who does laugh. In the presence of this prodigious fact, the fact that men laugh in different degrees, and at different things, shrivels not merely into insignificance but into invisibility. It is true that I have often felt the physical universe as something like a firework display: the most practical of all practical jokes. But if the cosmos is meant for a joke, men seem to be the only cosmic conspirators who have been let into the joke. There could be no fraternity like our freemasonry in that secret pleasure. It is true that there are no limits to this jesting faculty, that it is not confined to common human jests; but it is confined to human jesters. Mr. Moore may burst out laughing when he beholds the morning star, or be thrown into convulsions of amusement by the effect of moonrise seen through a mist. He may, to quote his own catalogue, see all the fun of an eagle or an oak tree. We may come upon him in some quiet dell rolling about in uproarious mirth, at the sight of a violet. But we shall not find the violet in a state of uproarious mirth at Mr. Moore. He may laugh at the worm;

but the worm will not turn and laugh at him. For that comfort he must come to his fellow-sinners: I shall always be ready to oblige.

The truth involved here has had many names; that man is the image of God; that he is the microcosm; that he is the measure of all things. He is the microcosm in the sense that he is the mirror, the only crystal we know in which the fantasy and fear in things are, in the double and real sense, things of reflection. In the presence of this mysterious monopoly the differences of men are like dust. That is what the equality of men means to me; and that is the only intelligible thing it ever meant to anybody. The common things of men infinitely outclass all classes. For a man to disagree with this it is necessary that he should understand it; Mr. Moore may really disagree with it; but the ordinary modern anti-egalitarian does not understand it, or apparently anything else. If a man says he had some transcendental dogma of his own, as Mr. Moore may possibly have, which mixes man with nature or claims to see other values in men, I shall say no more than that my religion is different from his, and I am uncommonly glad of it. But if he simply says that men cannot be equal because some of them are clever and some of them are stupid—why then I shall merely agree (not without tears) that some of them are very stupid.

THE SENTIMENTALISM OF
DIVORCE

DIVORCE is a thing which the newspapers now not only advertise, but advocate, almost as if it were a pleasure in itself. It may be, indeed, that all the flowers and festivities will now be transferred from the fashionable wedding to the fashionable divorce. A superb iced and frosted divorce-cake will be provided for the feast, and in military circles will be cut with the co-respondent's sword. A dazzling display of divorce presents will be laid out for the inspection of the company, watched by a detective dressed as an ordinary divorce guest. Perhaps the old divorce breakfast will be revived; anyhow, toasts will be drunk, the guests will assemble on the door-step to see the husband and wife go off in opposite directions; and all will go merry as a divorce-court bell. All this, though to some it might seem a little fanciful, would really be far less fantastic than the sort of things that are really said on the subject. I am not going to discuss the depth and substance of that subject. I myself hold a mystical view of marriage; but I am not going to debate it here. But merely in the interests of light and logic I would protest against the way in which it is frequently debated. The process cannot rationally be called a debate at all. It is a sort of chorus of sentimentalists in the sensational newspapers, perpetually intoning some such formula as this: "We respect marriage, we reverence marriage, holy, sacred, ineffably exquisite and ideal marriage. True marriage is love, and when love alters, marriage alters, and when love stops or begins again, marriage does the same; wonderful, beautiful, beatific marriage."

Now, with all reasonable sympathy with everything sentimental, I may remark that all that talk is tosh. Marriage is an institution like any other, set up deliberately to have certain functions and limitations; it is an institution like private property, or conscription, or the legal liberties of the subject. To talk as if it were made or melted with certain changing moods is a mere waste of words. The object of private property is that as many citizens as possible should have a certain dignity and pleasure in being masters of material things. But suppose a dog-stealer were to say that as soon as a man was bored with his dog it ceased to be his dog, and he ceased to be responsible for it. Suppose he were to say that by merely coveting the dog, he could immediately morally possess the dog. The answer would be that the only way to make men responsible for dogs was to make the relation a legal one, apart

146

SENTIMENTALISM OF DIVORCE

from the likes and dislikes of the moment. Suppose a burglar were to say: " Private property I venerate, private property I revere; but I am convinced that Mr. Brown does not truly value his silver Apostle spoons as such sacred objects should be valued; they have therefore ceased to be his property; in reality they have already become my property, for I appreciate their precious character as nobody else can do." Suppose a murderer were to say: " What can be more amiable and admirable than human life lived with a due sense of its priceless opportunity! But I regret to observe that Mr. Robinson has lately been looking decidedly tired and melancholy; life accepted in this depressing and demoralizing spirit can no longer truly be called life; it is rather my own exuberant and perhaps exaggerated joy of life which I must gratify by cutting his throat with a carving-knife."

It is obvious that these philosophers would fail to understand what we mean by a rule, quite apart from the problem of its exceptions. They would fail to grasp what we mean by an institution, whether it be the institution of law, of property, or of marriage. A reasonable person will certainly reply to the burglar: " You will hardly soothe us by merely poetical praises of property; because your case would be much more convincing if you denied, as the Communists do, that property ought to exist at all.

147

There may be, there certainly are, gross abuses in private property; but, so long as it is an institution at all, it cannot alter merely with moods and emotions. A farm cannot simply float away from a farmer, in proportion as his interest in it grows fainter than it was. A house cannot shift away by inches from a householder, by certain fine shades of feeling that he happens to have about it. A dog cannot drift away like a dream, and begin to belong to somebody else who happens just then to be dreaming of him. And neither can the serious social relation of husband and wife, of mother and father, or even of man and woman, be resolved in all its relations by passions and reactions of sentiment." This question is quite apart from the question of whether there are exceptions to the rule of loyalty, or what they are. The primary point is that there is an institution to which to be loyal. If the new sentimentalists mean what they say, when they say they venerate that institution, they must not suggest that an institution can be actually identical with an emotion. And that is what their rhetoric does suggest, so far as it can be said to suggest anything.

These writers are always explaining to us why they believe in divorce. I think I can easily understand why they believe in divorce. What I do not understand is why they believe in marriage. Just as the philosophical burglar would be more philosophical if he were a Bolshevist, so this sort of divorce advocate would be more philosophical if he were a free-lover. For his arguments never seem to touch on marriage as an institution, or anything more than an individual experience. The real explanation of this strange indifference to the institutional idea is, I fancy, something not only deeper, but wider; something affecting all the institutions of the modern world. The truth is that these sociologists are not at all interested in promoting the sort of social life that marriage does promote. The sort of society of which marriage has always been the strongest pillar is what is sometimes called the distributive society; the society in which most of the citizens have a tolerable share of property, especially property in hand. Everywhere, all over the world, the farm goes with the family and the family with the farm. Unless the whole domestic group hold together with a sort of loyalty or local patriotism, unless the inheritance of property is logical and legitimate, unless the family quarrels are kept out of the courts of officialism, the tradition of family ownership cannot be handed on unimpaired. On the other hand, the Servile State, which is the opposite of the distributive state, has always been rather embarrassed by the institution of marriage. It is an old story that the negro slavery of " Uncle Tom's Cabin " did its worst work in the breaking-up of families. But, curiously enough, the same story is told from both sides. For the apologists of the Slave States, or, at least, of the Southern States, make the same admission even in their own defence. If they denied breaking up the slave family, it was because they denied that there was any slave family to break up.

Free love is the direct enemy of freedom. It is the most obvious of all the bribes that can be offered by slavery. In servile societies a vast amount of sexual laxity can go on in practice, and even in theory, save when now and then some cranky speculator or crazy squire has a fad for some special breed of slaves like a breed of cattle. And even that lunacy would not last long; for lunatics are the minority among slave-owners. Slavery has a much more sane and a much more subtle appeal to human nature than that. It is much more likely that, after a few such fads and freaks, the new Servile State would settle down into the sleepy resignation of the old Servile State; the old pagan repose in slavery, as it was before Christianity came to trouble and perplex the world with ideals of liberty and chivalry. One of the conveniences of that pagan world is that, below a certain level of society, nobody really need bother about pedigree or paternity at all. A new world began when slaves began to stand on their dignity as virgin martyrs. Christendom is the civilization that such martyrs made; and slavery is its returning enemy. But of all the bribes that the old pagan slavery can offer, this luxury and laxity is the strongest; nor do I deny that the influences desiring the degradation of human dignity have here chosen their instrument well.

STREET CRIES AND STRETCH-ING THE LAW

ABOUT a hundred years ago some enemy sowed among our people the heresy that it is more practical to use a corkscrew to open a sardine-tin, or to employ a door-scraper as a paper-weight. Practical politics came to mean the habit of using everything for some other purpose than its own; of snatching up anything as a substitute for something else. A law that had been meant to do one thing, and had conspicuously failed to do it, was always excused because it might do something totally different and perhaps directly contrary. A custom that was supposed to keep everything white was allowed to survive on condition that it made everything black. In reality this is so far from being practical that it does not even rise to the dignity of being lazy. At the best it can only claim to save trouble, and it does not even do that. What it really means is that some people will take every other kind of trouble in the world, if they are saved the trouble of thinking. They will sit for hours trying to open the tin with a corkscrew, rather than make the mental effort of *m.a.l.*

pursuing the abstract, academic, logical connexion between a corkscrew and a cork.

Here is an example of the sort of thing I mean, which I came across in a daily paper to-day. A headline announces in staring letters, and with startled notes of exclamation, that some abominable judicial authority has made the monstrous decision that musicians playing in the street are not beggars. The journalist bitterly remarks that they may shove their hats under our very noses for money, but yet we must not call them beggars. He follows this remark with several notes of exclamation, and I feel inclined to add a few of my own. The most astonishing thing about the matter, to my mind, is that the journalist is quite innocent in his own indignation. It never so much as crosses his mind that organ-grinders are not classed as beggars because they are not beggars. They may be as much of a nuisance as beggars; they may demand special legislation like beggars; it may be right and proper for every philanthropist to stop them, starve them, harry them, and hound them to death just as if they were beggars. But they are not beggars, by any possible definition of begging. Nobody can be said to be a mere mendicant who is offering something in exchange for money, especially if it is something which some people like and are willing to pay for. A street singer is no more of a mendicant than Madame Clara

Butt, though the method (and the scale) of re-
muneration differs more or less. Anybody who sells
anything, in the streets or in the shops, is begging
in the sense of begging people to buy. Mr. Selfridge
is begging people to buy; the Imperial International
Universal Cosmic Stores is begging people to buy.
The only possible definition of the actual beggar is
not that he is begging people to buy, but that he has
nothing to sell.

Now, it is interesting to ask ourselves what the
newspaper really meant, when it was so wildly illogical in what it said. Superficially, and as a matter
of mood or feeling, we can all guess what was meant.
The writer meant that street musicians looked very
much like beggars, because they wore thinner and
dirtier clothes than his own; and that he had grown
quite used to people who looked like that being
treated anyhow and arrested for everything. That
is a state of mind not uncommon among those whom
economic security has kept as superficial as a varnish. But what was intellectually involved in his
vague argument was more interesting. What he
meant was, in that deeper sense, that it would be a
great convenience if the law that punishes beggars
could be *stretched* to cover people who are certainly
not beggars, but who may be as much of a bothera-
tion as beggars. In other words, he wanted to use
the mendicity laws in a matter quite unconnected

with mendicity; but he wanted to
use the old laws because it would
save the trouble of making new
laws—as the corkscrew would save
the trouble of going to look for
the tin-opener. And for this notion of the crooked and anomalous
use of laws, for ends logically
different from their own, he could,
of course, find much support in the
various sophists who have attacked
reason in recent times. But, as I
have said, it does not really save
trouble; and it is becoming increasingly doubtful whether it will
even save disaster. It used to be
said that this rough-and-ready
method made the country richer; but
it will be found less and less consoling to explain why the country
is richer when the country is
steadily growing poorer. It will
not comfort us in the hour of failure to listen to long and ingenious
explanations of our success. The
truth is that this sort of practical compromise has not led to
practical success. The success of
England came as the culmination of
the highly logical and theoretical
eighteenth century. The method
was already beginning to fail by
the time we came to the end of the

compromising and constitutional
nineteenth century. Modern scientific civilization was launched by
logicians. It was only wrecked
by practical men. Anyhow, by this
time everybody in England has
given up pretending to be particularly rich. It is, therefore, no
appropriate moment for proving t
that a course of being consistently unreasonable will always lead
to riches.

In truth, it would be much more
practical to be more logical. If
street musicians are a nuisance,
let them be legislated against for
being a nuisance. If begging is
really wrong, a logical law should
be imposed on all beggars, and not
merely on those whom particular
persons happen to regard as being
also nuisances. What this sort of
opportunism does is simply to prevent any question being considered
as a whole. I happen to think the
whole modern attitude towards
beggars is entirely heathen and inhuman. I should be prepared to
maintain, as a matter of general
morality, that it is intrisically
for human assistance. I should say
that is is intrinsically insane to
urge people to give charity and

156

forbid people to accept charity.
Nobody is penalized for crying
for help when he is drowning;
why should he be penalized for
crying for help when he is starving? Every one would expect to
have to help a man to save his
life in a shipwreck; why not a
man who has suffered a shipwreck
of his life? A man may be in such
a position by no conceivable
fault of his own; but in any case
his fault is never urged against
him in the parallel cases. A man
is saved from shipwreck without
inquiry about whether he has
blundered in the steering of his
ship; and we fish him out of a
pond before asking whose fault
it was that he fell into it. A
striking social satire might be
written about a man who was rescued again and again out of
mere motives of humanity in all
the wildest places of the world;
who was heroically rescued from
a lion and skilfully saved out of
a sinking ship; who was sought out
on a desert island and scientifically recovered from a deadly
swoon; and who only found himself
suddenly deserted by all humanity

when he reached the city that was
was his home.

In the ultimate sense, therefore, I do not myself disapprove
of mendicants. Nor do I disapprove of musicians. It may not
unfairly be retorted that this
is because I am not a musician.
I allow full weight to the fair-
ness of the retort, but I cannot think it a good thing that
even musicians should lose all
their feelings except the feeling for music. And it may surely be said that a man must have
lost most of his feelings if he
does not feel the pathos of a
barrel-organ in a poor street.
But there are other feelings besides pathos covered by any comprehensive veto upon street
music and minstrelsy. There are
feelings of history, and even
of patriotism. I have seen in
certain rich and respectable
quarters of London a notice saying that all street cries are
forbidden. If there were a notice up to say that all old
tombstones should be carted a-
way like lumber, it would be
rather less of an act of vanda-

lism. Some of the old street
cries of London are among the last
links that we have with the London
of Shakespeare and the London of
Chaucer. When I meet a man who
utters one I am so far from regarding as a beggar; it is I who
should be a beggar, and beg him to
say it again.

But in any case it should be
made clear that we cannot make one
law do the work of another. If we
have real reasons for forbidding
something like a street cry, we
should give the reasons that are
real; we should forbid it because
it is a cry, because it is a
noise, because it is a nuisance,
or perhaps, according to our tastes
because it is old, because it is
popular, because it is historic and
a memory of Merry England. I suspect that the sub-conscious prejudice against it is rooted in the
fact that the pedlar or hawker is
one of the few free men left in the
modern city; that he often sells his
own wares directly to the consumer,
and does not pay rent for a shop.
But if the modern spirit wishes to
veto him, to harry him, or to bang,
draw, and quarter him for being

158-A

free, at least let it so far
recognize his dignity as to define
him; and let the law deal with
him in principle as well as in
practice.

WHY REFORMS GO WRONG

EVERYBODY says that each generation revolts against the last. Nobody seems to notice that it generally revolts against the revolt of the last. I mean that the latest grievance is really the last reform. To take but one example in passing. There is a new kind of novel which I have seen widely reviewed in the newspapers. No; it is not an improper novel. On the contrary, it is more proper—almost in the sense of prim—than its authors probably imagine. It is really a reaction towards a more old-fashioned morality, and away from a new-fashioned one. It is not so much a revolt of the daughters as a return of the grandmothers.

Miss May Sinclair wrote a novel of the kind I mean, about a spinster whose life had been blighted by a tender and sensitive touch in her education, which had taught her—or rather, expected her—always to "behave beautifully." Mrs. Delafield wrote a story with the refreshing name of "Humbug" on somewhat similar lines. It suggests that children are actually trained to deception, and especially self-deception, by a delicate and considerate treatment that continually appealed to their better feelings, which was always saying, "You would not hurt father." Now, certainly a more old-fashioned and simple style of education did not invariably say "You would not hurt father." Sometimes it preferred to say, "Father will hurt you." I am not arguing for or against the father with the big stick. I am pointing out that Miss Sinclair and the modern novelists really *are* arguing for the father with the big stick, and against a more recent movement that is supposed to have reformed him. I myself can remember the time when the progressives offered us, as a happy prospect, the very educational method which the novelists now describe so bitterly in retrospect. We were told that true education would only appeal to the better feelings of children; that it would devote itself entirely to telling them to live beautifully; that it would use no argument more arbitrary than saying, "You would not hurt father." That ethical education was the whole plan for the rising generation in the days of my youth. We were assured beforehand how much more effective such a psychological treatment would be than the bullying and blundering idea of authority. The hope of the future was in this humanitarian optimism in the training of the young; in other words, the hope was set on something which, when it is established, Mrs. Delafield instantly calls humbug and Miss Sinclair appears to hate as a sort of hell. What they are suffering from, apparently, is not the abuses of their grandfathers, but the most modern reforms of their fathers. These complaints are the first fruits of reformed education, of ethical societies, and social idealists. I repeat that I am for the moment talking about their opinions and not mine. I am not eulogizing either big sticks or psychological scalpels; I am pointing out that the outcry against the scalpel inevitably involves something of a case for the stick. I have never tied myself to a final belief in either; but I point out that the progressive, generation after generation, does elaborately tie himself up in new knots, and then roar and yell aloud to be untied.

It seems a little hard on the late Victorian idealist to be so bitterly abused merely for being kind to his children. There is something a little unconsciously comic about the latest generation of critics, who are crying out against their parents, " Never, never can I forgive the tenderness with which my mother treated me." There is a certain irony in the bitterness which says, " My soul cries for vengeance when I remember that papa was always polite at the breakfast-table; my soul is seared by the persistent insolence of Uncle William in refraining from clouting me over the head." It seems harsh to blame these idealists for idealizing human life, when they were only following what was seriously set before them as the only ideal of education. But, if this is to be said for the late Victorian idealist, there is also something to be said for the early Victorian authoritarian. Upon their own argument, there is something to be said for Uncle William if he did clout them over the head. It is rather hard, even on the great-grandfather with the big stick, that we should still abuse him merely for having neglected the persuasive methods that we have ourselves abandoned. It is hard to revile him for not having discovered to be sound the very sentimentalities that we have since discovered to be rotten.

For the case of these moderns is worst of all when they do try to find any third ideal, which is neither the authority which they once condemned for not being persuasion, nor the persuasion which they now condemn for being worse than authority. The nearest they can get to any other alternative is some notion about individuality; about drawing out the true personality of the child, or allowing a human being to find his real self. It is, perhaps, the most utterly meaningless talk in the whole muddle of the modern world. How is a child of seven to decide whether he has or has not found his true individuality? How, for that matter, is any grown-up person to tell it for him? How is anybody to know whether anybody has become his true self? In the highest sense it can only be a matter of mysticism; it can only mean that there was a purpose in his creation. It can only be the purpose of God, and even then it is a mystery. In anybody who does not accept the purpose of God, it can only be a muddle. It is so unmeaning that it cannot be called mystery but only mystification. Humanly considered, a human personality is the only thing that does in fact emerge out of a combination of the forces inside the child and the forces outside. The child cannot grow up in a void or vacuum with no forces outside. Circumstances will control or contribute to his character, whether they are the grandfather's stick or the father's persuasion or the conversations among the characters of Miss May Sinclair. Who in the world is to say positively which of these things has or has not helped his real personality?

What is his real personality? These philosophers talk as if there was a complete and complex animal curled up inside every baby, and we had nothing to do but to let it come out with a yell. As a matter of fact, we all know, in the case of the finest and most distinguished personalities, that it would be very difficult to disentangle them from the trials they have suffered, as well as from the truths they have found. But, anyhow, these thinkers must give us some guidance as to how they propose to tell whether their transcendental notion of a true self has been realized or no. As it is, anybody can say of any part of any personality that it is or is not an artificial addition obscuring that personality. In fiction, most of the wild and anarchical characters strike me as entirely artificial. In real life they would no doubt be much the same, if they could ever be met with in real life. But anyhow, they would be the products of experience as well as of elemental impulses; they would be influenced in some way by all they had gone through; and anybody would be free to speculate on what they would have been like if they had never had such experiences. Anybody might amuse himself by trying to subtract the experiences and find the self; anybody who wanted to waste his time.

Therefore, without feeling any fixed fanaticism for all the old methods, whether coercive or persuasive, I do think they both had a basis of common sense which is wanting in this third theory. The parent, whether persuading or punishing the child, was at least aware of one simple truth. He knew that, in the most serious sense, God alone knows what the child is really like, or is meant to be really like. All we can do to him is to fill him with those truths which we believe to be equally true whatever he is like. We must have a code of morals which we believe to be applicable to all children, and impose it on this child because it is applicable to all children. If it seems to be a part of his personality to be a swindler or a torturer, we must tell him that we do not want any personalities to be swindlers and torturers. In other words, we must believe in a religion or philosophy firmly enough to take the responsibility of acting on it, however much the rising generations may knock or kick at the door. I know all about the word education meaning drawing things out, and mere instruction meaning putting things in. And I respectfully reply that God alone knows what there is to draw out; but we can be reasonably responsible for what we are ourselves putting in.

THE INNOCENCE OF THE CRIMINAL

A PHRASE, which we have all heard, is sometimes uttered by some small man sentenced to some small town of imprisonment, for either or both of the two principal reasons for imprisoning a man in modern England: that he is known to the police, and that he is not known to the magistrate. When such a man receives a more or less temperate term of imprisonment, he is often reported as having left the dock saying that he would "do it on his head." In his own self-consciousness, he is merely seeking to maintain his equilibrium by that dazed and helpless hilarity which is the only philosophy allowed to him. But the phrase itself, like a great part of really popular slang, is highly symbolic. The English pauper (who tends to become numerically the preponderant Englishman) does really reconcile himself to existence by putting himself in an inverted and grotesque posture towards it. He does really stand on his head, because he is living in topsy-turvydom. He finds himself in an Upsidonia fully as fantastic as Mr. Archibald Marshall's, and far less fair and logical; in a landscape as wild as if the trees grew downwards or the moon hung below his feet. He lives in a world in which the man who lends him money makes him a beggar; in which, when he is a beggar, the man who gives him money makes him a criminal; in which, when he is a criminal and " known to the police," he becomes permanently liable to be arrested for other people's crimes.

He is punished if his home is neglected though there is nobody to look after it, and punished again if it is not neglected, and the children are kept from school to look after it. He is arrested for sleeping on private land, and arrested again for sleeping on public land, and arrested, be it noted, for the positive and explicit reason that he has no money to sleep anywhere else. In short, he is under laws of such naked and admitted lunacy that they might quite as well tell him to pluck all the feathers off the cows, or to amputate the left leg of a whale. There is no possible way of behaving in such a pantomime city except as a sort of comic acrobat, a knockabout comedian who does as many things as possible on his head. He is, both by accident and design, a tumbler. It is a proverb about his children that they tumble up; it is the whole joke about his drunkenness that he tumbles down. But he is in a world in which standing straight or standing still have become both impossible and fatal. Meredith rightly conceived the only possible philosophy of this modern outlaw as that of Juggling Jerry; and even what is called his swindling is mostly this sort of almost automatic juggling. His nearest approach to social status is mere kinetic stability, like a top. There was, indeed, another tumbler called in tradition Our Lady's Tumbler, who performed happier antics before a shrine in the days of superstition; and whose philosophy was perhaps more positive than Juggling Jerry's, or Meredith's. But a strenuous reform has passed through our own cities, careful of the survival of the fittest, and we have been able to preserve the antic while abolishing the altar.

But though this form of reaction into ridicule, and even self-ridicule, is very natural, it is also very national; it is not the only human reaction against injustice, nor perhaps the most obvious. The Irishman has shot his landlord, the Italian has joined a revolutionary Secret Society, the Russian has either thrown a bomb or gone on a pilgrimage, long before the Englishman has come finally to the conclusion that existence is a joke. Even as he does so he is too fully conscious that it would be too bad as a tragedy if it were not so good as a farce. It is further to be noticed, for the fact is of ominous importance, that this topsy-turvy English humour has, during the last six or seven generations, been more and more abandoned to the poorer orders. Sir John Falstaff is a knight; Tony Weller is a coachman;

his son Sam is a servant to the middle classes, and the recent developments of social discipline seem calculated to force Sam Weller into the status of the Artful Dodger. It is certain that a youth of that class who should do to-day a tenth of the things that Sam Weller did would in one way or another spend most of his life in jail. To-day, indeed, it is the main object of social reform that he should spend the whole of his life in jail; but in a jail that can be used as a factory. That is the real meaning of all the talk about scientific criminology and remedial penalties. For such outcasts punishment is to be abolished by being perpetuated. When men propose to eliminate retribution as "vindictive," they mean two very simple things: ceasing altogether to punish the few who are rich, and enslaving all the rest for being poor.

Nevertheless this half-conscious buffoon who is the butt of our society is also the satirist of it. He is even the judge of it, in the sense that he is the normal test by which it will be judged. In a number of quite practical matters it is he who represents historic humanity, and speaks naturally and truthfully where his judges and critics are crooked, crabbed and superstitious. This can be seen, for instance, if we see him for a moment not in the dock but in the witness-box. In several books and newspapers I happened to read lately, I have noticed a certain tone touching the uneducated witness; phrases like " the vagueness characteristic of their class," or " easily confused, as such witnesses are." Now such vagueness is simple truthfulness. Nine times out of ten, it is the confusion any man would show at any given instant about the complications which crowd human life. Nine times out of ten, it is avoided in the case of educated witnesses by the mere expedient of a legal fiction. The witness has a brief, like the barrister: he has consulted dates, he has made memoranda, he has frequently settled with solicitors exactly what he can safely say. His evidence is artificial even when it is not fictitious; we might almost say it is fictitious even when it is not false. The model testimony, regarded as the most regular of all in a law court, is constabulary testimony; if what the soldier said is not evidence, what the policeman says is often the only evidence. And what the policeman says is incredible, as he says it. It is something like this: " I met the prisoner coming out of Clapham Junction Station and he told me he went to see Mrs. Nehemiah Blagg, of 192 Paardeburg Terrace, West Ealing, about a cat which he had left there last Tuesday week which she was going to keep if it was a good mouser, and she told him it had killed a mouse in the back kitchen on Sunday morning so he had better leave it. She gave him a shilling for his trouble, and he went to West Ealing post-office where he bought two half-penny stamps and a ball of string, and then to the Imperial Stores at Ealing Broadway, and bought a pennyworth of mixed sweets. Coming out he met a friend, and they went to the Green Dolphin and made an appointment for 5.30 next day at the third lamp-post in Eckstein Street," and so on. It is frankly impossible for anybody to say such a sentence; still more for anybody to remember it. If the thing is not a tissue of mere inventions, it can only be the arbitrary summary of a very arbitrary cross-examination, conducted precisely as are the examinations of a secret police in Russia. The story was not only discovered bit by bit, but discovered backwards. Mountains were in labour to bring forth that mouse in West Ealing. The police made a thorough official search of the man's mental boxes and baggage, before that cat was let out of the bag. I am not here supposing the tale to be untrue—I am pointing out that the telling of it is unreal. The right way to tell a story is the way in which the prisoner told it to the policeman, and not the way in which the policeman tells it to the court. It is the way in which all true tales are told, the way in which all men learn the news about their neighbours, the way in which we all learned everything we know in childhood; it is the only real evidence for anything on this earth, and it is not evidence in a court of law. The man who tells it is vague about some things, less vague about others, and so on in proportion; but at his very vaguest, among the stiff unreason of modern conditions, he is a judgment on those conditions. His very bewilderment is a criticism, and his very indecision is a decision against us. It is an old story that we are judged by the innocence of a child, and every child is, in the French phrase, a terrible child. There is a true sense in which all our laws are judged by the innocence of a criminal.

In politics, of course, the case is the same. I will defer the question of whether the democracy knows how to answer questions until the oligarchy knows how to ask them. Asking a man if he approves of Tariff Reform is not only a silly but an insane question, for it covers the wildest possibilities, just as asking him whether he approves of Trouser Reform might mean anything from wearing no trousers to wearing a particular pattern of yellow trousers decorated with scarlet snakes. Talking about Temperance, when you mean pouring wine down the gutter, is quite literally as senseless as talking about Thrift, when you mean throwing money into the sea. The rambling speech of yokels and tramps is as much wiser than this as a rambling walk in the woods is wiser than the mathematical straightness of a fall from a precipice. The present leaders of progress are, I think, very near to that precipice; about all their schemes and ideals there is a savour of suicide. But the clown will go on talking in a living and, therefore, a leisurely fashion, and the great truth of pure gossip which sprang up in simpler ages and was the fountain of all the literatures, will flow on when our intricate and tortured society has died of its sins.

THE PRUDERY OF THE FEMINISTS

In the ultimate and universal sense I am astonished at the lack of astonishment. Starting from scratch, so to speak, we are all in the position of the first frog, whose pious and compact prayer was "Lord, how you made me jump!" Matthew Arnold told us to see life steadily and see it whole. But the flaw in his whole philosophy is that when we do see life whole we do not see it steadily, in Arnold's sense, but as a staggering prodigy of creation. There is a primeval light in which all stones are precious stones; a primeval darkness against which all flowers are as vivid as fireworks. Nevertheless, there is one kind of surprise that does surprise me, the more, perhaps, because it is not true surprise but a supercilious fuss. There is a kind of man who not only claims that his stone is the only pebble on the beach, but declares it must be the one and only philosopher's stone, because he is the one and only philosopher. He does not discover suddenly the sensational fact that grass is green. He discovers it very slowly, and proves it still more slowly, bringing us one blade of grass at a time. He is made haughty instead of humble by hitting on the obvious. The flowers do not make him open his eyes, but, rather, cover them with spectacles; and this is even more true of the weeds and thorns. Even his bad news is banal. A young man told me he had abandoned his Bible religion and vicarage environment at the withering touch of the one line of Fitzgerald: " The flower that once has blown, for ever dies." I vainly pointed out that the Bible or the English burial service could have told him that man cometh up as a flower and is cut down. If that were self-evidently final, there would never have been any Bibles or any vicarages. I do not see how the flower can be any more dead, when a mower can cut it down, merely because a botanist can cut it up. It should further be remembered that the belief in the soul, right or wrong, arose and flourished among men who knew all there is to know about cutting down, not unfrequently cutting each other down, with considerable vivacity. The physical fact of death, in a hundred horrid shapes, was more naked and less veiled in times of faith or superstition than in times of science or scepticism. Often it was not merely those who had seen a man die, but those who had seen him rot, who were most certain that he was everlastingly alive.

There is another case somewhat analogous to this discovery of the new disease of death. I am puzzled in somewhat the same way when I hear, as we often hear just now, somebody saying that he was formerly opposed to Female Suffrage but was converted to it by the courage and patriotism shown by women in nursing and similar war work. Really, I do not wish to be superior in my turn, when I can only express my wonder in a question. But from what benighted dens can these people have crawled, that they did not know that women are brave? What horrible sort of women have they known all their lives? Where do they come from? Or, what is a still more apposite question, where do they think they come from? Do they think they fell from the moon, or were really found under cabbage-leaves, or brought over the sea by storks? Do they (as seems more likely) believe they were produced chemically by Mr. Schefer on principles of abiogenesis? Should we any of us be here at all if women were not brave? Are we not all trophies of that war and triumph? Does not every man stand on the earth like a graven statue as the monument of the valour of a woman?

As a matter of fact, it is men much more than women who needed a war to redeem their reputation, and who have redeemed it. There was much more plausibility in the suspicion that the old torture of blood and iron would prove too much for a somewhat drugged and materialistic male population long estranged from it. I have always suspected that this doubt about manhood was the real sting in the strange sex quarrel, and the meaning of the new and nervous tattoo about the unhappiness of women. Man, like the Master Builder, was suspected by the female intelligence of having lost his nerve for climbing that dizzy battle-tower he had built in times gone by. In this the war did certainly straighten out the sex tangle; but it did also make clear on how terrible a thread of tenure we hold our privileges—and even our pleasures. For even bridge parties and champagne suppers take place on the top of that toppling war-tower; an hour can come when even a man who cared for nothing but bridge would have to defend it like Horatius; or when the man who only lives for champagne would have to die for champagne, as certainly as thousands of French soldiers have died for that flat land of vines; when he would have to fight as hard for the wine as Jeanne D'Arc for the oil of Rheims.

Just as civilization is guarded by potential war, so it is guarded by potential revolution. We ought never to indulge in either without extreme provocation; but we ought to be cured for ever of the fancy that extreme provocation is impossible. Against the tyrant within, as against the barbarian without, every voter should be a potential volunteer. " Thou goest with women, forget not thy whip," said the Prussian philosopher; and some such echo probably infected those who wanted a war to make them respect their wives and mothers. But there would really be a symbolic sense in saying, "Thou goest with men, forget not thy sword." Men coming to the council of the tribe should sheathe their swords, but not surrender them. Now I am not going to talk about Female Suffrage at this time of day; but these were the elements upon which a fair and sane opposition to it were founded. These are the risks of real politics; and the woman was not called upon to run such a risk, for the very simple reason that she was already running another risk. It was not laws that fixed her in the family; it was the very nature of the family. If the family was a fact in any very full sense, and if popular rule was also a fact in any very full sense, it was simply physically impossible for the woman to play the same part in such politics as the man. The difficulty was only evaded because the democracy was not a free democracy or the family not a free family. But whether this view was right or wrong, it is at least clear that the only honourable basis for any limitations of womanhood is the same as the basis of the respect for womanhood. It consisted in certain realities, which it may be undesirable to discuss, but is certainly even more undesirable to ignore. And my complaint against the more fussy Feminists (so called from their detestation of everything feminine) is that they do ignore these realities. I do not even propose the alternative of discussing them; on that point I am myself content to be what some call conventional, and others, civilized. I do not in the least demand that anyone should accept my own deduction from them; and I do not care a brass farthing what deduction anybody accepts about such a rag as modern ballot paper. But I do suggest that the peril with which one half of humanity is perpetually at war should be at least present in the minds of those who are perpetually bragging about breaking conventions, rending veils, and violating antiquated taboos. And, in nine cases out of ten, it seems to be quite absent from their minds. The mere fact of using the argument before mentioned, of women's strength vindicated by war work, shows that it is absent from their minds.

If this oddity of the new obscurantism means, rather, that women have shown the moral courage and mental capacity needed for important concerns, I am equally unable to summon up any surprise at the revelation. Nothing can well be more important than our own souls and bodies; and they, at their most delicate and determining period, are almost always and almost entirely confided to women. Those who have been appointed as educational experts in every age are not surely a new order of priestesses? If it means that in a historic crisis all kinds of people must do all kinds of work, and that women are the more to be admired for doing work to which they are unaccustomed, or even unsuited, it is a point which I should quite as easily concede. But if it means that in planning the foundations of a future society we should ignore the one eternal and incurable contrast in humanity; if it means that we may now go ahead gaily as if there were really no difference at all; if it means, as I read in a magazine to-day, and as almost anyone may now read almost anywhere, that if such and such work is bad for women it must be bad for men; if it means that patriotic women in munition factories prove that any women can be happy in any factories; if, in short, it means that the huge and primeval facts of the family no longer block the way to a mere social assimilation and regimentation —then I say that the prospect is not one of liberty but of perpetuation of the dreariest sort of humbug. It is not emancipation, it is not even anarchy; it is simply prudery in the thoughts. It means that we have Bowdlerized our brains as well as our books. It is every bit as senseless a surrender to a superstitious decorum as it would be to force every woman to cut herself with a razor, because it was not etiquette to admit that she cannot grow a beard.

HOW MAD LAWS ARE MADE

ANY one of the strange laws we suffer is a compromise between a fad and a vested interest. The fashionable way of effecting a social reform is as follows. To make the story clearer, and worthier of its wild and pointless process, I will call the two chief agents in it the March Hare and the Hatter. The Hatter is mad, in a quiet way; but he is merely mad on making hats, or rather on making money. He has a huge and prosperous emporium which advertises all possible hats to fit all possible heads; but he certainly nourishes an occult conviction that it is really the duty of the heads to fit the hats. This is his mild madness; in other respects he is a stodgy and rather stupid millionaire. Now, the man whom we will call the March Hare is at first sight the flat contrary of this. He is a wild intellectual and the leader of the Hatless Brigade. It does not much matter why there is this quarrel between the Hare and the Hat; it may be any progressive sophistry. Perhaps it is because he is a March Hare; and finds it hard to keep his hat on in a March wind. Perhaps it is because his ears are too long to allow him to wear a hat; or perhaps he hopes that every emancipated member of the Hatless Brigade will eventually evolve ears as long as a hare's—or a donkey's. The point is that anyone would fancy that the Hare and the Hatter would collide. As a matter of fact they co-operate. In other words, every "reform" to-day is a treaty between the two most influential modern figures—the great capitalist and the small faddist. They are the father and mother of a new law; and therefore it is so much of a mongrel as to be a monster.

What happens is something like this. The line of least resistance is found between the two by a more subtle analysis of their real respective aims. The intuitive eye of friendship detects a fine shade in the feelings of the Hatter. The desire of his heart, when delicately apprehended, is not necessarily that people should wear his hats, but rather that they should buy them. On the other hand, even his fanatically consistent colleague has no particular objection to a human being purchasing a hat, so long as he does not wreck his health, blast his prospects and generally blow his brains out, by the one suicidal act of putting it on. Between them they construct a law called the Habitual Hat-Pegs Act, which lays it down that every householder shall have not less than twenty-three hat-pegs and that, lest these should accumulate unwholesome dust, each must be covered by a hat in uninterrupted occupation. Or the thing might be managed some other way; as by arranging that a great modern nobleman should wear an accumulation of hats, one on top of the other, in pleasing memory of what has often been the itinerant occupation of his youth. Broadly, it would be enacted that hats might be used in various ways; to take rabbits out of, as in the case of conjurers, or put pennies into, as in the case of beggars, or smash on the heads of scarecrows, or stick on the tops of poles; if only it were guaranteed that as many citizens as possible should be forced to go bareheaded. Thus, the two most powerful elements in the governing class are satisfied; of which the first is finance and the second fidgets. The Capitalist has made money; and he only wanted to make money. The Social Reformer has done something; and he only wanted something to do.

Now every one of the recent tricks about temperance and economy has been literally of this type. I have chosen the names from a nonsense story merely for algebraic lucidity and universality; what has really happened in our own shops and streets is every bit as nonsensical. But quite recent events have confirmed this analysis with an accuracy which even the unconverted can hardly regard as a coincidence. I have already traced the truth in the case of the liquor traffic; but many public-spirited persons of the Prohibitionist school have found it very difficult to believe. All " temperance legislation " is a compromise between a liquor merchant who wants to get rid of his liquor and a teetotaller who does not want his neighbours to get it. But as the capitalist is much stronger than the crank, the compromise is lop-sided as such; the neighbours do get it, but always in the wrong way. But again, since the crank has not a true creed, but only an intellectual itch, he cares much more to be up and doing than to understand what he has done. As I said above, he only wants to do something; he has increased drunkenness. Anyhow, all such reforms are upon the plan of my parable. Sometimes it is decreed that drink shall only be sold in large quantities suitable to large incomes; that is exactly like allowing one nobleman to wear twenty hats. Sometimes it is proposed that the State should take over the liquor traffic; we hardly need to be told what that means, when it is the Plutocratic State. It means quite simply this: the policeman goes to the hatter and buys his whole stock of hats at a hundred pounds a piece, and then parades the street handing out hats to those who may take his fancy, and by blows of the truncheon forcing every man Jack of the rest of them to pay a hundred pounds for a hat he does not get. Merely to divert the rivers of ale or gin from private power to public power or from poor men to rich men, or from good taverns to bad taverns, is the sort of effort with which the faddists are satisfied and the liquor lords much more than satisfied.

There was a curious case of the same thing in the attempt to economize food during the Great War. The reformers did not wish *really* to economize food; the great food profiteers would not let them. The fussy person wants to force or forbid something, under the conditions defining all such effort; it must be something that will interfere with the citizen and will not interfere with the profiteer. Given such a problem, we might almost predict, for instance, that he will propose the limitation of the number of courses at a restaurant. It will not save the beef; it is not meant to save the beef; but to save the beef merchant. There will actually be more food bought, if the cook is not allowed to turn the scraps into kickshaws. But why should a plutocracy including food profiteers object to more food being bought? Why, for that matter, should the pure-minded social idealist object to more food being bought, as long as it is the wrong food that is sold? His quite disinterested aim is not that food should be restricted, but merely that freedom should be restricted. When once he is assured that a sufficient number of thoughtless persons are really getting what they don't want, he says he is building Jerusalem in England's green and pleasant land. And so he is; if the expression signifies handing over England to the wealthier Jews.

Now the only way in which this conclusive explanation can be countered is by ridiculing as impossible the notion that so fantastic a compact can be clearly and coolly made. The two attitudes are not logically interlocked, like the antlers of stags; they simply squeeze each other out of shape, as in a wrestle of two rival jelly-fish. We should be far safer if they had the intellectual honesty of a bargain or a bribe. As it is, they have an almost creepy quality which justifies the comparison to shapeless beasts of the sea. I defy any rational man to deny that he has noticed something moonstruck and mis-shapen, as apart from anything unjust or uncomfortable, about the little laws which have lately been tripping him up; laws which may tell him at any minute that he must not purchase turpentine before a certain tick of the clock, or that if he buys a pound of tea he must also buy a pennyworth of tin-tacks. The strictly correct word for such things is half-witted; and they are half-witted because each of the two incongruous partners has only half his will. They have not, for instance, the sweeping simplicity of the old sumptuary laws or even the old Puritan persecutions. But they are also half-witted because even the one mind is not the whole mind; it is largely the sub-conscious mind, which dares not trust itself in speech. The Drink Capitalist dares not actually say to the teetotaller, " Let me sell a quart bottle of whisky to be drunk in a day, and then I will let you pester a poor fellow who makes a pot of beer last half an hour." That is exactly what happens in essence; but it is easy to guess what happens in external form. The teetotaller has twenty schemes for cutting off free citizens from the beverage of their fathers; and out of these twenty the liquor lord, without whose permission nothing can be done, selects the one scheme which will not interfere with him and his money. It is even more probable that the temperance reformer himself selects, by an instinct for what he would call practical politics, the one scheme which the liquor lord is likely to look at. And it matters nothing that it is a scheme too witless for Wonderland; a scheme for abolishing hats while preserving hatters.

It might be a good thing to give the control of drink to the State—if there were a State to give it to. But there is not. There is nothing but a congested compromise made by the pressure of powerful interests on each other. The liquor lords may bargain with the other lords to take their abnormal tribute in a lump instead of a lifetime; but not one of them will live the poorer. The main point is that, in passing through that plutocratic machinery, even a mad opinion will always emerge in a shape more maniacal than its own; and even the silliest fool can only do what the stupidest fool will let him.

THE PAGODA OF PROGRESS

THERE is one fashionable fallacy that crops up everywhere like a weed, until a man feels inclined to devote the rest of his life to the hopeless task of weeding it out. I take one example of it from a newspaper correspondence headed " Have Women Gone Far Enough? " It is immediately concerned with alleged impropriety in dress; but I am not directly interested in that. I quote one paragraph from a lady correspondent, not because it is any worse than the same thing as stated by countless scholars and thinkers, but rather because it is more clearly stated—

" 'Women have gone far enough.' That has always been the cry of the individual with the unprogressive mind. It seems to me that until Doomsday there will always be the type of man who will cry ' Women have gone far enough '; but no one can stop the tide of evolution, and women will still go on."

Which raises the interesting question of where they will go to. Now, as a matter of fact, every thinking person wants to stop the tide of evolution at some particular mark in his own mind. If I were to propose that people should wear no clothes at all, the lady might be shocked. But I should have as much right as anyone else to say that she was obviously an individual with an unprogressive mind. If I were to propose that this reform should be imposed on people by force, she would be justly indignant. But I could answer her with her own argument—that there had always been unprogressive people, and would be till Doomsday. If I then proposed that people should not only be stripped, but skinned alive, she might, perhaps, see several moral objections. But her own argument would still hold good, or as good as it held in her own case; and I could say that evolution would not stop and the skinning would go on. The argument is quite as good on my side as on hers; and it is worthless on both.

Of course, it would be just as easy to urge people to progress or evolve in exactly the opposite direction. It would be as easy to maintain that they ought to go on wearing more and more clothes. It might be argued that savages wear fewer clothes, that clothes are a mark of civilization, and that the evolution of them will go on. I am highly civilized if I wear ten hats, and more highly civilized if I wear twelve hats. When I have already evolved so far as to put on six pairs of trousers, I must still hail the appearance of the seventh pair of trousers with the joy due to the waving banner of a great reform. When we balance these two lunacies against each other, the central point of sanity is surely apparent. The man who headed his inquiry. " Have Women Gone Far Enough? " was at least in a real sense stating the point rightly. The point is that there *is* a " far enough." There is a point at which something that was once neglected becomes exaggerated; something that is valuable up to that stage becomes undesirable after that stage. It is possible for the human intellect to consider clearly at what stage, or in what condition, it would have enough complication of clothes, or enough simplification of clothes, or enough of any other social element or tendency. It is possible to set a limit to the pagoda of human hats, rising for ever into infinity. It is possible to count the human legs, and, after a brief calculation, allot to them the appropriate number of trousers. There is such a thing as the miscalculation of making hats for a hydra or boots for a centipede, just as there are such things as bare-footed friars or the Hatless Brigade. There are exceptions and exaggerations, good and bad; but the point is that they are not only both good and bad, but they are good and bad in opposite directions. Let a man have what ideal of human costume or custom he likes. That ideal must still consist of elements in a certain proportion; and if that proportion is disturbed that ideal is destroyed. Let him once be clear in his own mind about what he wants, and then, whatever it is that he wants, he will not want the tide of evolution to wash it away. His ideal may be as revolutionary as he likes or as reactionary as he likes, but it must remain as he likes it. To make it more revolutionary or more reactionary is distortion; to suggest its growing more and more reactionary or revolutionary for ever is demented nonsense. How can a man know what he wants, how can he even want what he wants, if it will not even remain the same while he wants it?

The particular argument about women is not primarily the point; but as a matter of fact it is a very good illustration of the point. If a man thinks the Victorian conventions kept women out of things they would be the happier for having, his natural course is to consider what things they are; not to think that any things will do, so long as there are more of them. This is only the sort of living logic everybody acts in life. Suppose somebody says, " Don't you think all this wood could be used for something else besides palings? " We shall very probably answer, " Well, I dare say it could," and perhaps begin to think of wooden boxes or wooden stools. But we shall not see, as in a sort of vision, a vista of wooden razors, wooden carving-knives, wooden coats and hats, wooden pillows and pocket-handkerchiefs. If people had made a false and insufficient list of the uses of wood, we shall try to make a true and sufficient list of them; but not imagine that the list can go on for ever, or include more and more of everything in the world. I am not establishing a scientific parallel between wood and womanhood. But there would be nothing disrespectful in the symbol, considered as a symbol; for wood is the most sacred of all substances: it typifies the divine trade of the carpenter, and men count themselves fortunate to touch it. Here it is only a working simile, but the point of it is this—that all this nonsense about progressive and unprogressive minds, and the tide of evolution, divides people into those who stick ignorantly to wood for one thing and those who attempt insanely to use wood for everything. Both seem to think it a highly eccentric suggestion that we should find out what wood is really useful for, and use it for that. They either profess to worship a wooden womanhood inside the wooden fences of certain trivial and temporary Victorian conventions; or else they profess to see the future as a forest of dryads growing more and more feminine for ever.

But it does not matter to the main question whether anybody else draws the line exactly where I do. The point is that I am not doing an illogical thing, but the only logical thing, in drawing the line. I think tennis for women normal, and football

for women quite abnormal; and I am no more incon-
consistent than I am in having a wooden walking-
stick and not a wooden hat. I do not particularly
object to a female despot; but I do object to a
female demagogue. And my distinction is as much
founded on the substance of things as my eccentric
conduct in having a wooden chair and table but not
a wooden knife and fork. You may think my division wrong; the point is that it is not wrong in being
a division. All this fallacy of false progress tends
to obscure the old common sense of all mankind,
which is still the common sense of every man in his
own daily dealings: that everything has its place and
proportion and proper use, and that it is rational
to trust its use and distrust its abuse. Progress, in
the good sense, does not consist in looking for a direction in which one can go on indefinitely. For
there is no such direction, unless it be in quite transcendental things, like the love of God. It would be
far truer to say that true progress consists in looking for the place where we can stop.

THE MYTH OF THE
"MAYFLOWER"

AGNOSTICISM, the ancient confession of ignorance, was a singularly sane and healthy thing so far as it went. Unfortunately it has not gone as far as the twentieth century. It has declared in all ages, as a heathen chief declared in the dark ages, that the life of a man is like the flight of a bird across a firelit room, because we know nothing of whence it comes or whither it goes. It would seem natural to apply it not only to man but to mankind. But the moderns do not apply the same principle but the very opposite principle. They specialize in the unknown origins and in the unknown future. They dwell on the prehistoric and on the post-historic or prophetic; and neglect only the historic. They will give a most detailed description of the habits of the bird when he was a sort of pterodactyl only faintly to be traced in a fossil. They will give an equally detailed description of the habits of the bird a hundred years hence, when he shall have turned into a super-bird, or the dove of universal peace. But the bird in the hand is worth far less to them than the two mysterious birds in these two impenetrable bushes. They will publish a portrait with life, letters, and table-talk of the Missing Link, although he is missing; they will publish a plan and documented history of how the Social Revolution happened, though it has not happened yet. It is the men who are not missing and the revolutions that have happened that they have rather a habit of overlooking. Anyone who has argued, for instance, with the young Jewish intellectuals who are the brain of Bolshevism knows that their whole system turns on the two pivots of the prehistoric and the prophetic. They talk of the Communism of prehistoric ages as if it were a thing like the Crusades in the Middle Ages; not even a probable conjecture but a proved and familiar fact. They will tell you exactly how private property arose in primitive times, just as if they had been there. And then they will take one gigantic leap over all human history, and tell you about the inevitable Communism of the future. Nothing seems to matter unless it is either new enough to be foretold or old enough to be forgotten.

Mr. H. G. Wells has hit off his human habit in the account of a very human character, the American girl who glorifies Stonehenge in his last novel. I do not make Mr. Wells responsible for her opinions, though she is an attractive person and much too good for her Lothario. But she interests me here because she typifies very truly another variation upon this same tendency. To the prehistoric and the post-historic must be added a third thing, which may be called the unhistoric. I mean the bad teaching of real history that such intelligent people so often suffer. She sums up exactly what I mean when she says humorously that Stonehenge has been " kept from her," that Notre Dame is far less important, and that this is the real starting-point of the " Mayflower."

Now the " Mayflower " is a myth. It is an intensely interesting example of a real modern myth. I do not mean of course that the " Mayflower " never sailed, any more than I admit that King Arthur never lived or that Roland never died. I do not mean that the incident had no historic interest, or that the men who figured in it had no heroic qualities; any more than I deny that Charlemagne was a great man because the legend says he was two hundred years old; any more than I deny that the resistance of Roman Britain to the heathen invasion was valiant and valuable, because the legend says that Arthur at Mount Badon killed nine hundred men with his own hand. I mean that there exists in millions of modern minds a traditional image or vision called the " Mayflower," which has far less relation to the real facts than Charlemagne's two hundred years or Arthur's nine hundred corpses. Multitudes of people in England and America, as intelligent and sympathetic as the young lady in Mr. Wells' novel, think of the "Mayflower" as an origin, or archetype, like the Ark or at least the Argo. Perhaps it would be an exaggeration to say that they think the "Mayflower" discovered America. They do really talk as if the "Mayflower" populated America. Above all, they talk as if the establishment of New England had been the first and formative example of the expansion of England. They believe that English expansion was a Puritan experiment; and that an expansion of Puritan ideas was also the expansion of what have been claimed as English ideas, especially ideas of liberty. The Puritans of New England were champions of religious freedom, seeking to found a newer and freer state beyond the sea, and thus becoming the origin and model of modern democracy. All this betrays a lack of exactitude. It is certainly nearer to exact truth to say that Merlin built the castle at Camelot by magic, or that Roland broke the mountains in pieces with his unbroken sword.

For at least the old fables are faults on the right side. They are symbols of the truth and not of the opposite of the truth. They described Roland as brandishing his unbroken sword against the Moslems, but not in favour of the Moslems. And the New England Puritans would have regarded the establishment of real religious liberty exactly as Roland would have regarded the establishment of the religion of Mahound. The fables described Merlin as building a palace for a king and not a public hall for the London School of Economics. And it would be quite as sensible to read the Fabian politics of Mr. Sidney Webb into the local kingships of the Dark Ages, as to read anything remotely resembling modern liberality into the most savage of all the savage theological frenzies of the seventeenth century. Thus the "Mayflower" is not merely a fable, but is much more false than fables generally are. The revolt of the Puritans against the Stuarts was really a revolt *against* religious toleration. I do not say the Puritans were never persecuted by their opponents; but I do say, to their great honour and glory, that the Puritans never descended to the hypocrisy of pretending for a moment that they did not mean to persecute their opponents. And in the main their quarrel with the Stuarts was that the Stuarts would not persecute those opponents enough. Not only was it then the Catholics who were proposing toleration, but it was they who had already actually established toleration in the State of Maryland, before the Puritans began to establish the most intolerant sort of intolerance in the State of New England. And if the fable is fabulous touching the emancipation of religion, it is yet more fabulous touching the expansion of empire. That had been started long before either New England or Maryland, by Raleigh who started it in Virginia. Virginia is still perhaps the most English of the states, certainly more English than New England. And it was also the most typical and important of the states, almost up to Lee's last battle in the Wilderness. But I have only taken the "Mayflower" as an example of the general truth; and in a way the truth has its consoling side. Modern men are not allowed to have any history; but at least nothing can prevent men from having legends.

We have thus before us, in a very true and typical modern picture, the two essential parts of modern culture. It consists first of false history and second of fancy history. What the American tourist believed about Plymouth Rock was untrue; what she believed about Stonehenge was only unfounded. The popular story of Primitive Man cannot be proved. The popular story of Puritanism can be disproved. I can fully sympathize with Mr. Wells and his heroine in feeling the imaginative stimulus of mysteries like Stonehenge; but the imagination springs from the mystery; that is, the imagination springs from the ignorance. It is the very greatness of Stonehenge that there is very little of it left. It is its chief feature to be featureless. We are very naturally and rightly moved to mystical emotions about signals from so far away along the path of the past; but part of the poetry lies in our inability really to read the signals. And this is what gives an interest, and even an irony, to the comparison half consciously invoked by the American lady herself when she asked "What's Notre Dame to this?" And the answer that should be given to her is: "Notre Dame, compared to this, is *true*. It is history. It is humanity. It is what has really happened, what we know has really happened, what we know is really happening still. It is the central fact of your own civilization. And it is the thing that has really been kept from you."

Notre Dame is not a myth. Notre Dame is not a theory. Its interest does not spring from ignorance but from knowledge; from a culture complicated with a hundred controversies and revolutions. It is not featureless, but carved into an incredible forest and labyrinth of fascinating features, any one of which we could talk about for days. It is not great because there is little of it, but great because there is a great deal of it. It is true that though there is a great deal of it, Puritans may not be allowed to see a great deal in it; whether they were those brought over in the "Mayflower" or only those brought up on the "Mayflower." But that is not the fault of Notre Dame; but of the extraordinary evasion by which such people can dodge to right or left of it, taking refuge in things more recent or things more remote. Notre Dame, on its merely human side, is mediæval civilization, and therefore not a fable or a guess but a great solid determining part of modern civilization. It is the whole modern debate about guilds; for such cathedrals were built by the guilds. It is the whole modern question of religion and irreligion; for we know what religion it stands for, while we really have not a notion what religion Stonehenge stands for. A Druid temple is a ruin, and a Puritan ship by this time may well be called a wreck. But a church is a challenge; and that is why it is not answered.

MUCH TOO MODERN HISTORY

ALL wise men will agree that history ought to be taught more fully in the form of world history. In that respect at least Mr. Wells gave us an excellent working model. England is meaningless without Europe, more meaningless than England without Empire. But those who would broaden history with human brotherhood too often suffer from a limitation not absent even from Mr. Wells. They exchange the narrowness of a nation for the narrowness of a theory, or even a fad. They think they have a world-wide philosophy because they extend their own narrowness to the whole world. A distinguished professor, who is a member of the League of Nations Union, has been telling an interviewer what he thinks history-books should teach. And it seems to me that, according to his views if correctly reported, the new histories would be rather more prejudiced and limited than the old.

He begins with a small but singular error, which itself shows some lack of the imagination that can see two sides of a question. He says, "Textbooks of history should aim at truth. It should not be possible for one version of the American War of Independence to be taught in American schools, and another in English schools."

Now, in point of fact, the same version of that story is taught both in English and American schools. It is the other version, a very tenable one, that is not allowed to be taught anywhere. No American historian, however American, could be more positive that George III was wrong and George Washington right than all the English historians are. What would show real independence of mind would be to state the case for George III. And there was a very real case for George III. I will not go into it here, but every honest historical student will agree with me. Perhaps the fairest way of putting it is this: that it was not really a case of a government resolved on tyranny, but of a nation resolved on independence.

But if we sympathize with national independence, surely there is something to be said for intellectual independence. And the professor is far from being really sympathetic with intellectual independence. He is so far from it that he wants both sides forced to tell the same story, apparently whether they like it or not. As a fact, they do agree; but apparently in any case the professor would coerce them into agreement. And his extraordinary reason for this course is that history should aim at truth.

But suppose I do aim at truth, and sincerely

come to the conclusion that North was a patriot and Burke a sophist? How would the professor prevent it being " possible " for me to teach what I think is true? The truth is that it has never occurred to these progressive professors that there could be any view of any question except their own, or what they call their own. For it is only a tradition they have been taught; a tradition as narrow as North's and now nearly as old.

But the professor goes on to say something much more interesting and curious. After saying very truly that the past, the Plantagenet period, for instance, should not be made a mere matter of kings and battles, he goes on to say, " What we want to see is the textbook of history and the teaching of it brought more closely into touch with the realities of the modern world—the world of the division of labour between different countries, of the application of science to industry, of the shortening of the spaces of the earth by improvements in transport— and with all that these realities imply."

Now it seems to me obvious that what we want is exactly the opposite. A child can see these realities of the modern world, whether he is taught any history or not. He will see them whether you want him to or not. As he grows up he will learn by experience all about the improvements in transport, its acceleration by Zeppelins and its interruption by submarines. He will realize for himself that the modern world is the world of the division of labour between nations. For he will know that England has been turned into an isolated workshop with hardly food enough for a fortnight, with the potential alternative of surrender or starvation or eating nails. He will by the light of nature know all about the application of science to industry—in war by chemical analyses of poison gas, in peace by bright little pamphlets about phossy jaw. He will know "all that these realities imply," about which also there is very much that might be said. But even if we consider only the somewhat cheerier products of the division of labour and the application of science to industry, there is quite as little need laboriously to instruct the infant in what he can see for himself. A child has a very pure and poetical love of machinery, a love in which there is nothing in the least evil or materialistic. But it is hardly necessary to devote years to proving to him that motor-cars have been invented, as he can see them going by in the street. It is not necessary to read up in the British Museum the details with which to demonstrate that there are really such things as tube stations or motor bicycles. The child can see these things everywhere, and the real danger obviously is that he should think they had existed always. The danger is that he should know nothing of humanity, except as it is under these special and sometimes cramping conditions of scientific industry and the division of labour. It is that he should be unable to imagine any civilization without tube stations, whatever its substitutes in the way of temples or trophies of war. It is that he should see man as a sort of cyclist-centaur, inseparable from his motor-bike. In short, the whole danger of historical ignorance is that he may be as limited to his local circumstances as a savage on an island, or a provincial in a decayed town, or a historical professor in the League of Nations Union.

The whole object of history is to enlarge experience by imagination. And this sort of history would enlarge neither imagination nor experience. The whole object of history is to make us realize that humanity could be great and glorious, under conditions quite different and even contrary to our own. It is to teach us that men could achieve most profitable labour without our own division of labour. It is to teach us that men could be industrious without being industrial. It is to make us understand that there might be a world in which there was far less improvement in the transport for visiting various places, and there might still be a very great improvement in the places visited.

The professor is perfectly right in saying that a history of the Plantagenet period ought not merely to record the succession of kings and battles. But what ought it to record? Is it to record only the absence of motors and electric lights? Should we say nothing of the Plantagenet period except that it did *not* have motor-bikes? I venture to suggest that we might record the presence of some things which the whole people had then and have not got now, such as the guilds, the great popular universities, the use of the common lands, the fraternity of the common creed.

I fear the professor will not follow me into matters so disturbing to his perfect picture of progress. But, in conclusion, there is one little question I should like to ask him, and it is this: If you cannot see Man, divine and democratic, under the disguises of all the centuries, why on earth should you suppose you will be able to see him under the disguises of all the nations and tribes? If the Dark Ages must be as dark as they look, why are the black men not so black as they are painted? If I may feel supercilious towards a Chaldean, why not towards a Chinaman? If I may despise a Roman for not having a steam-plough, why not a Russian for not wanting a steam-plough? If scientific industry is the supreme historical test, it divides us as much from backward peoples as from bygone peoples. It divides even European peoples from each other. And if that be the test, why bother to join the League of Nations Union?

THE EVOLUTION OF SLAVES

A VERY curious and interesting thing has recently happened in America. There has suddenly appeared an organized political attack on Darwinian Evolution, led by an old demagogue appealing entirely to the ideals of democracy. I mean no discredit to Mr. Bryan in calling him a demagogue; for I should have been far more heartily on his side in the days when he was a demagogue than in the days when he was a diplomatist. He was a much wiser man when he refused to allow the financiers to crucify humanity on a golden cross, than when he consented to allow the Kaiser to crucify it on an iron cross. The movement is religious and therefore popular; but it is Protestant and therefore provincial. Its opponents, the old guard of materialism, will of course do their best to represent it as something like the village that voted the earth was flat. But there is one sharp difference, which is the point of the whole position. If an ignorant man went about saying that the earth was flat, the scientific man would promptly and confidently answer, " Oh, nonsense; of course it's round." He might even condescend to give the real reasons, which I believe are quite different from the current ones. But when the private citizen rushes wild-eyed down the streets of Heliopolis, Neb., calling out " Have you heard the news? Darwin's wrong!" the scientific man does not say, " Oh, nonsense, of course he's right." He says tremulously, " Not entirely wrong; surely not entirely wrong "; and we can draw our conclusions. But I believe myself there is a deeper and more democratic force behind this reaction; and I think it worthy of further study.

I recently heard a debate on that American system of class privilege which we call for convenience Prohibition; and I was very much amused by one argument that was advanced in its favour. A very intelligent young American, a Rhodes scholar from Oxford, advanced the thesis that Prohibition was not a violation of liberty because, if it were fully established, its victims would never know what they had lost. If a generation of total abstainers could once grow up "without the desire" for drink, they would not be conscious of any restraint on their freedom. The argument is ingenious and promising and opens up a wide field of application. Thus, if I happen to find it convenient to keep miners or other proletarians permanently underground, I have only to make sure that all their babies are born in pitch darkness and they will certainly never imagine the light of day. My action therefore will not only be just and benevolent in itself, but will obviously involve not even the faintest infringement of the ideal of freedom. Or if I merely kidnap all the babies from all the mothers in the country, it is obvious that the infants will not remember their mothers, and in that sense will not miss them. There is therefore no reason why I should not adopt this course; and even if I hide the babies from their mothers by locking them up in boxes, I shall not be violating the principle of liberty; because the babies will not understand what I have done. Or, to take a comparison even closer in many ways, there is an ordinary social problem like dress. I come to the conclusion that ladies spend too much money on dress, that it is a social evil because families suffer from the extravagance, and rivalries and seductions distract the State. I therefore decree, on the lines of Prohibitionist logic, that the law shall forbid anybody to wear any clothes at all. Nobody who grows up naked, according to this theory, will ever have any regrets for beauty or dignity or decency; and therefore will have suffered no loss. I cannot sufficiently express my admiration for the extraordinary simplicity which can smooth the path of Prussianism with this large, elementary and satisfactory principle. So long as we tyrannize enough we are not tyrannizing at all; and so long as we steal enough our victims will never know what has been stolen.

Seriously, everybody knows that the rich planning the oppression of the poor will never lack a sycophant to act as a sophist. But I never dreamed that I should live to enjoy so crude and stark and startling a sophistry as this.

But the last example I gave, that of the normality of clothes or of nakedness, has a further relevance in this connection. What is really at the back of the minds of the people who say these strange things is one very simple error. They imagine that the drinking of fermented liquor has been an artifice and a luxury; something odd like the strange self-indulgences praised by the decadent poets. This is simply an accident of the ignorance of history and humanity. Drinking fermented liquor is not a fashion like wearing a green carnation. It is a habit like wearing clothes. It is one of the habits that are indeed man's second nature; if indeed they are not his first nature. Wine is purest and healthiest in the highest civilization, just as clothing is most complete in the highest civilization. But there is nothing to show that the savage has not shed the clothes of a higher civilization, retaining only the ornaments; as a good many fashionable people in our own civilization seem to be doing now. And there is nothing to show that ruder races who brew their " native beers " in Africa or Polynesia have not lost the art of brewing something better; just as Prohibitionist America, before

our very eyes, has left off brewing Christian beer
and taken to drinking fermented wood-pulp and
methylated spirit. The very example of modern
America falling from better to baser drinks, under
a dismal taboo, is a perfect model of the way in
which civilizations have relapsed into savagery, and
produced the savages we know. But the point is
that drink, like dress, is the rule; and the exceptions
only prove the rule. There are individuals who for
personal and particular reasons are right to drink
no liquor but water; just as there are individuals
who have to stay in bed, and wear no clothes but
bedclothes. There have been sects of Moslems and
there have been sects of Adamites. There have been,
as I have said, barbarized peoples fallen so far from
civilization as to wear grotesque garments or none,
or to drink bad beer or none. But nobody has ever
seen Primitive Man, naked and drinking water; he is
a myth of the modern mythologists. Man, as Aristotle saw long ago, is an abnormal animal whose
nature it is to be civilized. In so far as he ever
becomes uncivilized he becomes unnatural, and even
artificial.

Now at the back of all this, of course, the real
difference is religious. I only take this one case of
what is called temperance for the sake of the wider
philosophy that underlies it. When my young
American friend talked of the next generation grow-

ing up without the desire for " alcohol," he had at
the back of his mind a certain idea. It is the idea
which I have just seen expressed by another American in a high-brow article, in the words: " Evolution does not stand still. We are not finished. The
world is not finished." What it means is that the
nature of man can be modified to suit the convenience
of particular men; and this would certainly be very
convenient. If the rich man wants the miners to
live underground, he may really breed for it a new
race as blind as bats and owls. If he finds it cheaper
to run the school and school inspections on Adamite
principles, he can hope to produce Adamites not
merely as a sect but as a species. And the same will
be true of teetotalism or vegetarianism; nature, having evolved man, who is an ale-drinking animal, may
now evolve a super-man, or a sub-man, who shall be
a water-drinking animal. Having risen from a monkey who eats nuts to a man who eats mutton, he may
rise yet higher by eating nuts again.

Thinking people, of course, know that all that is
nonsense. They know there is no such constant flux
of adaption. So far from saying that the evolution
of man has not finished, they will point out that (as
far as we know) it has not begun. In all the five
thousand years of recorded history, and in all the
prehistoric indications before it, there is not a
shadow or suspicion of movement or change in the

human biological type. Even evolution, let alone natural selection, is only a conjecture about things unknown, compared with the broad daylight of things known in all those thousands of years. The only difference is that evolution seems a probable conjecture, and natural selection is on the face of it an extravagantly improbable one. All this, which is obvious to thinking people, has at last become obvious even to the most unthinking; and *that* is the meaning of the attack on Darwinism in America and the battle of Mr. Bryan against the Missing Link. The secret is out. The obscurantism of the professors is over. Those of us who have humbly hammered on this point from time to time suddenly find ourselves hammering on an open door. For these changes almost always come suddenly; which is alone enough to show that human history at least has never been merely an evolution. As Darwinism came with a rush, so anti-Darwinism has come with a rush; and just as people who accepted evolution could not be held back from embracing natural selection, so it is likely enough that many, who now see reason to reject natural selection, will not be stopped in their course till they have also rejected evolution. They will merely have a vague but angry conviction that the professors have been kidding them. But behind all this there will be a very real moral and religious reaction; the meaning of which is what I have described in this article. It is the profound popular impression that scientific materialism, at the end of its hundred years, is found to have been used chiefly for the oppression of the people. Of this the most evident example is that evolution itself can be offered as something able to evolve a people who can be oppressed. As in the argument about Prohibition, it will offer to breed slaves; to produce a new race indifferent to its rights. Morally the argument is quite indistinguishable from justifying assassination by promising to bring up children as suicides, who will prefer to be poisoned.

IS DARWIN DEAD?

MR. ERNEST NEWMAN, that lively and acute critic, once rebuked the arrogance of those of us who confessed that we knew nothing about music. Why he should suppose we are arrogant about it, if he does think so, I cannot quite understand. I, for one, am fully conscious of my inferiority to him and others through this deficiency; nor is it, alas, the only deficiency. I have sometimes thought it would be wholesome for anybody who has succeeded pretty well by some trick of some trade, to have a huge notice board or diagram hung in front of him all day; showing exactly where he stood in all the other crafts and competitions of mankind. Thus the poet's eye in a fine frenzy rolling, as it rose from the paper on which an entirely new type of villanelle had just sprung into being, would encounter the disconcerting facts and figures about his suitability to be a professional acrobat or a pearl-diver. On the other hand, the radiant victor in the great International Egg and Spoon Race can see at a glance how very far down he stands, so to speak, in the queue of those waiting for the post of Astronomer Royal. Most of us have at least one or two gaps in our general culture and information; and sometimes whole departments of knowledge·are practically hidden from whole generations and classes of mankind. There is something very defective and disproportionate about even the ideal culture of a modern man. It may be that Mr. Newman is deeply read in that mediæval theology which is still the sub-conscious basis of most morality; but it is also possible that he is not. He may have at his fingers' ends that military art which has often turned the fortunes of history; but he may not. He would be none the less a highly cultivated gentleman, if he did not. Yet the mystical and the military mind have been at least as pivotal and practical in history as the musical mind. I can admire them all, but I have no claim to possess any of them.

But my ignorance of music happens to assist me with a convenient metaphor in the more controversial matter of my ignorance of science. I once made some remarks about the decline of Darwinism, in a review of the Wells "Outline of History." This aroused rather excited criticism; but one comparatively calm critic challenged what really interests me in the matter: he said that my conundrums about the wing of the bat and similar things " could easily be solved on purely Darwinian lines by any competent zoologist, or even by one so incompetent as myself. The conundrum in question, of course, concerns the survival value of features in their unfin-

217

ished state. If a thing can fly it may survive, and if it has a wing it may fly; but if it cannot fly with half a wing, why should it survive with half a wing? Yet Darwinism pre-supposes that numberless generations could survive before one generation could fly. Now it is quite true that I am not even an incompetent zoologist; and that my critic is more competent than I, if only in the mere fact of being a zoologist at all. Nevertheless, I adhere to my opinion, and do so for a reason that seems to me worthy of some little consideration. I do it because this does happen to be exactly one of those questions on which, as it seems to me, the independent critic has really a right to check the specialist. For it is a larger question of logic, and not a smaller question of fact. It is like the difficulty of believing that a halfpenny can fall head or tail a hundred times running; which has nothing to do with the numismatic value of the coin. It is like the difficulty of believing that a mere tax could make a loaf cheaper, which has nothing to do with the agrarian craft of growing corn. There is a general tide of reason flowing against such improbabilities, even if they are possibilities; they would still be exceptions, and reason would be on the side of the rule. And whatever the details of natural history, this thing is against the very nature of things.

To explain what I mean I will take this parallel of the technique of music, of which I know even less than of the technique of natural history. To begin with a simple though moving musical instrument, suppose an expert told me that a coach-horn could be blown quite as well if it were only two feet long. I should believe him; partly because it seems probable enough, and partly because I know nothing about the matter. I am not even an incompetent coach-horn blower. But I should certainly not believe him if he told me, as a generalization about all musical instruments, that half a musical instrument was better than no music, or even as good as any music. I should disbelieve it because it is inconsistent with the general nature of a musical instrument, or any instrument. I should disbelieve it long before I had thought of the thousand particular instruments to which it does not apply. I should not primarily need to think of the particular examples, though they are obvious enough. A stringed instrument cannot even be called stringed without two fixed points to hold both ends of the string. At the stage when the fiddle-strings floated like filaments in the void, feeling their way towards an evolutionary other end of nowhere, there could be nothing serving any purpose of a fiddle. A drum with a hole in is not a drum at all. But an evolutionary drum has to turn slowly into a drum, when it has begun by being only a hole. I cannot see any survival for a bagpipe that begins by being slit; I think such bagpipes would die with all their music in them. I feel a faint

doubt, mingled with fascination, about the idea that
a violin could grow out of the ground like a tree;
it would at least make a charming fairy story. But
whether or no a fiddle could grow like a tree, I feel
sure nobody could play on it while it was still only
a twig. But all these, as I say, are only examples
that throng into the mind afterwards, of a principle
seen in a flash from the first. Of things serving particular purposes, by a balance and arrangement of
parts, it *cannot* be generally true that they are fit
for use before they are finished for use. It is against
the general nature of such things; and can only be
true by an individual coincidence. I can see for myself, for instance, that some particular case like the
trunk of an elephant might really be compared to
the simpler case of the coach-horn. Length and
flexibility *are* mere matters of degree; and I might
possibly find it convenient if my nose were six inches
longer, and sufficiently lively to be able to point
right and left at various objects on the tea-table.
But this is simply an accident of the particular
qualities of length and laxity, not a general truth
about the qualities of growth and use. It is not
in the least true that I should experience the least
convenience from the membrane between my fingers
thickening or widening a little; even if an evolution-
ist at my elbow comforted and inspired me with the
far-off divine event when my descendant should have
the wings of a bat. Until the membrane can really

be spread properly from point to point it is like the fiddle-string before it is stretched properly from point to point. It is no nearer serving its ultimate purpose than if it were not there at all. But it would be easy to find a similar animal parallel to the drum with a hole in it. There are monsters who would die instantly if they could not close the holes in their head under water. One supposes they would have died swiftly, before their closing apparatus could develop slowly. But the principle is a general one, and is involved in the very nature of any apparatus. It is only by way of figure of speech, in defence of the freedom of the ignorant, that I take the type of a musical apparatus. I take it because I am entirely ignorant of musical instruments. I am of the candid class of those who have " never tried " to perform on the violin. I cannot play upon this pipe; especially if it be a bag-pipe. But if anybody tells me that the wildest pibroch rose from a whisper gradually, as a hole in the wind-bag was filled up gradually—why then, I shall not be so rude, I hope, as to say that there is a wind-bag in his head, but I shall venture to say that there is a hole in his argument. And if he says that pieces of wood came together slowly, stick by stick, to form a fiddle, and that before it was yet a fiddle at all the sticks discoursed most excellent music—why, I fear I shall be content to say " fiddlesticks."

There is another answer often made which seems

to me even more illogical. The critic generally says it is unreasonable to expect from the geological record that continuous gradation of types which the challengers of Darwinism demand. He says that only a part of the earth can be examined and that it could not in any case prove so much. This mode of argument involves an amazing oblivion of what is the thing to be proved, and who is trying to prove it. By hypothesis the Darwinians are trying to prove Darwinism. The Anti-Darwinians are not trying to prove anything; except that the Darwinians have not proved it. I do not demand anything, in the sense of complaining anything or the absence of anything. I am quite comfortable in a completely mysterious cosmos. I am not reviling the rocks or cursing the eternal hills for not containing these things. I am only saying that these are the things they would have to contain to make me believe something that somebody else wants me to believe. These traces are not things that the Anti-Darwinian demands. They are things that the Darwinian requires. The Darwinian requires them in order to convince his opponent of Darwinism; his opponent may be right or wrong, but he cannot be expected to accept the mere absence of them as proof of Darwinism. If the evidences in support of the theory are unfortunately hidden, why then, we do not know whether they were in support of the theory. If the proofs of natural selection are lost, why then, there are no proofs of natural selection; and there is an end of it.

And I would respectfully ask these critics what would be thought of a theological or miraculous argument which thus based itself on the very gaps in its own evidence. Let them indulge in the flight of fancy that I have just told them, let us say, that I saw the Devil at Brighton: and that the proof of his presence there can still be seen on the sands, in gigantic marks of a cloven hoof as big as the foot of an elephant. Suppose we all search the sands of Brighton and find no such thing. And suppose I then say that, after all, the tide might have washed away the footprints, or that the fiend may have flown through the air from his little country seat at the Dyke, or that he may have walked along the hard asphalt of Brighton parade, as proudly as once upon the flaming marl. To those acquainted with Brighton parade this will seem probable enough; but there would be a fallacy in merely saying that the evil spirit may have done all this. The sceptic will not unnaturally reply: " Yes, he may; and he may not; and it may be a legend; and you may be a liar; and I thing our little investigation is now concluded." I am very far indeed from calling the Darwinian a liar; but I shall continue to say that he is not always a logician.

TURNING INSIDE OUT

WHEN the author of "If Winter Comes" brought out another book about the life of the family, it was almost as much criticized as the first book was praised. I do not say that there was nothing to criticize, but I do say that I was not convinced by the abstract logic of the criticism. Probably the critics would have accepted it as a true story if the author had not been so incautious as to give it a true moral. And the moral is not fashionable in the Press at the moment; for it is to the effect that a woman may gain a professional success at the price of a domestic failure. And it is the convention of journalism at this moment to support what is feminist against what is feminine. Anyhow, while the story might be criticized, the criticisms can certainly be criticized. It is not really conclusive to say that a woman may be ambitious in business without her children going to the bad. It is just as easy to say that a woman may be ambitious in politics without helping to murder an old gentleman in his bed. But that does not make "Macbeth" either inartistic or untrue. It is just as easy to say that a woman may be ambitious in society without tricking her husband into a debtor's prison, so that she may spend the time with a bald-headed nobleman with red whiskers. But that does not make the great scene in "Vanity Fair" unconvincing either in detail or design. The question in fiction is not whether that thing must occur, but whether that sort of thing may occur, and whether it is significant of larger things. Now this business of the woman at work and the woman at home is a very large thing, and this story about it is highly significant.

For in this matter the modern mind is inconsistent with itself. It has managed to get one of its rather crude ideals in flat contradiction to the other. People of the progressive sort are perpetually telling us that the hope of the world is in education. Education is everything. Nothing is so important as training the rising generation. Nothing is really important except the rising generation. They tell us this over and over again, with slight variations of the same formula, and never seem to see what it involves. For if there be any word of truth in all this talk about the education of the child, then there is certainly nothing but nonsense in nine-tenths of the talk about the emancipation of the woman. If education is the highest function in the State, why should anybody want to be emancipated from the highest function in the State? It is as if we talked

of commuting the sentence that condemned a man
to be President of the United States; or a reprieve
coming in time to save him from being Pope. If
education is the largest thing in the world, what is
the sense of talking about a woman being liberated
from the largest thing in the world? It is as if we
were to rescue her from the cruel doom of being a
poet like Shakespeare; or to pity the limitations of
an all-round artist like Leonardo da Vinci. Nor can
there be any doubt that there is truth in this claim
for education. Only precisely the sort of which it is
particularly true is the sort called domestic education. Private education really is universal. Public
education can be comparatively narrow. It would
really be an exaggeration to say that the schoolmaster who takes his pupils in freehand drawing is
training them in all the uses of freedom. It really
would be fantastic to say that the harmless foreigner
who instructs a class in French or German is talking
with all the tongues of men and angels. But the
mother dealing with her own daughters in her own
home does literally have to deal with all forms of
freedom, because she has to deal with all sides of a
single human soul. She is obliged, if not to talk
with the tongues of men and angels, at least to
decide how much she shall talk about angels and
how much about men.

In short, if education is really the larger matter,
then certainly domestic life is the larger matter; and

official or commercial life the lesser matter. It is a mere matter of arithmetic that anything taken from the larger matter will leave it less. It is a mere matter of simple subtraction that the mother must have less time for the family if she has more time for the factory. If education, ethical and cultural, really were a trivial and mechanical matter, the mother might possibly rattle through it as a rapid routine, before going about her more serious business of serving a capitalist for hire. If education were merely instruction, she might briefly instruct her babies in the multiplication tables, before she mounted to higher and nobler spheres as the servant of a Milk Trust or the secretary of a Drug Combine. But the moderns are perpetually assuring us that education is not instruction; they are perpetually insisting that it is not a mechanical exercise, and must on no account be an abbreviated exercise. It must go on at every hour. It must cover every subject. But if it must go on at all hours, it must not be neglected in business hours. And if the child is to be free to cover every subject, the parent must be free to cover every subject too.

For the idea of a non-parental substitute is simply an illusion of wealth. The advanced advocate of this inconsistent and infinite education for the child is generally thinking of the rich child; and all this particular sort of liberty should rather be called luxury. It is natural enough for a fashionable lady to leave her little daughter with the French governess or the Czecho-Slovakian governess or the Ancient Sanskrit governess, and know that one or other of these sides of the infant's intelligence is being developed; while she, the mother, figures in public as a money-lender or some other modern position of dignity. But among poorer people there cannot be five teachers to one pupil. Generally there are about fifty pupils to one teacher. There it is impossible to cut up the soul of a single child and distribute it among specialists. It is all we can do to tear in pieces the soul of a single schoolmaster, and distribute it in rags and scraps to a whole mob of boys. And even in the case of the wealthy child it is by no means clear that specialists are a substitute for spiritual authority. Even a millionaire can never be certain that he has not left out one governess, in the long procession of governesses perpetually under his marble portico; and the omission may be as fatal as that of the king who forgot to ask the bad fairy to the christening. The daughter, after a life of ruin and despair, may look back and say, "Had I but also had a Lithuanian governess, my fate as a diplomatist's wife in Eastern Europe would have been very different." But it seems rather more probable, on the whole, that what she would miss would not be one or other of these special accomplishments, but some common sense code of morals or general view of life. The millionaire could, no doubt, hire a mahatma or mystical prophet to give his child a general philosophy. But I doubt if the philosophy would be very successful even for the rich child, and it would be quite impossible for the poor child. In the case of comparative poverty, which is the common lot of mankind, we come back to a general parental responsibility, which is the common sense of mankind. We come back to the parent as the person in charge of education. If you exalt the education, you must exalt the parental power with it. If you exaggerate the education, you must exaggerate the parental power with it. If you depreciate the parental power, you must depreciate education with it. If the young are always right and can do as they like, well and good; let us all be jolly, old and young, and free from every kind of responsibility. But in that case do not come pestering us with the importance of education, when nobody has any authority to educate anybody. Make up your mind whether you want unlimited education or unlimited emancipation, but do not be such a fool as to suppose you can have both at once.

There is evidence, as I have noted, that the more hard-headed people, even of the most progressive sort, are beginning to come back to realities in this respect. The new work of Mr. Hutchinson's is only one of many indications among the really independent intelligences, working on modern fiction, that the cruder culture of merely commercial emancipation is beginning to smell a little stale. The work of Miss Clemence Dane and even of Miss Sheila Kaye-Smith contains more than one suggestion of what I mean. People are no longer quite so certain that a woman's liberty consists of having a latch-key without a house. They are no longer wholly convinced that every housekeeper is dull and prosaic, while every bookkeeper is wild and poetical. And among the intelligent the reaction is actually strengthened by all the most modern excitements about psychology and hygiene. We cannot insist that every trick of nerves or train of thought is important enough to be searched for in libraries and laboratories, and not important enough for anybody to watch by simply staying at home. We cannot insist that the first years of infancy are of supreme importance, and that mothers are not of supreme importance; or that motherhood is a topic of sufficient interest for men, but not of sufficient interest for mothers. Every word that is said about the tremendous importance of trivial nursery habits goes to prove that being a nurse is not trivial. All tends to the return of the simple truth that the private work is the great one and the public work the small. The human house is a paradox, for it is larger inside than out.

But in the problem of private versus public life there is another neglected truth. It is true of many masculine problems as well as of this feminine problem. Indeed, feminism falls here into exactly the same mistake as militarism and imperialism. I mean that anything on a grand scale gives the illusion of a grand success. Curiously enough, multiplication acts as a concealment. Repetition actually disguises failure. Take a particular man, and tell him to put on a particular kind of hat and coat and trousers, and to stand in particular attitudes in the back garden; and you will have great difficulty in persuading yourself (or him) that he has passed through a triumph and transfiguration. Order four hundred such hats, and eight hundred such trousers, and you will have turned the fancy costume into a uniform. Make all the four hundred men stand in the special attitudes on Salisbury Plain, and there will rise up before you the spirit of a regiment. Let the regiment march past, and, if you have any life in you above the brutes that perish, you will have an overwhelming sense that something splendid has just happened, or is just going to begin. I sympathize with this moral emotion in militarism; I think it does symbolize something great in the soul, which has given us the image of St. Michael. But I also realize that in practical relations that emotion can get mixed up with an illusion. It is not really possible to know the characters of all the four hundred men in the marching column as well as one might know the character of the one man attitudinizing in the back garden. If all the four hundred men were

individual failures, we could still vaguely feel that
the whole thing was a success. If we know the one
man to be a failure, we cannot think him a success.

That is why a footman has become rather a foolish figure, while a foot-soldier remains rather a
sublime one. Or rather, that is one of the reasons;
for there are others much more worthy. Anyhow,
footmen were only formidable or dignified when they
could come in large numbers like foot-soldiers—
when they were in fact the feudal army of some great
local family, having some of the loyalty of local
patriotism. Then a livery was as dignified as a uniform, because it really was a uniform. A man who
said he served the Nevilles or rode with the Doug-
lases could once feel much like a man fighting for
France or England. But military feeling is mob
feeling, noble as mob feeling may be. Parading one
footman is like lunching on one pea, or curing bald-
ness by the growth of one hair. There ought not
to be anything but a plural for flunkeys, any more
than for measles or vermin or animalculæ or the
sweets called hundreds and thousands. Strictly
speaking, I suppose that a logical Latinist could say,
" I have seen an animalcula "; but I never heard of
a child having the moderation to remark, " I have
eaten a hundred and thousand." Similarly, any one
of us can feel that to have hundreds and thousands
of slaves, let alone soldiers, might give a certain imaginative pleasure in magnificence. To have one

slave reveals all the meanness of slavery. For the solitary flunkey really is the man in fancy dress, the man standing in the back garden in the strange and the fantastic coat and breeches. His isolation reveals our illusion. We find our failure in the back garden, when we have been dreaming a dream of success in the market-place. When you ride through the streets amid a great mob of vassals (you may have noticed) you have a genial and not ungenerous sense of being at one with them all. You cannot remember their names or count their numbers, but their very immensity seems a substitute for intimacy. That is what great men have felt at the head of great armies; and the reason why Napoleon or Foch would call his soldiers "*mes enfants.*" He feels at that moment that they are a part of him, as if he had a million arms and legs. But it is very different if you disband your army of lackeys; or if (as is, after all, possible) you have not got an army of lackeys. It is very different if you look at one lackey; one solitary solemn footman standing in your front hall. You never have the sense of being caught up into a rapture of unity with *him.* All your sense of social solidarity with your social inferiors has dropped from you. It is only in public that people can be so intimate as that. When you look into the eyes of the lonely footman, you see that his soul is far away.

In other words, you find yourself at the foot of

a steep and staggering mountain crag, that is the real character and conscience of a man. To be really at one with that man, you would have to solve real problems and believe that your own solutions were real. In dealing with the one man you would really have a far huger and harder job than in dealing with your throng of thousands. And *that* is the job that people run away from when they wish to escape from domesticity to public work, especially educational work. They wish to escape from a sense of failure which is simply a sense of fact. They wish to recapture the illusion of the market-place. It is an illusion that departs in the dark interiors of domesticity, where the realities dwell. As I have said, I am very far from condemning it altogether; it is a lawful pleasure, and a part of life, in its proper proportion, like any other. But I am concerned to point out to the feminists and the faddists that it is not an approach to truth, but rather the opposite. Publicity is rather of the nature of a harmless romance. Public life at its very best will contain a great deal of harmless romancing, and much more often a very harmful romancing. In other words, I am concerned with pointing out that the passage from private life to public life, while it may be right or wrong, or necessary or unnecessary, or desirable or undesirable, is always of necessity a passage from a greater work to a smaller one, and from a harder work to an easier one. And that is why most of the moderns do wish to pass from the great domestic task to the smaller and easier commercial one. They would rather provide the liveries of a hundred footmen than be bothered with the love-affairs of one. They would rather take the salutes of a hundred soldiers than try to save the soul of one. They would rather serve out income-tax papers or telegraph forms to a hundred men than meals, conversation, and moral support to one. They would rather arrange the educational course in history or geography, or correct the examination papers in alegbra or trigonometry, for a hundred children, than struggle with the whole human character of one. For anyone who makes himself responsiblle for one small baby, as a whole, will soon find that he is wrestling with gigantic angels and demons.

In another way there is something of illusion, or of irresponsibility, about the purely public function, especially in the case of public education. The educationist generally deals with only one section of the pupil's mind. But he always deals with only one section of the pupil's life. The parent has to deal, not only with the whole of the child's character, but also with the whole of the child's career. The teacher sows the seed, but the parent reaps as well as sows. The schoolmaster sees more children, but it is not clear that he sees more childhood; certainly he sees less youth and no maturity. The number of little girls who take prussic acid is necessarily small. The boys who hang themselves on bedposts, after a life of crime, are generally the minority. But the parent has to envisage the whole life of the individual, and not merely the school life of the scholar. It is not probable that the parent will exactly anticipate crime and prussic acid as the crown of the infant's career. But he will anticipate hearing of the crime if it is committed; he will probably be told of the suicide if it takes place. It is quite doubtful whether the schoolmaster or schoolmistress will ever hear of it at all. Everybody knows that teachers have a harassing and often heroic task, but it is not unfair to them to remember that in this sense they have an exceptionally happy task. The cynic would say that the teacher is happy in never seeing the results of his own teaching. I prefer to confine myself to saying that he has not the extra worry of having to estimate it from the other end. The teacher is seldom in at the death. To take a milder theatrical metaphor, he is seldom there on the night. But this is only one of many instances of the same truth: that what is called public life is not larger than private life, but smaller. What we call public life is a fragmentary affair of sections and seasons and impressions; it is only in private life that dwells the fullness of our life bodily.

STRIKES AND THE SPIRIT OF WONDER

THERE is a story which pleases me so much that I feel sure I have repeated it in print, about an alleged and perhaps legendary lady secretary of Madam Blavatsky or Mrs. Besant, who was so much delighted with a new sofa or ottoman that she sat on it by preference when resting or reading her correspondence. At last it moved slightly, and she found it was a mahatma covered with his Eastern robe and rigid in prayer, or some more impersonal ecstasy. That a lady secretary should have a seat any gentleman will approve; that a mahatma should be sat on no Christian will deny; nevertheless, there is another possible moral to the fable which is a reproach rather to the sitter than the seat. It might be put, as in a sort of vision or allegory, by imagining that all our furniture really was made thus of living limbs instead of dead sticks. Suppose the legs of the table were literally legs—the legs of slaves standing still. Suppose the arms of an armchair really were arms—the arms of a patient domestic permanently held out, like those of an old nurse waiting for a baby. It would be calculated to make the luxurious occupant of the easy chair feel rather like a baby; which might do him good. Suppose every sofa were like that of Mrs. Besant's secretary—simply made of a man. They need not be made merely of Theosophists or Buddhists—God forbid. Many of us would greatly prefer to trust ourselves to a Moslem or Turk. This might, with strict accuracy, be called sitting on an Ottoman. I have even read, I think, of some oriental potentate who rejoiced in a name sounding like "sofa." It might even be hinted that some of them might be Christians, but there is no reason, of course, why all of them should not be praying. To sit on a man while he was praying would doubtless require some confidence. It would also give a more literal version of the possession of a prie-dieu chair. It would be easy to expand the extravagance into a vision of a whole house alive, an architecture of arms and legs, a temple of temples of the spirit. The four walls might be made of men like the squares in military formation. There is even, perhaps, a shadow of the fantasy in the popular phrases that compare the roof to the human head, that name the chimney-pot hat after the chimney, or lightly allude to all modern masculine head-dresses as "tiles." But the only value of the vision, as of most visions—even the most topsy-turvy ones—is a moral value. It figures forth, in emblem enigma, the truth that we do treat merely as furniture a number of people who are, at the very least, live stock. And the proof of it is that when they move we are startled like the secretary sitting on the praying man; but perhaps it is we who should begin to pray.

In the current criticisms of the Strikes there is a particular tone, which affects me not as a matter of politics, but rather of philosophy, or even of poetry. It is, indeed, the servile spirit expressed, if not in its poetry, at least in its rhetoric. But it is a spirit I can honestly claim to have hated and done my best to hammer long before I ever heard of the Servile State, long before I ever dreamed of applying this test to Strikes, or indeed of applying it to any political question. I felt it originally touching things at once elemental and everyday—things like grass or daylight, like stones or daisies. But in the light of it at least, I always rebelled against the trend or tone of which I speak. It may roughly be described as the spirit of taking things for granted. But, indeed, oddly enough, the very form of this phrase rather misses its own meaning. The spirit, I mean, strictly speaking, does not take things for granted. It takes them as if they had not been granted. It takes them as if it held them by something more autocratic than a right; by a cold and unconscious occupation, as stiff as a privilege and as baseless as a caprice. As a fact, things generally are granted ultimately by God, but often immediately by men. But this type of man is so unconscious of what he has been given that he is almost unconscious of what he has got; not realizing things as gifts, he hardly realizes them as goods. About the natural things, with which I began, this oblivion has only inward and spiritual, and not outward and political, effects. If we forget the sun the sun will not forget us, or, rather, he will not remember us to revenge himself by " striking " at us with a sunstroke. The stars will not go on strike or extinguish the illumination of the universe as the electricians would extinguish the illumination of the city. And so, while we repeat that there is a special providence in a falling star, we can ignore it in a fixed star. But when we at once ignore and assume thousands of thinking, brooding, free, lonely and capricious human creatures, they will remind us that we can no more order souls than we can order stars. This primary duty of doubt and wonder has nothing to do with the rights or wrongs of special industrial quarrels. The workmen might be quite wrong to go on strike, and we should still be much more wrong in never expecting them to go on strike. Ultimately, it is a mystical but most necessary mood of astonishment at everything outside one's own soul—even one's own body. It may even involve a wild vision in which one's own boots on one's own feet seem to be things distant and unfamiliar. And if this sound a shade fantastic, it is far less fantastic than the opposite extreme—the state of the man who feels as if he owned not only his own feet, but hundreds of other human feet like a huge centipede, or as if he were a universal octopus, and all rails, tubes and tramlines were his own tentacles, the nerves of his own body, or the circulation of his own blood. That is a much worse nightmare, and at this moment a much commoner one.

Tennyson struck a true note of the nineteenth century when he talked about "the fairy tales of science and the long result of time." The Victorians had a very real and even childlike wonder at things like the steam-engine or the telephone, considered as toys. Unfortunately the long result of time, on the fairy tales of science, has been to extend the science and lessen the fairy tale, that is, the sense of the fairy tale. Take for example the current case of the Tubes. Suppose that at an age of innocence you had met a strange man who had promised to drive you by the force of the lightning through the bowels of the earth. Suppose he had offered, in a friendly way, to throw you from one end of London to the other, not only like a thunderbolt, but by the same force as a thunderbolt. Or if we picture it a pneumatic and not an electric railway; suppose he gaily promised to blow you through a pea-shooter to the other side of London Bridge. Suppose he indi-

cated all these fascinating opportunities by pointing
to a hole in the ground and telling you he would
take you there in a sort of flying or falling room.
I hope you would have agreed that there was a special providence in a falling room. But whether or
no you could call it providential, you would agree
to call it special. You would at least think that the
strange man was a very strange man. You would
perhaps call him a very strange and special liar, if
he merely undertook to do it. You might even call
him a magician, if he did do it. But the point is
this, that you would not call him a Bolshevik merely
because he did not do it. You would think it a wonderful thing that it should be done at all; passing in
that swift car through those secret caverns, you
would feel yourself whirled away like Cinderella carried off in the coach that had once been a pumpkin.
But though such things happened in every fairy
tale, they were not expected in any fairy tale. Nobody turned on the fairies and complained that they
were not working because they were not always working wonders. The Press in those parts did not break
into big headlines of " Pumpkins held up; no Transformation Scenes," or " Wands Won't Work; Famine of Coaches." They did not announce with horror
a " Strike of Fairy Godmothers." They did not
draw panic-stricken pictures of mobs of fairy godmothers, meeting in parks and squares, merely be-

cause the majority of pumpkins still continued to be pumpkins. Now I do not argue that we ought to treat every tube-girl as our fairy godmother; she might resent the familiarity, especially the suggestion of anything so near to a grandmother. But I do suggest that we should, by a return to earlier sentiments, realize that the tube servants are doing something for us that we could not do for ourselves; something that is no part of our natural capacities, or even of our natural rights. It is not inevitable, or in the nature of things, that when we have walked as we can or want to, somebody else should carry us further in a cart, even for hire: or that when we have wandered up a road and come to a river, a total stranger should take us over in a boat, even if we bribe him to do so. If we would look at things in this plain white daylight of wonder, that shines on all the roads of the fairy tales, we come to see at last the simplest truth about the Strikes, which is utterly missed in all contemporary comments on them. It is merely the fact that Strikers are not *doing* something: they are doing nothing. If you mean that they should be *made* to do something, say so, and establish slavery. But do not be muddled by the mere word "strike" into mixing it up with breaking a window or hitting a policeman on the nose. Do not be stunned by a metaphor; there are no metaphors in fairy tales.

A NOTE ON OLD NONSENSE

THE Suffragettes have found out that they were wrong; I might even be so egotistical as to say they have found out that we were right. At least they have found out that the modern plutocratic parliamentary franchise is what I for one always said it was. In other words, they are startled and infuriated to find that the most vital modern matters are not settled in Parliament at all, but mostly by a conflict or compromise between Trusts and Trade Unions. Hence Mrs. Flora Drummond actually cries aloud that she is being robbed of her precious vote; and says dramatically, " We women are being disenfranchised "—apparently by " Soviets." It is as if somebody who had just spent half a million on a sham diamond, that ought never to have deceived anybody, should shriek from the window that thieves had stolen the real diamond that never existed at all.

Whether or no there are Soviets, there are undoubtedly Strikes; and I do not under-rate the difficulty or danger of the hour. There is at least a case for blaming men for striking right and left, illogically and without a system; there is a case for blaming them for striking steadily and logically in accordance with a false system; there is a case for saying that "direct action" implies such a false system. But there is no case whatever for blaming them for having depreciated the waste paper of the Westminster ballot-box; for that was depreciated long before the war, and long before the word "Soviet" came to soothe and satisfy the mind of Mrs. Drummond. It is absurd to blame the poor miners for discrediting the members of Parliament, who could always be trusted to discredit themselves. It was not the wild destructive Soviet which decided that Parliament should not know who paid the bills of its own political parties; it was Parliament itself. It was not a mad Bolshevist addressing a mob who said that the men of the parliamentary group have to treat charges of corruption among themselves differently from those outside; it was the greatest living parliamentarian in a great parliamentary debate. Miners had no more to be with it than missionaries in the Cannibal Islands; it was not because men could not get coal that they wanted to get coronets; and the empty coal-scuttle did not fill the party chest. But in any case the policy of people like Mrs. Drummond seems to require explanation. I can only fall back on the suggestion I have already made; that she and her friends insisted on taking shares in a rotten concern. They were quite sincere; so far as anybody can be quite sincere who flatly refuses to listen to reason. They have no right to complain if those who had to listen to their lawlessness will not listen to their legalism.

As a fact such a lady is rather contemptuous than complaining. She says the miners do not want Nationalization; which may or may not be true. But she explains the demand by the old disdainful allusion to agitators; or Labour leaders who "have to beat the big drum or lose their jobs." Nobody of course could possibly connect Mrs. Flora Drummond with the idea of a big drum; any more than with a big horse or a uniform or a self-created military rank. But this particular school of Feminists must not be too fastidious in the present case. The miners are poor and rudely instructed men; and cannot be expected to have that touch of quiet persuasiveness and softening courtesy, by which the Militant Suffragettes did so much to defend the historic dignity of their sex. They have to fall back on something only too like a big drum, having no skill in the silvery flutings of the W.S.P.U., or that tender lute which Miss Pankhurst touched at twilight. But under all the disadvantages of the coarser sex, the advocates of Nationalization have not yet used all the methods that precedent might suggest to them. Mr. Smillie has not cut up any Raphaels or Rembrandts at the National Gallery; nor even set fire to any of the theatres he may happen to pass when he is out for a walk. Mr. Bonar Law, on returning home at evening, does not find Mr. Sidney Webb, a solitary figure chained to his railings. One of the Suffragettes distinguished herself by getting inside a grand piano; but it is seldom that we open our own private piano and find a large coal-miner inside the instrument. The coal-miner may be better at the big drum than the grand piano; but he remains on the outside of both; and his drum is really smaller than some. The big drum, however, is rather a convenient metaphor for something obvious and loud and hollow; and the true moral in the matter is that recent English history was a procession led far too much by the big drum; and the agitation about mere Parliamentary votes was one of the most recent and most remarkable examples of it.

What will be the future of the present industrial crisis I will not prophesy; but I do know that every element in the past, which has led to this impasse in the present, has been thus glorified as a mere novelty by such a noisy minority. It was just because sanguine and shallow people found it easier to act than to write, and easier to write than to think, that every one of the changes came which now complicate our position. The very industrialism which makes us dependent on coal, and therefore on coal-miners and coal-owners, was forced on us by fussy inefficient fools, for whom anything fresh seemed to be free.

A NOTE ON OLD NONSENSE

Neither miners nor mine-owners could have put out the fire by which Shakespeare told his Winter's Tale. The unequal ownership, which has justly alienated the workers, was hurried happily through because the owners were new, and it did not matter that they were few. The blind hypocrisy with which our press and publicists hardened their hearts in the great strikes before the war, was made possible by loud evasions about political progress and especially by the big drum of Votes for Women. I have begun this essay on a controversial note, with the echo of an old controversy; and yet I do not mean to be merely provocative. The Suffragettes are only doing what we all do; and I have only put them first as an example of accumulated abuses for which we are all responsible. I do not mean to blame the Suffragettes as they blame the Socialists; but only to point to an impasse of impenitence for which we are all to blame.

I am more and more convinced that what is wanted nowadays is not optimism or pessimism, but a sort of reform that might more truly be called repentance. The reform of a State ought to be a thing more like the reform of a thief, which involves the admission that he has been a thief. We ought not to be merely inventing consolations, or even merely prophesying disasters; we ought, first and foremost, to be confessing our own very bad mistakes. It is easy enough to say that the world is getting better, by some mysterious thing called progress—which seems to mean providence without purpose. But it is almost as easy to say the world is getting worse, if we assume that it is only the younger generation that has just begun to make it worse. It is easy enough to say that the country is going to the dogs, if we are careful to identify the dogs with the puppies. What we need is not the assertion that other people are going to the dogs, but the confession that we ourselves have only just come back from the swine. We also are the younger generation, in the sense of being the Prodigal Son. As somebody said, there is such a thing as the Prodigal Father. We could purchase hope at the dreadful price of humility. But all thinkers and writers, of all political parties and philosophical sects, seem to shrink from this notion of admitting they are on the wrong road and getting back on to the right one. They are always trying to pretend, by hook or crook, that they are all on the same somewhat meandering road, and that they were right in going east yesterday, though they are right in going west to-day. They will try to make out that every school of thought was an advance on the last school of thought, and that no apology is due to anybody. For instance, we might really have a moderate, cautious, and even conservative reform of the evils affecting Labour, if we would only confess that Capitalism itself was a blunder which it is very difficult to undo. As it is, men seem to be divided into those that think it an achievement so admirable that it cannot be improved upon, and those who think it an achievement so encouraging that it *can* be improved upon. The former will leave it in chaos, and the latter will probably improve it into slavery. Neither will admit what is the truth— that we have got to get *back* to a better distribution of property, as it was before we fell into the blunder of allowing property to be clotted into monstrous monopolies. For that involves admitting that we have made a mistake; and that we none of us have the moral courage to do.

I suggest very seriously that it will do good to our credit for courage and right reason if we drop this way of doing things. The conversions that have converted the world were not effected by this sort of evolutionary curve. St. Paul did not pretend that he had changed slowly and imperceptibly from a Pharisee to a Christian. Victor Hugo did not maintain that he had been very right to be a Royalist, and only a little more right to be a Republican. If we have come to the conclusion that we have been wrong, let us say so, and congratulate ourselves on being now right; not insinuate that in some relative fashion we were just as right when we were wrong. For in this respect the progressive is the worst sort of conservative. He insists on conserving, in the most obstinate and obscurantist fashion, all the courses that have been marked out for progress in the past. He does literally, in the rather unlucky metaphor of Tennyson, " let the great world spin for ever down the ringing grooves of change." For anyone who changes in that fashion has only got into a groove. There is no obligation on anybody to invent evolutionary excuses for all these experiments. There is no need to be so much ashamed of our blunders as all that. It is human to err; and the only final and deadly error, among all our errors, is denying that we have ever erred.

MILTON AND MERRY ENGLAND

MR. FREEMAN, in contributing to the " London Mercury " some of those critical analyses which we all admire, remarked about myself (along with compliments only too generous and strictures almost entirely just) that there was very little autobiography in my writings. I hope the reader will not have reason to curse him for this kindly provocation, watching me assume the graceful poses of Marie Bashkirtseff, but I feel tempted to plead it in extenuation or excuse for this article, which can hardly avoid being egotistical. For though it concerns one of those problems of literature, of philosophy and of history that certainly interest me more than my own psychology, it is one on which I can hardly explain myself without seeming to expose myself.

That valuable public servant, " The Gentleman with the Duster," has passed on from Downing Street, from polishing up the Mirrors and polishing off the Ministers, to a larger world of reflections in " The Glass of Fashion." I call the glass a world of reflections rather than a world of shadows: especially as I myself am one of those tenuous shades. And the matter which interests me here is that the critic in question complains that I have been very unjust to Puritans and Puritanism, and especially to a certain ethical idealism in them, which he declares to have been more essential than the Calvinism of which I "make so much." He puts the point in a genial but somewhat fantastic fashion by saying that the world owes something to the jokes of Mr. G. K. Chesterton, but more to the moral earnestness of John Milton. This involves rather a dizzy elevation than a salutary depression; and the comparison is rather too overwhelming to be crushing. For I suppose the graceful duster of mirrors himself would hardly feel crushed if I told him he did not hold the mirror up to Nature quite so successfully as Shakespeare. Nor can I be described as exactly reeling from the shock of being informed that I am a less historic figure than Milton. I know not how to answer, unless it be in the noble words of Sam Weller: "That's what we call a self-evident proposition, as the cats'-meat-man said to the housemaid when she said he was no gentleman." But for all that I have a controversial issue with the critic about the moral earnestness of Milton, and I have a confession to make which will seem to many only too much in the personal manner referred to by Mr. Freeman.

My first impulse to write, and almost my first impulse to think, was a revolt of disgust with the Decadents and the æsthetic pessimism of the 'nineties.

It is now almost impossible to bring home to anybody, even to myself, how final that *fin de siècle*
seemed to be; not the end of the century but the end
of the world. To a boy his first hatred is almost as
immortal as his first love. He does not realize that
the objects of either can alter; and I did not know
that the twilight of the gods was only a mood. I
thought that all the wit and wisdom in the world
were banded together to slander and depress the
world, and in becoming an optimist I had the feelings of an outlaw. Like Prince Florizel of Bohemia,
I felt myself to be alone in a luxurious Suicide Club.
But even the death seemed to be a living or rather
everlasting death. To-day the whole thing is merely
dead; it was not sufficiently immortal to be damned,
but then the image of Dorian Gray was really an
idol, with something of the endless youth of a god.
To-day the picture of Dorian Gray has really grown
old. Dodo then was not merely an amusing female;
she was the eternal feminine. To-day the Dodo is
extinct. Then, above all, everyone claiming intelligence insisted on what was called " Art for art's
sake." To-day even the biographer of Oscar Wilde
proposes to abandon " art for art's sake," and to
substitute " art for life's sake." But at the time I
was more inclined to substitute " no art, for God's
sake." I would rather have had no art at all than
one which occupies itself in matching shades of pea-

cock and turquoise for a decorative scheme of blue
devils. I started to think it out, and the more I
thought of it the more certain I grew that the whole
thing was a fallacy; that art could not exist apart
from, still less in opposition to, life; especially the
life of the soul, which is salvation; and that great art
never had been so much detached as that from conscience and common sense, or from what my critic
would call moral earnestness. Unfortunately, by the
time I had exposed it as a fallacy it had entirely
evaporated as a fashion. Since then I have taken
universal annihilations more lightly. But I can still
be stirred, as man always can be by memories of
their first excitements or ambitions, by anything
that shows the cloven hoof of that particular blue
devil. I am still ready to knock him about, though
I no longer think he has a cloven hoof or even a
lame leg to stand on. But for all that there is one
real argument which I still recognize on his side;
and that argument is in a single word. There is
still one word which the æsthete can whisper; and the
whisper will bring back all my childish fears that the
æsthete may be right after all. There is one name
that does seem to me a strong argument for the
decadent doctrine that " art is unmoral." When
that name is uttered, the world of Wilde and Whis-
tler comes back with all its cold levity and cynical
connoisseurship; the butterfly becomes a burden, and

the green carnation flourishes like the green bay-tree. For the moment I do believe in " art for art's sake." And that name is John Milton.

It does really seem to me that Milton was an artist, and nothing but an artist; and yet so great an artist as to sustain by his own strength the idea that art can exist alone. He seems to me an almost solitary example of a man of magnificent genius whose greatness does not depend at all upon moral earnestness, or upon anything connected with morality. His greatness is in a style, and a style which seems to me rather unusually separate from its substance. What is the exact nature of the pleasure which I, for one, take in reading and repeating some such lines, for instance, as those familiar ones:

> Dying put on the weeds of Dominic
> Or in Franciscan think to pass disguised.

So far as I can see, the whole effect is in a certain unexpected order and arrangement of words, independent and distinguished, like the perfect manners of an eccentric gentleman. Say instead " Put on in death the weeds of Dominic," and the whole unique dignity of the line has broken down. It is something in the quiet but confident inversion of " Dying put on " which exactly achieves that perpetual slight novelty which Aristotle profoundly said was the lan-

guage of poetry. The idea itself is at best an obvious
and even conventional condemnation of superstition,
and in the ultimate sense a rather superficial one.
Coming where it does, indeed, it does not so much
suggest moral earnestness as rather a moralizing
priggishness. For it is dragged in very laboriously
into the very last place where it is wanted, before a
splendidly large and luminous vision of the world
newly created, and the first innocence of earth and
sky. It is that passage in which the wanderer
through space approaches Eden; one of the most
unquestionable triumphs of all human literature.
That one book at least of " Paradise Lost " could
claim the more audacious title of " Paradise Found."
But if it was necessary for the poet going to Eden
to pass through Limbo, why was it necessary to pass
through Lambeth and Little Bethel? Why should
he go there via Rome and Geneva? Why was it necessary to compare the débris of Limbo to the details
of ecclesiastical quarrels in the seventeenth century,
when he was moving in a world before the dawn of all
the centuries, or the shadow of the first quarrel?
Why did he talk as if the Church was reformed before the world was made, or as if Latimer lit his can-
dle before God made the sun and moon? Matthew
Arnold made fun of those who claimed divine sanc-
tion for episcopacy by suggesting that when God
said, " Let there be light," He also said " Let there

be Bishops." But his own favourite Milton went
very near suggesting that when God said, " Let there
be light," He soon afterwards remarked, " Let there
be Nonconformists," I do not feel this merely because
my own religious sympathies happen to be rather on
the other side. It is indeed probable that Milton did
not appreciate a whole world of ideas in which he
saw merely the corruptions: the idea of relics and
symbolic acts and the drama of the deathbed. It
does not enlarge his place in the philosophy of history that this should be his only relation either to the
divine demagogy of the Dogs of God or to the fantastical fraternity of the Jugglers of God. But I
should feel exactly the same incongruity if the theological animus were the other way. It would be
equally disproportionate if the approach to Eden
were interrupted with jokes against Puritans, or if
Limbo were littered with steeple-crowned hats and
the scrolls of interminable Calvinistic sermons. We
should still feel that a book of " Paradise Lost " was
not the right place for a passage from Hudibras.
So far from being morally earnest, in the best sense,
there is something almost philosophically frivolous
in the incapacity to think firmly and magnanimously
about the First Things, and the primary colours of
the creative palette, without spoiling the picture with
this ink-slinging of sectarian politics. Speaking
from the standpoint of moral earnestness, I confess

it seems to me trivial and spiteful and even a little vulgar. After which impertinent criticism, I will now repeat in a loud voice, and for the mere lust of saying it as often as possible:

> Dying put on the weeds of Dominic
> Or in Franciscan think to pass disguised.

And the exuberant joy I take in it is the nearest thing I have ever known to art for art's sake.

In short it seems to me that Milton was a great artist, and that he was also a great accident. It was rather in the same sense that his master Cromwell was a great accident. It is not true that all the moral virtues were crystallized in Milton and his Puritans. It is not true that all the military virtues were concentrated in Cromwell and his Ironsides. There were masses of moral devotion on the one side, and masses of military valour on the other side. But it did so happen that Milton had more ability and success in literary expression, and Cromwell more ability and success in military science, than any of their many rivals. To represent Cromwell as a fiend or Milton as a hypocrite is to rush to another extreme and be ridiculous; they both believed sincerely enough in certain moral ideas of their time. Only they were not, as seems to be supposed, the only moral ideas of their time. And they were not, in my private opinion, the best moral ideas of their time. One of them was the idea that wisdom is more or less weakened by laughter and a popular taste in pleasure; and we may call this moral earnestness if we like. But the point is that Cromwell did not succeed by his moral earnestness, but by his strategy; and Milton did not succeed by his moral earnestness, but by his style.

And, first of all, let me touch on the highest form of moral earnestness and the relation of Milton to the religious poetry of his day. " Paradise Lost " is certainly a religious poem; but, for many of its admirers, the religion is the least admirable part of it. The poet professes indeed to justify the ways of God to men; but I never heard of any men who read it in order to have them justified, as men do still read a really religious poem, like the dark and almost sceptical Book of Job. A poem can hardly be said to justify the ways of God, when its most frequent effect is admittedly to make people sympathize with Satan. In all this I am in a sense arguing against myself; for all my instincts, as I have said, are against the æsthetic theory that art so great can be wholly irreligious. And I agree that even in Milton there are gleams of Christianity. Nobody quite without them could have written the single line: " By the dear might of Him that walked the waves." But it is hardly too much to say that it is the one place where that Figure walks in the whole world of Milton. Nobody, I imagine, has ever been able to recognize Christ in the cold conqueror who drives a chariot in the war in Heaven, like Apollo warring on the Titans. Nobody has ever heard Him in the stately disquisitions either of the Council in Heaven or of " Paradise Regained." But apart from all these particular problems, it is surely the general truth that the great religious epic strikes us with a sense of disproportion; the sense of how little it is religious considering how manifestly it is great. It seems almost strange that a man should have written so much and so well without stumbling on Christian tradition.

Now in the age of Milton there was a riot of religious poetry. Most of it had moral earnestness, and much of it had splendid spiritual conviction. But most of it was not the poetry of the Puritans; on the contrary, it was mostly the poetry of the Cavaliers. The most real religion—we might say the most realistic religion—is not to be found in Milton, but in Vaughan, in Traherne, in Crashaw, in Herbert, and even in Herrick. The best proof of it is that the religion is alive to-day, as religion and not merely as literature. A Roman Catholic can read Crashaw, an Anglo-Catholic can read Herbert, in a direct devotional spirit; I gravely doubt whether many modern Congregationalists read the theology of " Paradise Lost " in that spirit. For the moment I mention

only this purely religious emotion; I do not deny
that Milton's poetry, like all great poetry, can
awaken other great emotions. For instance, a man
bereaved by one of the tragedies of the Great War
might well find a stoical serenity in the great lines
beginning, "Nothing is here, for tears." That
sort of consolation is uttered, as nobly as it
could be uttered, by Milton; but it might be uttered by Sophocles or Goethe, or even by Lucre-
tius or Voltaire. But supposing that a man were
seeking a more Christian kind of consolation, he
would not find it in Milton at all, as he would find it
in the lines beginning, "They are all gone into the
world of light." The whole of the two great Puritan
epics do not contain all that is said in saying, "O
holy hope and high humility." Neither hope nor
humility were Puritan specialties.

But it was not only in devotional mysticism that
these Cavaliers could challenge the great Puritan;
it was in a mysticism more humanistic and even
more modern. They shine with that white mystery
of daylight which many suppose to have dawned
with Wordsworth and with Blake. In that sense
they make earth mystical where Milton only made
Heaven material. Nor are they inferior in philosophic freedom; the single line of Crashaw, addressed
to a woman, "By thy large draughts of intellectual
day," is less likely, I fancy, to have been addressed

by Adam to Eve, or by Milton to Mrs. Milton. It seems to me that these men were superior to Milton in magnanimity, in chivalry, in joy of life, in the balance of sanity and subtlety, in everything except the fact (not wholly remote from literary criticism) that they did not write so well as he did. But they wrote well enough to lift the load of materialism from the English name and show us the shining fields of a Paradise that is not wholly lost.

Of such was the anti-Puritan party; and the reader may learn more about it from the author of " The Glass of Fashion." There he may form a general idea of how, but for the Puritans, England would have been abandoned to mere ribaldry and licence; blasted by the blasphemies of George Herbert; rolled in the mire of the vile materialism of Vaughan; tickled to ribald laughter by the cheap cynicism and tap-room familiarities of Crashaw and Traherne. But the same Cavalier tradition continued into the next age, and indeed into the next century; and the critic must extend his condemnation to include the brutal buffooneries of Bishop Ken or the gay and careless worldliness of Jeremy Collier. Nay, he must extend it to cover the last Tories who kept the tradition of the Jacobites; the careless merriment of Dean Swift, the godless dissipation of Dr. Johnson. None of these men were Puritans; all of them were strong opponents of political and religious Puritanism. The truth is that English literature bears a very continuous and splendid testimony to the fact that England was not merely Puritan. Ben Jonson in " Bartholomew Fair " spoke for most English people, and certainly for most English poets. Anti-Puritanism was the one thing common to Shakespeare and Dryden, to Swift and Jonson, to Cobbett and Dickens. And the historical bias the other way has come, not from Puritan superiority, but simply from Puritan success. It was the political triumph of the party, in the Revolution and the resultant commercial industrialism, that suppressed the testimony of the populace and the poets. Loyalty died away in a few popular songs; the Cromwellians never had any popular song to die. English history has moved away from English literature. Our culture, like our agriculture, is at once very native and very neglected. And as this neglect is regrettable, if only as neglect of literature, I will pause in conclusion upon the later period, two generations after Milton, when the last of the true Tories drank wine with Bolingbroke or tea with Johnson.

The truth that is missed about the Tories of this tradition is that they were rebels. They had the virtues of rebels; they also had the vices of rebels. Swift had the fury of a rebel; Johnson the surliness of a rebel; Goldsmith the morbid sensibility of a rebel; and Scott, at the end of the process, something of the despair and mere retrospection of a defeated rebel. And the Whig school of literary criticism, like the Whig school of political history, has omitted or missed this truth about them, because it necessarily omitted the very existence of the thing against which they rebelled. For Macaulay and Thackeray and the average of Victorian liberality the Revolution of 1688 was simply an emancipation, the defeat of the Stuarts was simply a downfall of tyranny and superstition; the politics of the eighteenth century were simply a progress leading up to the pure and happy politics of the nineteenth century; freedom slowly broadening down, etc., etc. This makes the attitude of the Tory rebels entirely meaningless; so that the critics in question have been forced to represent some of the greatest Englishmen who ever lived as a mere procession of lunatics and ludicrous eccentrics. But these rebels, right or wrong, can only be understood in relation to the real power against which they were rebelling; and their titanic figures can best be traced in the light of the lightning which they defied. That power was a positive thing; it was anything but a mere negative emancipation of everybody. It was as definite as the monarchy which it had replaced; for it was an aristocracy that replaced it. It was the oligarchy of the great Whig families, a very close corporation indeed, having Parliament for its legal form, but the new wealth for its essential substance. That is why these lingering Jacobites appear most picturesque when they are pitted against some of the princes of the new aristocratic order. That is why Bolingbroke remains in the memory, standing in his box at the performance of " Cato," and flinging forth his defiance to Marlborough. That is why Johnson remains rigid in his magnificent disdain, hurling his defiance at Chesterfield. Churchill and Chesterfield were not small men, either in personality or in power; they were brilliant ornaments of the triumph of the world. They represented the English governing class when it could really govern; the modern plutocracy when it still deserved to be called an aristocracy also. And the whole point of the position of these men of letters is that they were denying and denouncing something which was growing every day in prestige and prosperity; which seemed to have, and indeed had, not only the present but the future on its side. The only thing it had not got on its side was the ancient tradition of the English populace. That populace was being more and more harried by evictions and enclosures, that its old common lands and yeomen freeholds might be added to the enormous estates of the all-powerful aristocracy. One of the Tory rebels has himself made that infamy immortal in the great lines of the " Deserted Village." At least, it is immortal in the sense that it can never now be lost for lovers of English literature; but even this record was for a long time lost to the public by under-valuation and neglect. In recent times the " Deserted Village " was very much of a deserted poem. But of that I may have occasion to speak later. The point for the moment is that the psychology of these men, in its evil as well as its good, is to be interpreted not so much in terms of a lingering loyalty as of a frustrated revolution. Some of them had, of course, elements of extravagance and morbidity peculiar to their own characters; but they grew ten times more extravagant and more morbid as their souls swelled within them at the success of the shameless and the insolence of the fortunate. I doubt whether anybody ever felt so bitter against the Stuarts. Now this misunderstanding has made a very regrettable gap in literary criticism. The masterpieces of these men are represented as much more crabbed or cranky or inconsequent than they really were, because their objective is not seen objectively. It is like judging the raving of some Puritan preacher without allowing for the fact that the Pope or the King had ever possessed any power at all. To ignore the fact of the great Whig families because of the legal fiction of a free Parliament is like ignoring the feelings of the Christian martyrs about Nero, because of the legal fiction that the Imperator was only a military general. These fictions do not prevent imaginative persons from writing books like the "Apocalypse" or books like "Gulliver's Travels."

I will take only one example of what I mean by this purely literary misunderstanding: an example from "Gulliver's Travels" itself. The case of the under-valuation of Swift is a particularly subtle one, for Swift was really unbalanced as an individual, which has made it much easier for critics not to keep the rather delicate balance of justice about him. There is a superficial case for saying he was mad, apart from the physical accident of his madness; but the point is that even those who have realized that he was sometimes mad with rage have not realized what he was in a rage with. And there is a curious illustration of this in the conclusion of the story of Gulliver. Everyone remembers the ugly business about the Yahoos, and the still uglier business about the real human beings who reminded the returned traveller of Yahoos; how Gulliver shrank at first from his friends, and would only gradually consent to sit near his wife. And everybody remembers the picturesque but hostile sketch which Thackeray gives of the satire and the satirist; of Swift as the black and evil blasphemer sitting down to write his terrible allegory, of which the only moral is that all things are, and always must be, valueless and vile. I say that everybody remembers both these

literary passages; but, indeed, I fear that many remember the critical who do not really remember the
creative passage, and that many have read Thackeray who have not read Swift.

Now it is here that purely literary criticism has a
word to say. A man of letters may be mad or sane
in his cerebral constitution; he may be right or
wrong in his political antipathies; he may be anything we happen to like or dislike from our own individual standpoint. But there is one thing to which
a man of letters has a right, whatever he is, and that
is a fair critical comprehension of any particular literary effect which he obviously aims at and achieves.
He has a right to his climax, and a right not to be
judged without reference to his climax. It would
not be fair to leave out the beautiful last lines of
" Paradise Lost " as mere bathos; without realizing
that the poet had a fine intention in allowing that
conclusion, after all the thunder and the trumps of
doom, to fall and fade away on a milder note of
mercy and reasonable hope. It would not be fair to
stigmatize the incident of Ignorance, damned at the
very doors of Heaven at the end of Bunyan's book,
as a mere blot of black Calvinist cruelty and spite,
without realizing that the writer fully intended its
fearful irony, like a last touch of the finger of fear.
But this justice which is done to the Puritan masters
of imagination has hardly been done to the great

Tory masters of irony. No critic I have read has noticed the real point and climax of that passage about the Yahoos. Swift leads up to it ruthlessly enough, for an artist of that sort is often ruthless; and it is increased by his natural talent for a sort of mad reality of detail, as in his description of the slowly diminished distance between himself and his wife at the dinner-table. But he was working up to something that he really wished to say, something which was well worth saying, but which few seem to have thought worth hearing. He suggests that he gradually lost the loathing for humanity with which the Yahoo parallel had inspired him, that although men are in many ways petty and animal, he came to feel them to be normal and tolerable; that the sense of their unworthiness now very seldom returns; and indeed that there is only one thing that revives it. If one of these creatures exhibits Pride.

That is the voice of Swift, and the cry arraigning aristocracy. It is natural for a monkey to collect nuts, and it may be pardonable for John Churchill to collect guineas. But to think that John Churchill can be proud of his heap of guineas, can convert them into stars and coronets, and can carry that calm and classic face disdainful above the multitude! It is natural for she-monkeys to be mated somehow; but to think that the Duchess of Yarmouth is proud of being the Duchess of Yarmouth! It may not be be surprising that the nobility should have scrambled like screaming Yahoos for the rags and ribbons of the Revolution, tripping up and betraying anybody and everybody in turn, with every dirty trick of treason, for anything and everything they could get. But that those of them who had got everything should then despise those who had got nothing, that the rich should sneer at the poor for having no part of the plunder, that this oligarchy of Yahoos should actually feel superior to anything or anybody—that does move the prophet of the losing side to an indignation which is something much deeper and nobler than the negative flippancies that we call blasphemy. Swift was perhaps more of a Jeremiah than an Isaiah, and a faulty Jeremiah at that; but in his great climax of his grim satire he is none the less a seer and a speaker of the things of God; because he gives the testimony of the strongest and most searching of human intellects to the profound truth of the meanness and imbecility of pride.

And the other men of the same tradition had essentially the same instinct. Johnson was in many ways unjust to Swift, just as Cobbett was afterwards unjust to Johnson. But looking back up the perspective of history we can all see that those three great men were all facing the same way; that they all regretted the rise of a rapacious and paganized commercial aristocracy, and its conquest over the old popular traditions, which some would call popular prejudices. When Johnson said that the devil was the first Whig, he might have merely varied the phrase by saying that he was the first aristocrat. For the men of this Tory tradition, in spirit if not in definition, distinguished between the privilege of monarchy and that of the new aristocracy by a very tenable test. The mark of aristocracy is ambition. The king cannot be ambitious. We might put it now by saying that monarchy is authority; but in its essence aristocracy is always anarchy. But the men of that school did not criticize the oligarch merely as a rebel against those above; they were well aware of his activities as an oppressor of those below. This aspect, as has already been noted, was best described by a friend of Johnson, for whom Johnson had a very noble and rather unique appreciation—Oliver Goldsmith.

I hope that the author of an admirable study of Mr. Belloc in this magazine will not think that I am merely traversing one of his criticisms if I venture to add something to it. He used the phrase that Mr. Belloc had been anticipated by Disraeli in his view of England as having evolved into a Venetian oligarchy. The truth is that Disraeli was anticipated by Bolingbroke and the many highly intelligent men who agreed with him; and not least by Goldsmith. The whole view, including the very parallel with

Venice, can be found stated with luminous logic and cogency in the " Vicar of Wakefield." And Goldsmith attacked the problem entirely from the popular side. Nobody can mistake his Toryism for a snobbish submission to a privilege or title:

> Princes and lords, the shadow of a shade,
> A breath can make them, as a breath has made:
> But a bold peasantry, a nation's pride,
> When once destroyed can never be supplied.

I hope he was wrong; but I sometimes have a horrible feeling that he may have been right.

But I have here, thank God, no cause for touching upon modern politics. I was educated, as much as my critic, in the belief that Whiggism was a pure deliverance; and I hope I am still as willing as he to respect Puritans for their individual virtue as well as for their individual genius. But it moves all my memories of the unmorality of the 'nineties to be charged with indifference to the importance of being earnest. And it is for the sake of English literature that I protest against the suggestion that we had no purity except Puritanism, or that only a man like the author of " Paradise Lost " could manage to be on the side of the angels.

On Peace Day I set up outside my house two torches, and twined them with laurel; because I thought at least there was nothing pacifist about laurel. But that night, after the bonfire and the fireworks had faded, a wind grew and blew with gathering violence, blowing away the rain. And in the morning I found one of the laurelled posts torn off and lying at random on the rainy ground; while the other still stood erect, green and glittering in the sun. I thought that the pagans would certainly have called it an omen; and it was one that strangely fitted my own sense of some great work half fulfilled and half frustrated. And I thought vaguely of that man in Virgil, who prayed that he might slay his foe and return to his country; and the gods heard half the prayer, and the other half was scattered to the winds. For I knew we were right to rejoice; since the tyrant was indeed slain and his tyranny fallen for ever; but I know not when we shall find our way back to our own land.

THE END

FEB 2 1926

NOV 30 1923

DEC 10 1926

NOV 30 1954

YO-BRK-808

Wireless Internet
Enterprise Applications

A Wiley Tech Brief

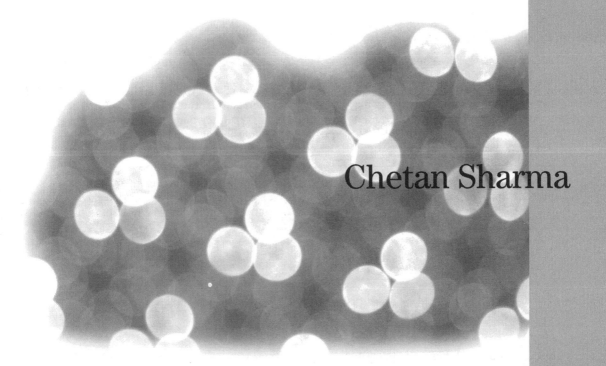

Chetan Sharma

Wiley Computer Publishing

John Wiley & Sons, Inc.

NEW YORK · CHICHESTER · WEINHEIM · BRISBANE · SINGAPORE · TORONTO

This book is dedicated to my parents.

Publisher: Robert Ipsen
Editor: Carol Long
Associate Editor: Margaret Hendrey
Managing Editor: Micheline Frederick
Text Design & Composition: Benchmark Productions, Inc.

Designations used by companies to distinguish their products are often claimed as trademarks. In all instances where John Wiley & Sons, Inc., is aware of a claim, the product names appear in initial capital or ALL CAPITAL LETTERS. Readers, however, should contact the appropriate companies for more complete information regarding trademarks and registration.

This book is printed on acid-free paper. ∞

Copyright © 2001 by Chetan Sharma. All rights reserved.

Published by John Wiley & Sons, Inc.

Published simultaneously in Canada.

No part of this publication may be reproduced, stored in a retrieval system or transmitted in any form or by any means, electronic, mechanical, photocopying, recording, scanning or otherwise, except as permitted under Sections 107 or 108 of the 1976 United States Copyright Act, without either the prior written permission of the Publisher, or authorization through payment of the appropriate per-copy fee to the Copyright Clearance Center, 222 Rosewood Drive, Danvers, MA 01923, (978) 750-8400, fax: (978) 750-4744. Requests to the Publisher for permission should be addressed to the Permissions Department, John Wiley & Sons, Inc., 605 Third Avenue, New York, NY 10158-0012, (212) 850-6011, fax: (212) 850-6008, e-mail: PERMREQ@WILEY.COM.

This publication is designed to provide accurate and authoritative information in regard to the subject matter covered. It is sold with the understanding that the publisher is not engaged in professional services. If professional advice or other expert assistance is required, the services of a competent professional person should be sought.

Library of Congress Cataloging-in-Publication Data:

ISBN 0-471-39382-7 (pbk. : alk. paper)

Printed in the United States of America.

10 9 8 7 6 5 4 3 2 1

Wiley Tech Brief Series

Other books in the series:

Ray Rischpater, *Palm Enterprise Applications*. 0471-39379-7

Steve Mann and Scott Sbihli, *The Wireless Application Protocol (WAP)*. 0471-39992-2

William Ruh, Francis Maginnis, and William Brown, *Enterprise Application Integration*. 0471-37641-8

Contents

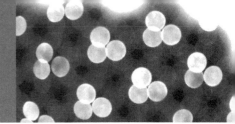

List of Illustrations

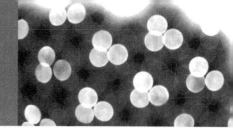

List of Tables

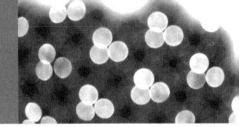

Acknowledgments

● ●

Wireless Internet Enterprise Applications would not have happened without help from the following fine individuals. I am forever indebted to:

> ➤ Carol Long, for the opportunity to pen my thoughts on wireless Internet technology.

> ➤ Margaret Hendrey, Micheline Frederick, Darlene Bordwell and others at John Wiley & Sons for their efforts, attention to detail, continuous feedback, and support throughout the length of this project.

> ➤ Colin Hendricks, Eswar Eluri, and Casey Krub for their research and contributions to the manuscript of this book.

> ➤ My colleagues in the Pervasive Computing Practice at Luminant Worldwide for our endless conversations and brainstorming sessions on the future of wireless Internet.

> ➤ My friends from Cellular Technical Services, especially Dmitry Kaplan, Evan Green, and the TPA gang for jump-starting my career in wireless communications.

> ➤ My teachers and friends from the University of Roorkee and Kansas State University.

> ➤ My parents, Dr. C. L. Sharma and Prem L. Sharma, and my brother Rahul for their encouragement and support throughout my life.

> ➤ My wife Sarla, whose endless love, immense patience, good humor, constant encouragement, and dedicated support kept me sane during this two-month project.

This project owes its successful completion to these people.

I would also like to express my gratitude to the companies, organizations, and individuals who provided permission to include their material at short notice.

—*Chetan Sharma, Summer 2000*

Introduction

We live in interesting times. The rate at which technology increasingly impacts our personal lives, our businesses, and our society is simply astonishing. The past decade of the Information Revolution has transformed economies globally and, in turn, laid a solid foundation that assures even more exciting things to come.

In the past decade, the Internet has been at the nucleus of a majority of innovative solutions and services, whether of hardware or software. As we all know, the Internet is a great enabler of communication among humans and machines. Whether involving simple applications such as email or more complicated ones such as knowledge management, the ease of communication provides increased efficiencies and hence value to both the supplier and the recipient of information. These days, there is hardly a successful business that isn't an ebusiness. The accelerated evolution of communication has forced traditional companies to rethink, regroup, and look at the consumer and business landscape from an Internet perspective. Corporations that fail to move fast are left behind or routed by innovative startups. Previous business models have become relics.

While we are still absorbing the virtues of this amazing revolution, another one is sneaking up on us. The 1990s saw the pre-existing client/server model evolve into today's Internet-centric model, in which computers (primarily desktops and mainframes) are interconnected and Web browsers have become the predominant client technology. This change enabled users(provided they have the right privileges) to access information from any desktop PCs, as long as the PCs are connected to the "net". The constraint to this model is obvious: lack of *mobility*. Even though the Internet radically transforms the way we interact with information and the value proposition thereof, for the most part we still need to be attached to a physical desktop to access information. This constraint hinders both ease of use and appropriate dissemination and access of information. The natural evolution of the Internet model is to extend its reach to multiple devices so that a bidirectional information exchange is possible from almost any computing device, simply by virtue of the fact that the device is connected to the Internet. These computing devices can vary in form, functionality, and connectivity. Connectivity can occur via local area networks (LANs) or wireless networks. The use of wireless networks to access the Internet represents a fundamental paradigm shift in the way we view and access information.

The two main benefits of wireless Internet communication are as follows:

➤ Wireless technology allows us to solve the problem of mobility, which in turn has huge implications. A user doesn't have to be shackled to a desktop to get time-sensitive information; a user doesn't have to carry computers and network paraphernalia wherever he or she goes. Merely carrying a simple, convenient, network-enabled phone or personal digital assistant (PDA) would do.

➤ Information can be made available to users who don't have PCs. This is especially true in countries other than the United States.

With the rapid convergence of the computing and communications industries, wireless phones and PDAs are fast evolving into powerful multipurpose devices. They not only allow users to communicate and organize phone numbers and to-do lists, but they also check, send, and receive emails and faxes, provide driving directions, and let users surf the Internet, participate in live auctions, buy and sell stocks—the list goes on.

The Internet Revolution started with business-to-consumer (B2C) applications and services, from simple information lookups to serious ecommerce applications such as online auctions. Gradually, businesses started building more complicated enterprise applications, such as streamlining of the supply chain. Similarly, the first wireless Internet applications revolved around enabling the existing B2C information for various wireless devices. Today services such as stock price or weather lookup on a wireless device are common. The wireless infrastructure and component technologies are just beginning to explore the realms of *wireless Internet enterprise applications*.

Overview of the Book and Technology

Wireless data communication methods have been around for some time. However, lack of standards, robust infrastructure and enabling technologies, and prohibitive costs have limited the use of wireless networks for information exchange. Over the past couple of years, things have changed dramatically. With the advent of several new technologies and standards, it's possible to expel the hype and realize the potential of wireless data.

This book provides an overview of the wireless Internet marketplace, including some predominant technologies such as Wireless Application Protocol (WAP), VoiceXML, Bluetooth, and 3G, and guides the reader through the critical success factors for executing a profitable wireless Internet business plan. The main purpose of this book is to provide users with the **"big picture"** of the wireless Internet industry and where it will go in the future. A picture is worth a thousand words, they say, so I have used graphics and figures throughout the book to help you visualize and understand the technology, applications, and services under discussion.

How This Book Is Organized

The book is organized into ten chapters, as follows:

Chapter 1, "Wireless Internet Enterprise Applications," walks the reader through the various network computing models: client/server, Internet-centric, and pervasive computing. An introduction to wireless Internet applications and services is also provided.

Chapter 2, "A Wireless Primer," is for users who want to gain insights into the history of wireless communication, learn about the various standards prevalent on the world's continents, and understand the basics of wireless communication.

Chapter 3, "Market Drivers," discusses the key market drivers of the wireless Internet industry and trends that are fueling this rapidly growing industry.

Chapter 4, "Wireless Internet Applications and Services Landscape," walks users through various examples of applications and services being introduced in different market sectors: B2C, business-to-business (B2B), and business-to-employee (B2E).

Chapter 5, "Technology Landscape," takes a deeper look into various technologies in both the computing and communications industries that are making all these changes possible. We will discuss technologies such as WAP, voice recognition, position location, biometrics, and personalization.

Chapter 6, "Players," discusses the wireless Internet value chain and lists major players in various segments of that chain.

Chapter 7, "Evaluating Wireless Internet Solutions," evaluates various vendors' solutions offerings intended to meet particular needs of organizations. Several developer references are also provided.

Chapter 8, "Wireless Internet Strategy: Critical Success Factors and Guiding Principles," offers a few guiding principles that are critical to successful implementation of wireless Internet projects.

Chapter 9, "Wireless Internet Tomorrow," looks at the future of wireless Internet technologies and how research and development activities of today will evolve into exciting applications and services of tomorrow.

Chapter 10, "The Last Word," summarizes the discussions in this book.

If you would like to further research the topics mentioned in this book, the book's appendix lists references and recommended readings. A list of useful Web sites is also provided. If you are new to the industry, you will find the book useful and a good reference. If you are a strategist, Chapters 1–4, 6, and 7 are for you. If you are a technologist and an architect, Chapters 5 and 6 cover most of what you might be looking for. If your role in your organization is to successfully plan and implement wireless Internet solutions, Chapters 7 and 8 are must-reads. Readers familiar with wireless technologies may skip the first two chapters.

Who Should Read This Book?

This book is aimed at corporate managers who have responsibility for keeping their corporations on the cutting edge of technology and services. The goal of this book is to familiarize users with the complex wireless Internet business and technology landscape so that they can make informed and successful decisions in their own environments. Developers will also find this book useful for gaining a holistic view of the wireless Internet industry.

References and examples are provided throughout the book. The chapters include substantial coverage of several technologies that are shaping wireless Internet computing.

Summary

Technology is changing at a fierce pace. For that reason, some of the technical specifications mentioned in this book will eventually become outdated, perhaps sooner rather than later. Readers are advised to refer to the latest standards and information sheets for updates; toward this end, the appendix provides a comprehensive list of helpful URLs.

I hope you enjoy the book as much as I had fun writing it and that it is a useful reference for you on projects in years to come. I apologize for any inaccuracies that might have inadvertently sneaked in. I am very much interested in learning your thoughts on the content and ideas presented in this book, how you found it useful, your suggestions, and advice for futurework. Please feel free to contact me at *chetan@ieee.org*. Happy reading, and best wishes.

—*Chetan Sharma*

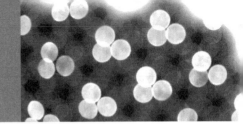

About the Author

Chetan Sharma
Principal, Pervasive Computing Practice

Chetan Sharma, an ardent evangelist of mobile computing, is the founder and Principal of Luminant's Pervasive Computing (PvC) Practice. In this role, he provides vision and strategic direction, directs PvC R&D efforts, identifies and establishes leading industry partnerships, oversees global client engagements, and provides industry leadership.

Before joining Luminant, Chetan held a number of positions with Cellular Technical Services — a wireless solutions firm. At CTS, he was instrumental in designing and implementing one of the first RF fingerprint-based fraud prevention solutions for the wireless industry and researched E911 position location systems.

Chetan has an MSEE from Kansas State University and a BSEE from University of Roorkee, India. He is a member of IEEE, IEEE Computer Society, Conference Committee Chair - NorthCon2000, and R & D Magazine's Judging Committee. He is a frequent invited speaker at several industry conferences including WAP Developer's Symposiums, MCommerce, Internet World. Chetan is frequently quoted in national press. He has published several articles and white papers on wireless Internet related topics. He has several patents (awarded and pending) in the field of wireless communications.

Wireless Internet Enterprise Applications

I n this chapter, we explore the definition and meaning of the term *wireless Internet enterprise applications (WIEA)*. We also take a look at the evolution of the network computing model. Over the past decade, enterprise models, paradigms, and architectures have changed to both leverage the new technologies and meet new business and customer needs. For corporations that invested heavily in legacy systems, deploying wireless applications could mean finding a way to build on the existing infrastructure rather than replacing it with a new one.

The Network Computing Model

Network computing is the fulcrum of our technology-based economy and has become the means to increased efficiencies in knowledge management, individual and group decision making, and performance improvement by several factors. Network computing promotes partnering with traditional allies and competition, leveraging existing knowledge and infrastructure to enter and define new markets. The better connected knowledge, employees, partners, and customers in the enterprise, the higher the chance of that enterprise's survival in this turbo-charged economy. If enterprise resources such as people and machines can make quick, informed, and educated decisions, efficiencies improve all the more. Instead of concentrating on mundane tasks that can be easily relegated to computers, corporations can better focus on important tasks at hand, such as aligning with new partners, entering new markets, or pleasing another dissatisfied customer. Network computing not only accelerates growth and innovation—it is essential for survival.

NOTE

Knowledge management is the systematic process of finding, selecting, organizing, distilling, and presenting information in a way that improves an employee's comprehension in a specific area of interest. Knowledge management helps an organization's employees gain insight and understanding from their own experiences.

Network computing at a high level consists of three main components: a server, a client, and a communication mechanism. A *client* is a program that requests services or information; a *server* is the provider of the services or information. The *communication mechanism* connects clients and servers. A server can request information from other servers and hence become the client for those servers.

Let's consider an example: a simple banking application. To check your bank account balance from your computer, the client software on your PC passes the request to the bank's server software. The bank's server, in turn, queries its database for an account balance and returns the information in a communication message back to the client. Typically, multiple clients are connected to a server at any given time. Figure 1.1 represents the three distinct generations in the life of network computing and how it has evolved in recent times.

The Client/Server Model

In the early 1990s, a simple *client/server model* (as represented in Figure 1.1a) defined network computing. The client/server architecture is a versatile, message-based and modular infrastructure that is intended to improve performance, usability, flexibility, interoperability, and scalability, compared with the previous centralized mainframe,

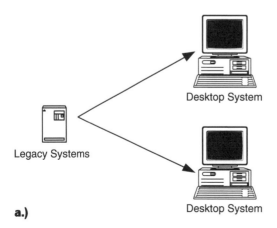

Legacy Systems

Desktop System

Desktop System

a.)

Figure 1.1   The evolution of network computing: a) The client/server model. b) The Internet-centric model. c) The pervasive computing model.

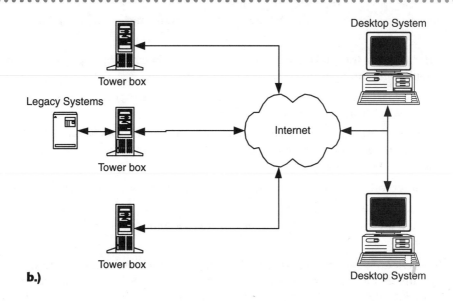

b.)

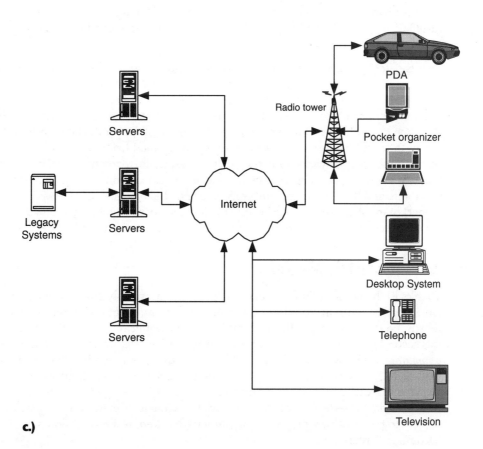

c.)

time-sharing computing. The following terms describe factors affecting the client/server model:

Performance is the total effectiveness of the system in terms of response times, availability, and throughput.

Usability is the ease with which a user can navigate the user interface by entering data and discerning output in a usable fashion.

Flexibility is the ease with which a component or a system can be modified for use in applications or environments other than those for which the component or system was specifically designed.

Interoperability is the ability of two or more components to exchange and use information.

Scalability is the ease with which the system or a component can be modified to fit a problem area.

In the client/server model, information and business logic reside on the servers, typically mainframes or UNIX servers, to be accessed by fat clients on proprietary or private networks. Although these systems are secure, they are highly expensive and problematic. Client software (such as a word processing application) requires installation at every terminal, which makes system rollouts and installations tedious and costly.

Because *user interfaces*—the look and feel of an application—differ greatly, users often need time and training to learn to interact with the new systems. It is also next to impossible to make two different applications or systems "talk" to each other in a cost-effective fashion. Once corporations buy one client/server system, it is cost-prohibitive to switch to another vendor, even if the performance of the product or vendor is below par. In the client/server world, information sharing and business intelligence are novel concepts usually seen only on paper. For example, if you have a Word document that you want to share with your customers and partners, you typically have to email it to them, and then the document's recipients need to have the same version (or higher) of the Word software to be able to view the document. Every time you update the document and need to share it, you again have to email it to colleagues and clients.

The Internet-centric Model

Thanks to the work of Tim Berners-Lee, the Web completely changed the way we work, interact with information, communicate, and innovate. The Internet has revamped the way people think about information sharing. The central theme of this second generation of network computing, the *Internet-centric model*, is *ease of communication* between machines and humans (as represented in Figure 1.1b). With this model, the limitations of a proprietary network vanishes. Client software has been standardized in the form of Internet browsers (Netscape Navigator, for example). This user interface revolution enables the same information on the back-end servers to be accessed from essentially any networked desktop. Rollouts have become instantaneous.

Information technology has become about "Web enabling" your enterprise, applications, and services. IBM branded this process *ebusiness*. Suddenly, if your company isn't an ebusiness—that is, if you can't reach your partners via extranets, employees via intranets, and customers via the Internet—your enterprise has become irrelevant.

Let's take a look at how the Web-based programming model works.

The Web Programming Model

In the *Web programming model*, the browser acts as a client and the Web server acts as the server responding to the browser's request (see Figure 1.2). Let's build an understanding of the model through an example. The communication steps are as follows:

1. The user enters *www.usbanks.com* into the *uniform resource locator* (URL) field of the browser.

2. The Web browser parses that URL and sends a HyperText Transfer Protocol (HTTP) or HTTPS (HTTP Secure) request to the Web server. The protocol is initiated when the server needs to authenticate the user before fulfilling the user's request.

3. The Web server receives the request, parses it, and responds back to the client. The response is generally formatted and displayed in a language that the browser can understand, such as HTML. The browser receives the message, parses it, and displays the contents to the user.

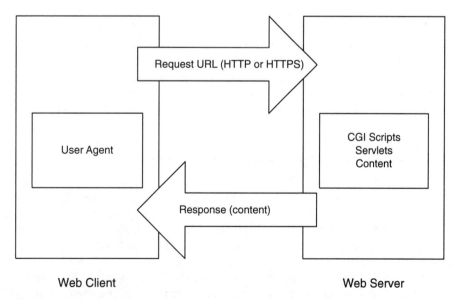

Web Client

Web Server

Figure 1.2 The Web programming model.

Advantages of the Internet-Centric Model

Advantages of the Internet model are clear:

➤ It propagates instantaneous information retrieval and dissemination.

➤ Organizations can be virtual and still be global in nature and operation.

➤ Infrastructure costs and deployment time decrease significantly.

➤ Nonbusiness entities such as government and consumers benefit equally.

➤ It fosters innovative business ideas and models so that consumers benefit.

Although this Web-enabled networking model is prevalent, we are still in the infancy of fully realizing the potential of the Internet network computing model. The biggest drawback to this model is mobility. Although it's possible to get to any information from any desktop in this information-centric economy, you can't be expected to carry a desktop computer wherever you go. The key elements of *anytime, anywhere* are missing from second-generation networking for information exchange to become truly pervasive. In this information age, if humans are mobile, shouldn't information be mobile as well?

A Pervasive Computing Model

> *Pervasive computing is a billion people interacting with a million ebusinesses*
> *with a trillion intelligent devices interconnected.*
>
> **LOU GERSTNER, CEO, IBM**

The third generation of networking is a *pervasive computing model* that is also Internet-centric (as depicted in Figure 1.1c). The key difference between the second- and third-generation network computing models is the introduction of the mobility factor, extending the information that was previously limited to a desktop to devices such as wireless phones or PDAs. The Internet has been around for almost a decade now, and wireless networks existed even before that. It has been only recently, through standards and advances in computing and communications technologies, that the convergence of wireless networks and the Internet is taking place.

The converged model is all about extending enterprises' reach to a disparate range of devices. So, devices such as wireless phones, PDAs, pagers, LAN phones, automobile PCs, game terminals, and cable TV can start performing like desktops connected to the Internet. Advances in wireless and Internet technologies are redefining the existing Internet model and its services. Technologies such as Wireless Application Protocol (WAP) are bringing Internet ebusinesses closer to the mobile world. For example, a bank that extended its operations arms to provide services over the Internet can now provide access to user data and services over the air. The bank can use WAP-based or similar technologies to put services at consumers' fingertips. As ecommerce vendors connect their warehouses, information databases, and applications to these wireless devices, they provide continual "anywhere" services and thereby evolve into *mbusinesses* (mobile businesses) and provide *mcommerce* (mobile commerce) services. Today, it's all about "wirelessization" of your Web-enabled enterprise and serving existing and new applications and services to the end users in ways never before thought possible.

Pervasive computing enables people to accomplish day-to-day personal and professional tasks using this new breed of intelligent and portable devices. It allows these devices to become extensions of powerful computers in your office or home, putting information within users' reach literally anytime, anywhere. In a few years, a majority of these devices will be Internet enabled. It's predicted that by 2003, there will be more cellular phones worldwide than TVs and PCs combined [Source: Phone.com, Nov. 1999].

The vision of pervasive computing is to provide easy access to any relevant data residing on any network to any device, anytime. This doesn't mean that a 5MB Acrobat file is available for viewing on a four-inch phone display—that simply doesn't make usability sense, but if it did, the user should be able to download and browse the file as he or she would on a wireless-enabled laptop or LAN-connected desktop.

With grand visions come added complexities for service and infrastructure providers and application developers. In addition to making their applications and services usable, flexible, scalable, and secure and so they can interoperate with other applications and services, these developers now have to add another dimension of devices to the whole picture. For political, market, and technical reasons, different devices communicate in different programming languages over different networks, are of different form factors, and provide different functionalities and capabilities. When designing new services and applications, application developers, UI designers, and usability experts need to consider all these issues.

Even with these challenges, the promise of pervasive computing is very lucrative to consumers and businesses alike. Consumers can have access to their daily calendars, receive and send emails, or access corporate intranets or personal information with a push of a button. Businesses can open up new channels, increase demand for their services and applications, explore new markets previously thought unreachable, and improve customer service, thus differentiating themselves in the marketplace.

The cost savings and time efficiencies of using pervasive computing are immense. Let's discuss an example to drive home this point. Every city has a government (more or less) and a utilities department, the responsibility of which is to ensure that all the city's basic infrastructure (electricity, water, transportation) is up and running all the time. Typically, this is done through staff called *field and service engineers*. These engineers go out into the field, responding to public calls or otherwise, to investigate problems and take notes in the field on paper forms. Once they get back to their offices, they either enter the information into a computer database or fill out some more forms before the data makes its way into the city's databases. Typically, a supervisor reviews the report produced from the database and analyzes the problem by geographic region so that the issues can be grouped and handled efficiently at one time. After task review, based on employee availability, the supervisor assigns an expert to look into each issue or problem. This expert picks up the paper report and goes to the site, does further investigation, and fixes the problem. On his or her return to the office, another paper copy report is filed, which the supervisor reviews before the issue is considered closed.

As you can imagine, the process of solving these problems from start to finish is very tedious and highly inefficient; it can take days, even months, to resolve small issues. Tracking the process gets in the way of solving real problems quickly and in a cost-effective manner.

If these field engineers, experts, and supervisors were armed with wireless PDAs enabled with a *global positioning system* (GPS) and appropriate task-specific applications, the process would be much quicker. Field engineers could file their reports while still on the spot; the supervisor could program business rules into the application and intelligently assign tasks to experts in the field in real time. Experts could get instant messages on their PDAs regarding work assignments based on their level of expertise and geographic coordinates. Once the problem was solved, experts could file their reports on their PDAs as well. This data would then automatically be entered into the back-end database servers. The tasks that took days and months could then be completed in a matter of hours, even minutes. More problems could be solved much more quickly. There would be no need for loads of paperwork and the confusion that results. Time and cost savings to the department, city, and, in turn, residents would be immense.

Can you imagine applying the benefits of automatic data entry and prescription tracking in the medical industry? Or, imagine having all your product and corporate information at your fingertips during a high-profile sales meeting. Table 1.1 lists some of the potential application and service areas in which pervasive computing will truly transform the landscape.

Table 1.1   Examples of Applications in the Pervasive Computing Era

APPLICATION AREA	APPLICATIONS
Information	• News, sports • Weather • Travel • Movies, restaurants • Traffic, airline schedules • Exchange rates • Yellow pages • Movie rental
Intranets	• Sales force automation • Access to intranet information such as emails, calendars • Contact list

Table 1.1 (Continued)

APPLICATION AREA	APPLICATIONS
	• Contract-signing workflow • Remote network diagnostics, analysis, and recovery • Workflow automation • Videoconferencing, shared whiteboard • Expense reports • Asset tracking
Medical	• Medical guidelines lookup • Doctors' prescriptions • Health-care monitoring • Remote diagnosis • Emergency services: dispatch and location
Ecommerce/ebusiness	• Shopping for books, jewelry, and other products • Auctions • Dynamic distribution • Customer service • Stock trading • Banking • Location-based services • Dispatch and delivery • Field services • Exception and business intelligence reports and data messaging • Customer relationship management • Enterprise resource planning • Supply chain management • Point of sale • Package pickup, delivery, and tracking • Inventory control • Credit/Smart Card verification
Entertainment	• Soap opera updates • Interactive multiuser games • Horoscopes • Puzzles, quizzes • Chat • Music • Gambling, betting • Lottery tickets
Personal	• Access to information such as email, calendar, contacts • Tracking of pets and children • "Myportal" consisting of links that are important to the user • Home and appliance networking

Continues

Table 1.1   Examples of Applications in the Pervasive Computing Era *(Continued)*

APPLICATION AREA	APPLICATIONS
Telemetry	• Engine and vehicle statistics • Burglar or fire alarm reporting • Vending machine status • Weather statistics such as temperature, wind velocity and direction, rainfall rate, barometric pressure • Stream statistics • Vehicular traffic statistics • Field measurements: gas, electric, water meters
Broadcast	• News • Weather advisory • Travel advisory • Advertising

It's clear that an era of pervasive computing is here to stay. The impact on our daily lives will be even more profound than that orchestrated by the Internet decade. In the next section, we explore the definition of wireless Internet enterprise applications using a real-world application and briefly discuss some of the key issues surrounding this technology area.

Wireless Internet Enterprise Applications

Let's dissect the term *wireless Internet enterprise applications* (WIEA). What does the term really mean, and what is its potential?

As we learned in the previous section, the Internet allows you to access information from your desktop. Wireless Internet is about accessing the Internet via wireless networks. The information flow is bidirectional, from server to client as well as client to server. (The same device can act as both server and client, a concept we will revisit in Chapter 5.)

Enterprise applications, in a nutshell, relate to services. An enterprise provides services to its customers, trading partners, channel partners, suppliers, and employees. These services can be horizontal or vertical. *Horizontal enterprise applications* service the needs of an entire community of users, with no focus on business functionality. *Vertical enterprise applications* service the needs of specific business functions (for example, sales, manufacturing, emergency management, and so on). When you enable these horizontal and vertical solutions for delivery and use by wireless devices over the Internet, you create wireless Internet enterprise applications.

Let's walk through a simple application to get a clear understanding of the WIEA concept. Smarttrek.org is a traffic information Web site offering real-time information on traffic congestion, schedules, directions, and much more. One of this Web site's really cool applications involves community transit buses. These buses carry a GPS to provide real-time tracking that can inform users (riders and potential riders) of the location of the bus at any given instant.

Figure 1.3 shows a typical bus schedule screen that provides information about the bus number, destination, schedule, and current status for any given bus stop. Transit status is very useful information for commuters, especially during rush hours. Let's say you are coming from an off-site meeting and you don't have your computer at your fingertips. You can go back to office to check the schedule, call the department of transportation's telephone information line to get the status of the bus, or take your chances and head for the bus stop. However, if the bus-positioning application were a wireless one, you could access the same information shown in Figure 1.3 using a wireless phone or a PDA, saving yourself time and hassle and doing it on the fly.

Figure 1.4 showcases a possible wireless application that could be made available via either WAP or Palm's Web Clipping technology, both of which we will discuss in Chapter 5. Add personalization, and the value of service is multiplied. For example, if you normally go home around 4:30 PM and take bus number 174, the schedule status information can automatically be sent to your phone (or pager or PDA) around 4:30 PM.

Better yet, since (let's assume) you have a GPS-enabled device and because the server is "aware" of the traffic conditions, your device could recommend at what speed you need to run to catch the bus.

The same concept can be easily applied to a majority of applications and services. Healthcare professionals could be armed with PDAs to check patient status, refer to a medical guide, or make notes; sales representatives could have valuable enterprise data at their fingertips; field workers could get rid of their arcane paper-based entry systems and instead enter information into the back-end databases right on the spot, where they're working. Improvements in efficiencies can be huge. Companies could channel these cost savings to, for example, better 401(k) plans for employees or finding new business opportunities. In fact, you should scan services at your organization and ask yourself: What other applications would benefit from being wirelessly

Route	Destination	Scheduled	At Bay	Depart Status
174	Downtown Seattle	4:43 PM	1	2 Min Delay
194	Downtown Seattle	4:35 PM	1	3 Min Delay
340	Bellevue Transit Ctr	4:47 PM	1	9 Min Delay

Sea-Tac Airport — 4:31 PM Fri Oct 08

Figure 1.3 A bus schedule available on a desktop.

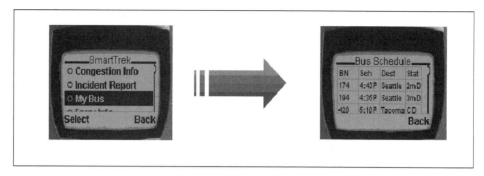

Figure 1.4   A bus schedule available on a WAP phone.

accessible? In Chapter 4, we will review some of the wireless Internet applications and services in the market today that could help you answer this question.

The same traffic information discussed in the Smarttrek.org example could be accessed not only by phones or PDAs but also by pagers, cable TVs, regular phones, autoPCs, and even wristwatches. Depending on the form factor and capability of the devices, the server would need to transform and package the information for appropriate display and use. This transformation of content on the fly will be one of the biggest challenges for any application or service. In Chapter 5, we will discuss content transformation in further detail and evaluate some of the solutions available in the marketplace today as well as how they are shaping up for tomorrow.

Another key element that we introduced in the traffic example is *personalization*. Due to restricted display size of these wireless devices, it's absolutely critical that the customer is sent only content he or she will find relevant and useful. Custom content delivery could be accomplished using some basic design features and available technologies. In Chapter 5, we will take a deeper look at the concept of personalization, what it means to different people, and how it can be integrated with almost all applications to ensure a pleasant user experience.

There is one other important aspect of WIEA that often goes unmentioned: the business plan. It's one thing to roll out interesting, innovative applications; it's another to recover investment and generate revenue of those services. Just because something is possible from a technology point of view might not make business sense, therefore it's essential to have a sound business plan going into any WIEA project.

You might ask why these enormous changes and convergence are happening all of a sudden. How is it possible to connect seemingly unrelated devices to the same information? In essence, what makes pervasive computing hum? Over the years, there has been a lot of talk about convergence of the worlds of computing and communications. The term *computing industry* primarily refers to the desktop applications and services industry, whereas *communications industry* refers to the wireless and telephone industry. With falling prices of semiconductor chips, it's possible to put more processing power in the tiniest of devices. Once you have processing power, you can implement more complex and networked applications in these devices.

Over the years, after many trials and tribulations, research technologies are emerging from the R&D labs to practical, real-world situations faster than ever before. Furthermore, there is a great deal of synergy and cooperation between the two industries in their attempts to come up with solutions for the common good—faster and better consumer acceptance and adoption of products and services. Chapter 3 looks at the market trends that are making the vision of WIEA possible. Finally, it's always important to keep taking the pulse of the technological and scientific innovations in the same or related industries, because any one of them can have a profound effect on your business and/or your industry in a way no one ever imagined. In Chapter 5, we will explore upcoming technologies that have the potential to propel the pervasive computing era into the next generation.

Anytime, anywhere, any device, any information—these are the promises of the next information revolution. Players in all industries will seek ways to leverage the wireless Internet phenomenon to reinvent themselves and extend their reach to customers, partners, and opportunities. Those that don't will risk being obliterated by competitors and missed opportunities.

The central theme of this book is to explore the business landscape of WIEA and look at the various options available to organizations that want to innovate and take the first-mover advantage in this competitive world.

In the next chapter, we will take a look at wireless network architecture and the wireless data technology landscape.

A Wireless Primer

I n this chapter, we will give you a very high-level overview of how wireless applications and services work, and we'll take a look at the evolution of wireless technologies. A detailed description and analysis of individual wireless technologies are outside the scope of this book; however, a comprehensive list of references is included at the end of the book for readers who are interested in more information on the nuts and bolts of these technologies.

Basic Wireless Network Architecture

To help you understand the architecture of a wireless network, this section describes each component and tells you how the components fit together. Figure 2.1 shows a basic wireless network with each of its major components; these components are briefly described in the following list:

Cell tower. A cell tower is the site of a cellular telephone transmission facility. Wireless coverage of any city is generally divided into rough hexagonal boundaries, with one cell tower to cover each region. Depending on the network's use and geographic coverage, this hexagonal shape could vary.

Base Station Controller (BSC). A BSC controls a cluster of cell towers. It is responsible for setting up a voice or data call with the mobile terminal and managing handoff when the mobile unit transitions from one cell tower boundary to another without disruption of service. For the purposes of our discussion, a BSC is also referred to as a *base station*.

Mobile Switching Center (MSC). An MSC connects all the base stations to pass communication signals and messages to and from subscribers operating on the network.

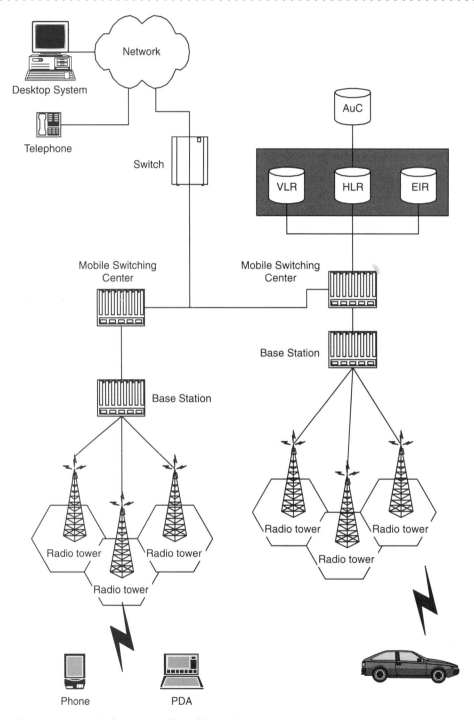

Figure 2.1   A wireless network and its major components.

An MSC is connected to a *visitor location register* (VLR), a *home location register* (HLR), an *authentication center* (AuC), and an *equipment identity register* (EIR).

Home Location Register (HLR). An HLR keeps track of information regarding the subscriber. For example, the HLR keeps a record of the last time the mobile unit (cell phone or Palm, for example) was registered on the network. *Note:* Mobile units register with a wireless network every few seconds to identify their location; this communication helps speed call setup when BSCs have to find the mobile device.

Visitor Location Register (VLR). A VLR records information about mobile units that have roamed into their network from other networks—that is, it tracks visitors. For example, if your cell phone is registered to operate with AT&T's network in Miami and you want to make a call in San Diego, the VLR registers details about the mobile and its plan in San Diego.

Mobile Identity Number (MIN) and electronic serial number (ESN). All phone equipment used in a wireless network carries these identification numbers. The MIN and ESN are used for verification, authentication, and billing purposes.

Equipment Identity Register (EIR). An EIR stores and checks the status of MINs and ESNs.

Authentication Center (AuC). An AuC is responsible for authentication and validation of services for each mobile device attempting to use the network.

Operations and Maintenance Center (OMC). An OMC is connected to the network to provide functions such as billing, network management, customer care, and service provisioning.

Radio Frequency (RF) transceiver. An RF transceiver is a combination transmitter/ receiver in a single package.

Data rate. Data rate refers to the speed with which data can be transferred from Point A to Point B. In a wireless context, it's the speed with which a wireless device can communicate with the wireless network.

To set up a call, a wireless device's RF transceiver sends a message request to the nearest base station. The base station recognizes the call signal and routes it to the MSC. The MSC queries the HLR or VLR (depending on the original registration of the mobile phone: If it's local, HLR will be queried; otherwise, VLR will be queried), EIR, and AuC for location, service qualification and features, and authentication. Depending on its destination, the call is either routed to another base station (or the same one, if the recipient is in the same area) or to a traditional wireline via the *public switched telephone network* (PSTN) or to an Internet device via the Internet. The call can be either a voice or data call. Figure 2.2 shows the message flow for a call originating from a wireless device and going to a LAN phone.

Wireless Data Networks

In this section, we examine the workings of wireless data transmission: how the data is transmitted from the wireless device to the wireless network, and vice versa. We

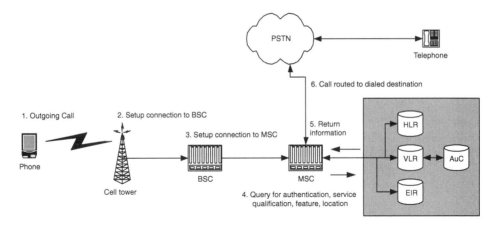

Figure 2.2 The call-setup process in a wireless network.

take a look at the two main transmission technologies for wireless data networks and review some of the wireless data networks in service.

Basics of Data Transmission

Wireless transmissions are broadly categorized into packet-switched or circuit-switched transmissions.

Packet-Switched Data Transmission

The term *packet-switched transmission* describes the type of network in which relatively small units of data, called *packets*, are routed through a network based on the destination address contained within each packet. Breaking communication into packets allows the same data path to be shared among many users in a network. This type of communication between sender and receiver is known as *connectionless* (rather than *dedicated*) communication. Most traffic over the Internet uses packet switching, and the Internet is basically a connectionless network. Users are generally charged based on the number of packets sent.

Circuit-Switched Data Transmission

Circuit-switched transmission describes a type of network in which a physical path is obtained for and dedicated to a single connection between two end points in the network for the duration of the connection (thus, it is called *dedicated communication*). For example, ordinary voice phone service is circuit-switched. The wireless operator reserves a specific physical path to the number you are calling for the duration of your call. During that time, no one else can use the physical lines involved. Users are generally charged for the duration of the connection time.

In order to understand the differences between packet- and circuit-switched technologies, consider a simple example. Suppose you wanted to send a 100-page document to a friend. You can write the friend's address on an envelope, put the 100-page document into the envelope, and mail it to your friend. This process is analogous to circuit-switched transmission in that the entire communication transaction takes place with one dedicated packet. On the other hand, if you were to take the 100 pages and put them individually into 100 corresponding envelopes, each labeled with the address of your friend, and then mail them, this process would be analogous to packet-switched transmission. All the packets might not arrive at the same time, but when they do, your friend can easily put them together.

Some of the key differences between packet- and circuit-based transmissions are highlighted in Table 2.1. The various types of wireless data networks are discussed in the following sections.

Public Packet Data Networks

The major public wireless data networks available today are listed in Table 2.2, along with available network speeds. These technologies are being used by paging and wireless data service providers such as Research in Motion (RIM), AT&T Wireless, Verizon, Palm.net, OmniSky, and others.

Private Packet Data Networks

In a private network, a company or a government agency builds out the network for its own use. One well-known private network was built by Federal Express. Since only the users associated with the builder organization are allowed on this kind of network, network availability and performance is high. Some examples of public packet data networks are Ericsson's Enhanced Digital Access Communications System (EDACS), Motorola's private DataTAC, and ASTROs. Terrestrial Trunked Radio (TETRA) is quite popular in Europe.

As businesses and consumers realize the benefits of wireless data communication, more and more applications and services will come to market. A majority of them will be on the wireless networks that are today used for voice communications. In the

Table 2.1   Packet Switching vs. Circuit Switching

PACKET SWITCHING	CIRCUIT SWITCHING
Efficient for short- to large-burst transmissions	Good for very large transmissions (for example, a 1MB data file)
Call setup and termination are almost immediate	There is a delay in call setup and termination
Carries broadcast capabilities	Enables point-to-point (P-to-P) connection
One logon at powerup	Logon (call) for every transmission
Airlink is generally secure	Airlink is not secure

Table 2.2   Public Data Networks and Data Rates

WAN TECHNOLOGY	DATA RATES	TRANSMISSION TECHNOLOGY
Ardis	19.2kbps	Packet
RAM	19.2kbps	Packet
Metricom	128kbps	Circuit switched/packet
CDPD	19.2kbps	Packet

next section, we briefly review the various wireless technologies and the data rate capabilities they offer.

Wireless Network Technologies: Past, Present, and Future

The acceptance of wireless phones is spreading at a speed that is hard to fathom. Over the past twenty years or so, wireless technologies have continuously evolved. Countries have adopted different sets of technologies depending on their needs and political alignments.

The analog technology that was the norm until the 1980s gave way to digital technologies in the 1990s. Each generation of technologies brought its own set of intricacies, performance enhancements, and problems. Adoption of a technology depended heavily on both the business model to attract new and existing customers and on the quality of service and performance of the technology. The emergence and continual growth of wireless networks are being driven by the need to lower the costs associated with network infrastructures and to support mobile networking applications that offer gains in process efficiency, accuracy, and lower business costs.

In this section we take a brief look at the timeline of these various technologies across three key geographic areas: Europe, Japan, and the United States. Table 2.3 depicts the wireless technology timelines for these major global markets; the technologies involved are described in the following list:

Code Division Multiple Access (CDMA). CDMA is an airlink interface coding scheme wherein multiple subscribers are granted access to the same radio frequency source by assigning subscribers' transmit and receive signals a spectrum-spreading code. CDMA is also referred to as Cellular IS-95, a digital spread-spectrum system initially developed by QUALCOMM and standardized by the Telecommunications Industry Association (TIA).

Time Division Multiple Access (TDMA). TDMA is an airlink interface coding scheme wherein multiple subscribers are granted access to the same radio frequency source by limiting subscribers' transmit and receive signals to time slots. TDMA is also referred to as the first digital cellular FM system standardized in North America.

Global System for Mobile Communications (GSM). GSM is similar to TDMA except that it uses 200KHz wide channels with eight users per channel and has a vocoder rate of 13kbps. It is the first digital cellular system to be used commercially and has been adopted in Europe and many Pacific Rim countries.

Universal Mobile Telecommunications System (UMTS). A project under the Special Mobile Group (SMG), a committee of the European Telecommunication Standards Institute (ETSI). UMTS is the first European implementation of the IMT2000 standard.

International Mobile Telecommunications by the Year 2000 (IMT2000) project. This project, under the subgroup IMT in the International Telecommunications Union (ITU), plans to facilitate cooperation in deciding global wireless access for the 21st century.

Nordic Mobile Telephone (NMT). NMT is the Japanese standard for analog cellular service.

Personal Digital Cellular (PDC). PDC is the Japanese standard for digital cellular service.

Advanced Mobile Phone System (AMPS). AMPS is the U.S. standard for analog cellular service.

Total Access Communication System (TACS). TACS is an analog FM communication system used in some parts of Europe and Asia (e.g. United Kingdom, Malaysia, etc.)

The *first generation* (1G) of wireless technologies, such as AMPS in North America, TACS in Europe, and NMT in Japan, was based on analog transmissions.

The *second generation* (2G) of technologies, such as TDMA and CDMA in the United States, PDC in Japan, and GSM in Europe, are digital in nature and provide improved system performance and security. Most new deployments are digital, with a few notable exceptions, such as those in South America and the United States. Even though digital networks are widely deployed, analog networks still service over 40 percent of cellular phones in the United States.

The *third generation* (3G) of technologies includes UMTS and CDMA2000 technologies.

As shown in Table 2.3, any given wireless technology has, on average, a 15-year maturity life cycle, divided distinctly into three phases: pain (coverage is poor, interference is high, customers are unhappy, devices are expensive and scarce), pleasure (coverage is the best it can be, interference is low, customers are happy, devices abound), and perfection (everything works as hoped for in the first phase, so it's time to move to something new).

Typical data rates available for the first generation of wireless technologies were 9.6kbps or lower. Second-generation technology data rates vary from 9.6kbps to 14.4kbps. Third-generation wireless technologies promise LAN-type data rates ranging from 144kbps to 2000kbps. This dramatic improvement in data rate is one of the major reasons for so much interest and excitement around wireless Internet applications and services.

Apart from these three distinct generations of technologies, there are additional technologies, which are referred as *2.5G wireless technologies*. These technologies are *High-*

Table 2.3 Timeline of Major Global Wireless Technologies, 1979–2020

JAPAN	1979–84	1984–89	1989–94	1994–99	1999–04	2004–09	2009–14
1G: NMT	Pain	Pleasure	Perfection				
2G: PDC			Pain	Pleasure	Perfection		
3G: WCDMA					Pain	Pleasure	Perfection

EUROPE	1982–87	1987–92	1992–97	1997–02	2002–07	2007–12	2012–17
1G: TACS	Pain	Pleasure	Perfection				
2G: GSM			Pain	Pleasure	Perfection		
3G: UMTS					Pain	Pleasure	Perfection

UNITED STATES	1982–87	1987–92	1992–97	1997–02	2002–07	2007–12	2012–17
1G: AMPS	Pain	Pleasure	Perfection				
2G: TDMA			Pain	Pleasure	Perfection		

	1995–00	2000–05	2005–10	2010–15	2015–20
2G: CDMA	Pain	Pleasure	Perfection		

	2002–07	2007–12	2012–17
3G: CDMA2000, UMTS	Pain	Pleasure	Perfection

Key:

Pain = Coverage is poor, interference is high, customers are unhappy, devices are expensive and scarce
Pleasure = Coverage is best it can be, interference is low, customers are happy, devices abound
Perfection = Everything works as hoped for in the first phase, so it's time to move to something new
(Copyright © 1998 RTT Programmes)

Speed Circuit-Switched Data (HSCSD), *General Packet Radio Service* (GPRS), and *Enhanced Data Rates for Global Evolution* (EDGE). They enhance the existing digital technologies and provide a nice transition to the 3G technologies. GPRS-based systems are already being deployed on some wireless networks. Available rates for HSCSD are up to 38.4kbps, GPRS are up to 144kbps, and theoretical data rates for EDGE hover around 384kbps. So, network operators have an option of deploying GPRS and EDGE before they invest in expensive 3G infrastructure More aggressive and bold operators—for example, NTT DoCoMo of Japan—see enough potential and benefits that they are choosing to go straight to 3G deployment (wide band CDMA).

Fourth-generation technologies (in research labs right now) focus on Wireless Asynchronous Transfer Mode (WATM) because it has the potential to provide data rates of 10Mbps to 150Mbps, low *bit error rate*, and high *quality of service*. Depending on how much growth 2.5 and 3G technologies are able to foster, the advent of fourth-generation technologies could be quicker than you think.

NOTE

Quality of service (QoS). QoS is a measurement of guarantees that can be made in meeting certain performance requirements.

Bit error rate (BER). BER is the number of error bits in a signal expressed as a fraction of the number of transmitted bits.

In this chapter we learned about the wireless network architecture and various wireless data and network technologies. In the next chapter we will discuss the market trends that are driving the wireless Internet market.

CHAPTER 3

Market Drivers

In Chapter 1, we got a glimpse of the potential and promise of wireless Internet-based applications. But why are these applications gaining so much momentum right now? Hardly a recent news or technical magazine hasn't carried wireless Internet as its cover story. Business alliances are being formed along these lines almost daily. In this chapter, we take a look at the key market drivers that are helping move theoretical wireless concepts to practical real-world applications, from marketing hype to business reality, and we discuss the consumer trends and technology evolution of the pervasive computing era.

As is true with any product or business idea, there's a fine equilibrium between consumer demand for and awareness of the product offering. If consumers aren't ready for a product, the best technologies and business ideas will be grounded before they reach the runway. Similarly, the product and business offerings need to be exciting and reasonable enough for consumers to pay attention to. If either supply or demand fumbles, the vision, however grand it might be, simply won't happen. Let's evaluate some of the key market drivers of the *anytime, anywhere* computing era.

The major forces driving innovation and enterpreneurship in this new marketplace are as follows:

➤ Mobile subscriber growth and market potential

➤ Trends in component technologies:

   ➤ Processing power

   ➤ Memory

   ➤ Power consumption

➤ New standards and technologies:
  ➤ Wireless Application Protocol (WAP)
  ➤ Bluetooth
  ➤ Predictive and other text-entry techniques
  ➤ eXtensible Markup Language (XML)
  ➤ Mobile Synchronization Protocol (SyncML)
  ➤ 2.5G and 3G wireless technologies
  ➤ Position location technologies
➤ The Internet Revolution
➤ Wireless data approaching ubiquity
➤ The need to streamline enterprise information
➤ The convergence of the computer and communications industries
➤ Competition
➤ Consumer awareness and demand

Each of these nine market drivers is discussed in a following section.

Mobile Subscriber Growth and Market Potential

We have come a long way since cellular phones were introduced some twenty years ago. Cell phones were once considered luxury items only for the wealthy, but they have since become household items that average people depend on in their day-to-day lives.

Wireless phones and networks were designed for what is still considered a *killer application*: voice communication. However, over the past decade, the novelty of wireless data has gained significant momentum on both fronts, consumer demand as well as technological innovation. During the past five years or so, wireless data-based instant messaging has become quite popular.

The following are some recent predictions from various consulting and news organizations around the world. Even though they differ in actual numbers, the crux of their messages is that subscriber growth for the next three to four years will be unprecedented; demand for new wireless applications and services will increase exponentially, and hence the market potential of WIEA will be large and lucrative.

Subscriber Growth

Worldwide wireless subscribers will grow from slightly over 400 million subscribers in 1999 to 1 billion in 2002.

–IDC, FEBRUARY 2000, QUOTED FROM BUSINESS WIRE OF FEBRUARY 29, 2000

By 2002, wireless phones will outnumber PCs and televisions combined and are projected to exceed 1 billion.

—STRATEGIC NEWS SERVICE, 2000

There will be nearly 24 million wireless data users by 2003. Wireless data services will be used by 9 million business consumers in three years, up from 784,000 in 1999.

—CAHNERS INSTAT GROUP, DEC 1999

The corporate market will be a huge target for wireless Internet services, with more than 32 million potential users for higher-cost mobile data services, compared to estimated 2.8 million workers who currently use such services.

—STRATEGIS GROUP, AUG 1999

Market Potential

The worldwide mobile commerce market will reach $200 billion by 2004.

—STRATEGY ANALYTICS, DEC 1999

By 2004, a full 40 percent of ecommerce transactions outside the US will be done via portable, cellular-enabled devices.

—GARTNER GROUP, NOV 1999

2002 revenues for wireless Internet applications alone could reach $37.5 billion.

—KILLEN & ASSOCIATES

Figure 3.1 provides several industry watchers' predicted wireless subscriber growth patterns across various countries.

Trends in Component Technologies

The three pillars of component technologies are processing power, memory, and power consumption. In this section, we take a look at the trends in these important areas.

Processing Power

Processing power can be measured in *millions of instructions per second* (MIPS). The higher the number of MIPS, the faster the processor. The lower the MIPS-per-dollar cost, the more MIPS a vendor can provide. More MIPS means more complex applications can be made available. In addition, if we can take advantage of new technologies that allow for better usage of MIPS, as Figure 3.2 shows, there will be an

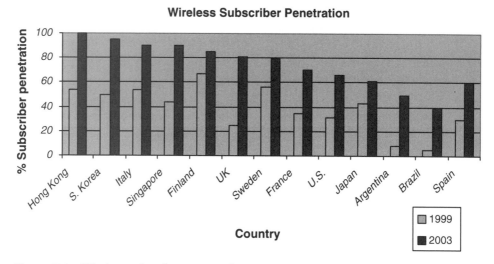

Figure 3.1   Wireless subscriber penetration rates.

(Sources Forrester Research, Ericsson, Strategic News Service, and The Yankee Group)

improvement in MIPS per dollar over time. MIPS per dollar is expected to double in the next two years.

Figure 3.3 lists the average number of MIPS required for various types of applications. The more complex an application, the higher the number of MIPS required for effective processing. With dropping costs and miniaturization of electronics, it's becoming possible to provide enough processing power to handhelds and phones to allow them to perform like desktop computers.

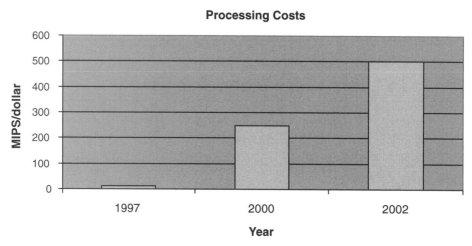

Figure 3.2   Trends in processing costs.

(Copyright © 1996, TI)

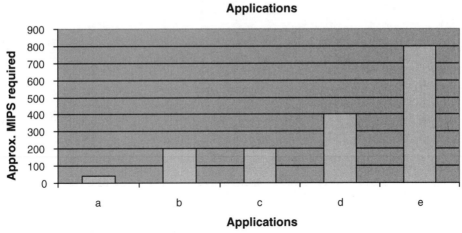

Applications

a   Handwriting recognition
b   Voice recognition (5000 words or phrases)
c   Simultaneous voice and data
d   Videoconferencing
e   TV-quality video

Figure 3.3   Processing requirements of common applications.
(Copyright © 1998, RTT Programmes)

Memory

Memory bandwidth is key to complex applications and services. With more memory available for a dollar (a trend expected to continue into the next decade), handhelds and phones are able to handle multiple applications at the same time. For example, you can simultaneously have a three-way conference call and transfer email headers. Figure 3.4 shows the trends in memory costs.

Power Consumption

Battery resources are scarce for mobile devices. Unlike desktops, mobile units have limited power resources. Complex applications drain battery resources fast, much to users' dismay. Improvements in power budgets will foster the development of exciting new applications. Figure 3.5 depicts trends in power consumption and costs.

New Standards and Technologies

Standardization is a process of vendors coming together for a common goal, standardizing the way an application or a technology works. This process has many advantages over proprietary technologies.

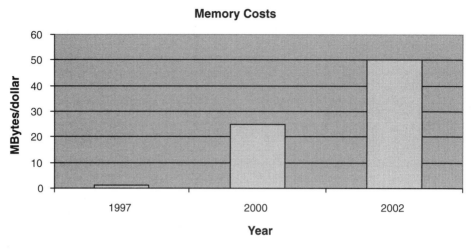

Figure 3.4 Trends in memory costs.

(Copyright © 1996, TI)

By way of explanation, let's consider an example of a wireless phone and examine how standardization helps the process. As we learned in Chapter 2, to set up a conversation, a wireless phone interacts with the base station controller for call setup. There are many handset and base station hardware and software providers around the world; Nokia, Motorola, and Ericsson are the three biggest suppliers of handsets and infrastructure equipment. If these handsets were to communicate with the base stations in a proprietary manner, two things would happen. First, Nokia phones, for example, would communicate only with Nokia base stations (and that would be true for other vendors' equipment as well). Second, if a carrier such as AT&T bought Nokia's base station, not only would it be locked into buying Nokia's handset and

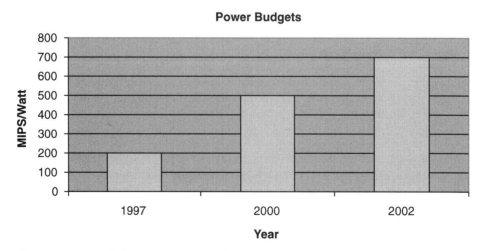

Figure 3.5 Trends in power consumption.

(Copyright © 1996, TI)

other related technology (such as MSC, HLR, VLR, and so on), but consumers could use only Nokia phones on AT&T's network. This extremely limited way of doing things would stifle innovation, services would be expensive and clumsy, and overall, it wouldn't be good for the industry or consumers.

Standards resolve compatibility problems among technologies from various vendors. An argument could be made that sometimes the large standards committees take too long to deliberate before some innovative solutions to come to market. However, the standards process is essential for meeting consumer demand for low prices and inter-operability among products from different vendors. Considering our example again, global air-interface standards such as CDMA, TDMA, and GSM allow vendors' technologies to interoperate with each other. So, AT&T could use Motorola's base station, Nokia's handset, and Ericsson's switching center, if it so desired. By adhering to standards, vendors can focus on improving their product offerings instead of expending energy making their products work with infrastructure from other suppliers.

The past couple of years have been instrumental in establishing several key standards in the computing and communications industries. These standards have truly kick-started the mobile business economy. Standards are key to adoption of technology and work for the benefit of consumers. These standards, coupled with several techno-logical innovations in the areas of semiconductors as well as communication and net-working technologies, have helped alleviate some of the severe constraints imposed on mobile devices. Now let's examine those constraints .

Less Powerful CPUs

In comparison to desktops, mobile devices such as PDAs and wireless phones are limited in their processing power. Although things in this area are changing, applica-tion developers, service providers, and users must still work within this constraint.

Limited Memory

Wireless devices are limited in memory. Writing memory-efficient programs and applications is still a huge challenge in the industry.

Restricted Power Consumption

Handsets and PDAs typically have two or three hours of battery life. The more complex an application, the more processing power it requires and the more quickly it drains power. So again, applications and new features have to work within power constraints.

Small Displays

Table 3.1 shows some examples of small displays that exist on some of the popular wireless data devices. It is critical that the information communicated to a device is packaged in a way that the user finds both useful and navigable.

Table 3.1   Screen Capabilities for Various Devices

DEVICE	SCREEN SIZE IN INCHES	CHARACTERS PER LINE	LINES PER SCREEN
Motorola Timeport	1.3 x 0.8	16	4
QUALCOMM pdQ	2.4 x 1.9	12	36
Sanyo SCP-4000	1.1 x 0.9	15	4
Sprint PCS Touchpoint	1.3 x 1.3	15	5
Palm V	2.25 x 3	40	13
Psion Revo	5 x 1.73	26	80

Difficult Input Devices

Punching in numbers is tedious on small keypads of handsets and PDAs. It's even more cumbersome to have to type short messages or emails on these devices. For wireless Internet to really take off, improvements in user interface technologies are essential.

Limited Bandwidth

Over the next five to ten years, data transmission rates of wireless networks will rival the data rates available on LAN networks, but it will take some time to get there. Moreover, technology evolution and implementation will vary by region. So, to provide access to the masses, it's critical for application and service developers and providers to keep the limited bandwidth in mind. Most wireless networks available today offer 9.6kbps to 19.2kbps.

Latency

Due to the inherent nature of wireless networks, setting up a connection involves a latency period. Unlike the Internet, these networks have limited resources, so, depending on how many customers are on the network at any given time, service could be delayed or even denied. With the spotty coverage and interference characteristic of today's wireless networks, a user's experience can be extremely discouraging.

Standards and Technologies

The technologies discussed in the sections that follow address many of the constraints on mobile devices. A high-level introduction to the standards and technologies is provided here; the topics are covered in more detail in Chapters 5 and 6.

Wireless Application Protocol (WAP)

> *Over 95 percent of mobile phones shipped
> in 2004 will be WAP enabled.*
>
> **–GARTNER GROUP, NOVEMBER 1999**

Although the industry has been buzzing with talk of mobile data applications and services, only recently—when WAP started to hit the developer and consumer communities—did the promise of wireless applications and services catch fire. In mid-1997, three of the largest phone manufacturers—Ericsson, Nokia, and Motorola—joined forces with Phone.com (previously known as Unwired Planet) to form the WAP Forum to work toward a common goal of forming a development framework that will expedite the development and implementation of wireless Internet-based applications.

WAP architecture consists of a suite of protocols and a markup language designed for wireless environments. This language, Wireless Markup Language (WML), is drawn from Handheld Device Markup Language (HDML) from Phone.com and is based on Extensible Markup Language (XML). (See the "Extensible Markup Language (XML)" section of this chapter as well as Chapter 5 for more details.)

The popularity of WAP arises from the fact that it has been adopted by a majority of players, both small and large, in the computing and communications industries. The forum recently boasted more than 250 corporate members worldwide.

Let's take a look at the WAP programming model and its advantages.

The WAP Programming Model

The WAP programming model, shown in Figure 3.6, is quite similar to the Web model shown in Figure 1.2. There are, however, a few differences.

In the Web model, the client directly communicates to the server. However, in the WAP programming model, the WAP gateway acts as an intermediary between the Web server and the WAP client (the browser on a wireless phone or alternate device). Using an example of connecting to the news service CNN's Web site, the communication steps in a WAP model are as follows:

1. The user enters the URL www.cnn.com into the WAP client (the browser).

2. The WAP user agent converts the URL into a compact binary message to decrease the size of the request message for efficient transmission over the air interface.

3. On receipt of the message, the WAP gateway converts it into an HTTP message and sends it to the www.cnn.com Web server.

4. The Web server recognizes the request and responds by sending appropriate HTML and JavaScript content back to the WAP gateway.

5. The WAP gateway converts the HTML and JavaScript content into WML and WMLScript and transforms that data into a compact binary format before sending it to the WAP client on the user's device.

6. The WAP client decodes the binary data and displays the appropriate content to the user.

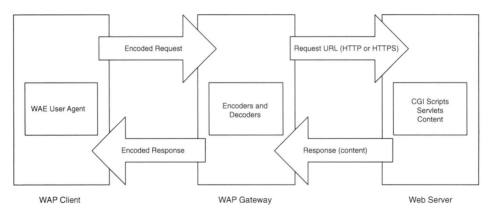

Figure 3.6 The WAP programming model.

A WAP gateway and the server can be on the same machine or on different machines or even on different networks. The server can also serve up WML content. In that case, the WAP gateway is needed only for encoding and decoding of WML and WMLScript content. In the future we will see these gateways become part of Web servers so that more efficiencies are realized. (For example, the Web server will be able to directly produce compact binary code instead of going through a separate gateway.)

Communication between the client and the server is achieved using WAP protocols such as Wireless Session Protocol (WSP), a compact, binary version of HTTP 1.1.

Advantages of the WAP Model

The following are some of the advantages of the WAP model:

➢ Encoding and decoding of Web content allows for decreasing the size of the transmitted information between the wireless device and the Web server. This decrease in size allows for faster transmission over narrowband wireless networks and improves latency.

➢ As we will see in Chapter 5, WAP works with a majority of bearers—namely, GSM, CDMA, TDMA, CDPD, Short Messaging Services (SMS), FLEX (a family of wireless technologies introduced by Motorola), and so on.

➢ WML supports text and images as well as user input and provides a variety of user navigation mechanisms. It also supports multiple languages and dialects (through the use of the Unicode character set) and provides state and context management features for faster performance.

➢ WAP allows for a wireless telephony applications interface. With such an interface, a user can, for example, look up a telephone number on the Web and dial it by simply pressing a key instead of dialing the entire number.

➢ WAP user agent information can be used for formatting highly personalized information. (We'll cover more details of this topic in Chapter 5.)

Right now, a majority of the carriers worldwide are jumping on the bandwagon of providing WAP-based services to their customers. However, critics of WAP argue that WAP provides a very constricted form of access to the Web by limiting the nature of content to basic text and that, with the advent of higher-bandwidth networks, WAP will soon become irrelevant. At this stage, though, it's difficult to deny WAP's popularity, and we must remember that it is an evolving standard. The WAP Forum is working with several Internet industry forums such as the World Wide Web Consortium (W3C) and the Internet Engineering Task Force (IETF). It is very likely that the standards of WAP, Synchronized Multimedia Markup Language (SMIL), eXtensible HyperText Markup Language (XHTML), and XML will merge at some point to provide enhanced personalization capabilities, applications, and services that are device and network independent.

It's worth mentioning here two other flavors of WML that are equally popular. They are Web Clipping and Compact HTML (CHTML). Web Clipping is the programming language used for Palm Pilots, which are very popular handheld devices in the United States. Web Clipping's programming model is quite similar to that of WAP. The idea is to translate HTML content into smaller Web "clipping" content for Palm devices that communicate to the Web server via wireless networks. As for CHTML, the carrier NTT DoCoMo's iMode service uses CHTML as its language for publishing Web content to wireless devices. iMode has been an instant hit in Japan, where NTT DoCoMo was able to sign on more than 2 million subscribers within eight months, at a staggering rate of 90,000 subscribers per week (source: *On Magazine*, Ericsson, December 1999).

As you might infer, today, in various regions of the world, multiple standards exist for presenting content to wireless devices, and the future will be no different. Only time will tell which standards will survive or which new standards will merge.

Bluetooth

> *More than 75 percent of new handsets shipped in 2004*
> *will be Bluetooth enabled.*
>
> **–GARTNER GROUP, NOVEMBER 1999**

> *About 95 percent of smart phones shipped to the United States*
> *and Western Europe in 2003 will be WAP enabled, and*
> *70 percent will have Bluetooth technology.*
>
> **–STRATEGY ANALYTICS, JULY 1999**

Bluetooth, named for a tenth-century Viking king, is a mobile communications technology that allows a wide variety of devices to communicate with each other. Typically, on a daily basis, you might interact with at least three common devices: a PC, a mobile phone, and a PDA. To see Bluetooth's role in wireless communication, let's consider a simple task of entering a new contact into your address book. Most likely, you would enter the information into each of these devices separately, or you might synchronize the devices using some software. The latter method is convenient but still requires some manual work. Now consider this: What if, as soon as you entered the contact information on your PC, the mobile phone and PDA immediately and automatically picked up that information! Bluetooth makes that magic happen.

Bluetooth is a technology for the use of short-range wireless communications for both voice and data. It enables peer-to-peer communications among all imaginable devices, from PDAs and phones to toasters and refrigerators. So, instead of dealing with cables between devices, seamless communication among them is possible if they are Bluetooth enabled.

Predictive and Other Text-Entry Techniques

Mobile phones and PDAs, with their small form factors, are difficult for most people to use comfortably. For applications such as email, chat, or instant messaging, it's hard and often frustrating for users to work with small keypads for text entry. Tegic Communications, recently acquired by America Online (AOL), pioneered predictive text-entry technology. Tegic's product helped predict words the user is likely to key in. T9 keeps a dictionary of your most commonly used words and predicts words as you key in letters. For example, normally, if you want to enter the word *FINE* as text on one of these devices, you press the keys labeled 3-4-6-3 for a total of ten taps, but with the help of Tegic's T9 technology, you will only have to press four keys (see Figure 3.7).

This technology is useful for any kind of small keyboard entry device such as those on mobile phones, PDAs, WebTV remotes, MP3 players, Nintendo game terminals, autoPCs, and information appliances. T9 technology is available in more than 14 languages, including Chinese, Spanish, and English. All the major global phone and PDA manufacturers have licensed this technology, so a majority of new phones come with Tegic's predictive text-entry technology.

Other popular modes of text entry, shown in Figure 3.8, are as follows:

Touch-screen entry. Using this technique, users can bring up the familiar qwerty keyboard on a small form factor device.

Handwriting recognition. One of the most natural ways to enter text is via handwriting. Using handwriting recognition software, users can input text as they write using a stylus.

In addition to these text-input technologies, the real promise lies with voice recognition-based input technologies. We will review some of the emerging technologies and standards in this area in Chapter 5.

eXtensible Markup Language (XML)

The programming language that has allowed content and application providers to publish information over the Internet is HTML. Over the past couple of years, XML has evolved into the next-generation ebusiness markup language. From the early days of static HTML content, applications rapidly started to serve interactive HTML content created dynamically, on the fly. HTML does a good job of formatting and pre-

Figure 3.7   Example of the use of Tegic's T9 technology.

senting the content but lacks the ability to apply meaning to the content. That's where XML's value can be realized. XML makes the data "smart," allowing it to be extracted for use in other applications and for providing other services across partner extranets or the consumer Internet.

For example, in HTML, if you'd like to italicize sine text, you use the <I> tag. This tag instructs the browser where to start italicizing the text; the ending tag </I> tells the browser where to end it. For example:

```
<I>Barcelona</I>
```

Figure 3.8   Text-input techniques: QWERTY and handwriting recognition.

Table 3.2.   Markup Languages

MARKUP LANGUAGE	PROPOSING VENDOR(S)	COMMENTS
Web Clipping	Palm HTML	IA proprietary format based on
VoiceXML	IBM, Lucent, Motorola, Nokia	Based on XML; mainly for creating content to be accessed by voice phones
Compact HTML	Microsoft, Ericsson	Based on HTML
iMode CHTML	NTT DoCoMo	Based on HTML; primarily popular in Japan

The markup in XML works essentially the same way:

```
<Capital City>Barcelona</Capital City>
```

Unlike HTML, however, XML allows you to create your own tags to describe exactly what you want the data to mean. Document type definition (DTD) helps standardize the structure of the XML documents that can be exchanged with others. DTDs define the rules that define the tags that can be used in XML files and their valid values. Extensible Style Language (XSL) is the style standard for XML. It specifies the presentation and appearance of an XML document.

The same XML document can be transformed into a variety of formats using XSL, the language that controls the presentation aspects of data. As mentioned before, WML is based on XML. As things stand today, multiple markup languages exist. Some of the other popular languages are listed in Table 3.2.

HTML developers know the efforts to which they must go in order to provide content to different browsers (for example, rivals Internet Explorer and Netscape Navigator). Imagine the conundrum that would result if developers had to format the content for multiple microbrowsers, each with its own markup language. Fortunately, by design, XML provides a solution for that very problem. Using style sheets, as shown in Figure 3.9, the same content can be displayed in a variety of formats that are applicable for different browsers and devices. This way, a single content source can be used to publish content in different formats (WML, HTML, CHTML, and so on) instead of keeping multiple content sources based on markup language formats.

Mobile Synchronization Protocol (SyncML)

Mobile Synchronization Protocol, known as *SyncML,* is a new industry initiative to develop and promote a single, common data synchronization protocol that can be used industrywide, across multiple devices and applications. The founders of the initiative and the SyncML Forum are IBM, Lotus, Motorola, Nokia, Palm, Psion, and Starfish Software. The goals of the protocol are as follows:

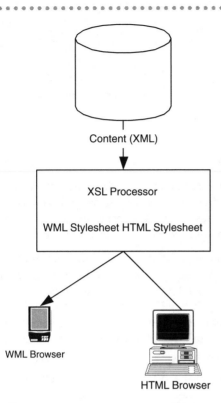

Figure 3.9   XML content processing.

➤ Support synchronization of any networked data with any mobile device

➤ Operate effectively with both wireless and wireline networks

➤ Support a variety of transport protocols

➤ Enable data access across a variety of applications

➤ Address the resource limitations of the mobile devices

➤ Build on existing Internet, Web, and wireless technologies

Forum members expect to release an open protocol sometime during 2000.

2.5G and 3G Wireless Technologies

In Chapter 2, we talked about 2.5G and 3G wireless technologies. They not only promise better coverage and improved performance; they also significantly increase bandwidth, making possible more complex wireless Internet applications. Since these technologies allow packet-based data transmission, devices can be "always on," and data transmission takes place whenever needed. The 2.5G and 3G network systems will also be compatible with 2G devices. The goal of these new technologies is twofold:

➤ Provide the user high-bandwidth services:

  ➤ Mobile data rates up to 384kbps

  ➤ Fixed data rates up to 2 Mbps

➤ Provide users with a full range of voice, data, fax, Internet, conference, and video services

Position Location Technologies

The term *position location technologies* refers to techniques for physically locating a wireless device by providing x, y, z (horizontal, vertical, azimuthal) geographic coordinates. Location-based services are the services these technologies enable, such as providing driving directions based on your location and desired destination.

Strategis Group estimates that the position location market will amount to in excess of $8 billion per year by 2005 (source: *Wireless Location Services Report*, Strategis Group, 1997). With the help of triangulation techniques such as angle of arrival, time difference of arrival, fingerprinting, and falling GPS chip prices, it's possible for a wireless device to be located from a remote spot within a few meters of accuracy. Once you know the location of a device and that of its owner, the horizon for value-added services and applications is endless.

Growth in the position location market has been significantly fueled by the Federal Communications Commission (FCC) mandate for E911 in the United States, which requires all U.S. carriers to be able to locate wireless phones within 50 to 100 meters— with 67 percent or better accuracy—by 2001. Position location applications will also be very popular for the automotive market. In Chapter 5, we will look into the various available technologies and applications in the position location marketplace and why it is such a critical element in designing good wireless Internet-based applications and services.

In this section we reviewed a whole range of standards and technologies in the Internet and wireless industries that are helping overcome some of the constraints imposed by the wireless environment. In Chapter 5, we will discuss these and some other technologies in more detail.

The Internet Revolution

Few revolutions in our history have so completely transformed economies and societies around the world as the Internet Revolution. Invented by Tim Berners-Lee, the Internet changed the way we collaborate, share, and disseminate information. Benefits and efficiencies gained using the Internet are ever growing. Although the concept of the Internet was born in Europe, it blossomed in the United States before spreading globally. Every second, thousands and thousands of new users across the globe discover the Internet. Figure 3.10 shows Internet penetration rates for various countries. They are predicted to go up across the board.

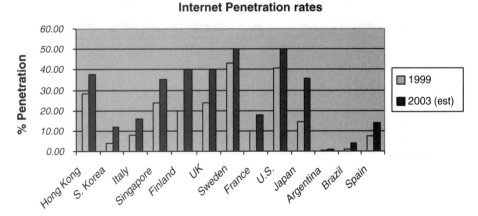

Figure 3.10   Internet penetration rates.
(Copyright © 2000, The Standard)

One of the main reasons the Internet has so permeated our lives is its effect on B2C and B2B applications and services. These applications and services define electronic commerce. The revenues from ecommerce are on the rise and are expected to grow exponentially, as shown in Figure 3.11.

Wireless Internet-based applications will be successful for the following two clear reasons:

➤ Existing users want to access the Internet using their wireless devices. For users who have already experienced the benefits of the Internet, wireless Internet applications will be easier to learn.

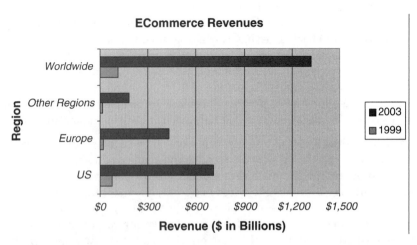

Figure 3.11   Ecommerce revenues.
(Copyright © 2000, The Standard)

Table 3.3. Wireless versus PC Penetration by Selected Country, 1999 and 2003

COUNTRY	1999	EST. 2003
Italy	6.4:1	5.6:1
Spain	4.0:1	4.2:1
Brazil	4.6:1	9.5:1
France	3.6:1	3.9:1
Argentina	14:1	41:1

➤ If you compare Figures 3.1 and 3.10, you will notice that in certain countries, especially in Europe, wireless device penetration far outreaches Internet penetration, even for the next three years or so; this fact is backed up by the data in Table 3.3. This means that these consumers' only way of accessing the Internet is by using a wireless Internet-enabled device. In turn, businesses have only the means of the wireless device to connect to these consumers instantly and profitably.

Wireless Data Moves toward Ubiquity

Next-generation wireless technologies promise enhanced bandwidth and significant performance improvements. These benefits, coupled with broadband wireless roll-outs, will accelerate the realization of wireless network ubiquity.

Increased demand for high-speed network access has generated new opportunities for service providers, but bandwidth limitations between the service providers' core networks and the end user, often referred to as "the last mile," have constrained service providers from exploiting these opportunities. In addition, although many wide area network (WAN) backbones have been upgraded to fiber optic cable and have used technologies that allow operation at speeds up to 9Gbps, the local access telephone network typically consists of older copper wires originally designed to transmit fixed-speed voice signals at a fraction of that fiber optic speeds. This "last mile" bottleneck is frustrating a broad base of business users, many of whom require symmetrical access to high-speed data that requires transmission at varying speeds.

Broadband wireless access technology can solve many of the problems faced by wired networks. Broadband wireless technology enables high-speed network access, unrestricted by traditional wired infrastructures. Broadband wireless technology is also a cost-effective alternative to wired networks, one that can be quickly implemented. A broadband wireless connection is often the best option for high-speed communication in remote areas and in many developing countries due to the lack of an existing wired infrastructure. In these regions, wireless technologies provide clear advantages over wired networks—advantages that include lower cost, faster deployment, greater flexibility, and increased reliability.

Need to Streamline Enterprise Information

Whatever the business, all successful enterprises have two key engines running well for them: communication and access to information. A well-informed employee is critical to the growth and success of a company. Changing times enforce the need and desire for information to be available to employees, anytime, anywhere. Since workers generally don't carry their desktops or laptops everywhere they go, it also means availability via any device. This is especially true for "road warriors" such as members of the sales team or department heads who need access to contact lists, emails, up-to-the-second sales forecasts, and other critical information. IT managers need to keep abreast of the status of their network infrastructures. Instead of replying to your favorite customers, "I will get back to you," imagine what would happen if you could give them the information they seek right then and there—it would have a huge impact on the way customers view you and your corporation.

So, it's imperative for enterprise workforce to be well informed and well equipped. Wireless Internet directly ties into that mission. Corporations will be the first to appreciate the benefits of distributed information and will be the early adopters of this technology. In Chapter 1, we reviewed some of the types of applications that will become prominent within the enterprise.

Convergence of Computing and Communications Industries

The convergence of the computing and communications industries promises exciting applications. Vendors from these growing sectors are working together on standards and technologies that blur the lines between desktop PCs and mobile communication devices.

As we reviewed earlier in this chapter, the costs of memory, power, and processing are dropping rapidly. This cost reduction is allowing yesterday's mobile devices to become powerful and useful extensions of the computing world. As is evident from Figure 3.12, computing and communications devices are converging into devices that not only communicate but that can also be used for many complex computing applications such as address book, email, calendar, browsing, games, and so on. Devices such as Nokia's Communicator or QUALCOMM's pdQ phones are popular examples of such convergence. Each of these devices is a PDA and phone in one unit. With time, their costs will come down and the form factor will improve to make them acceptable to mass markets.

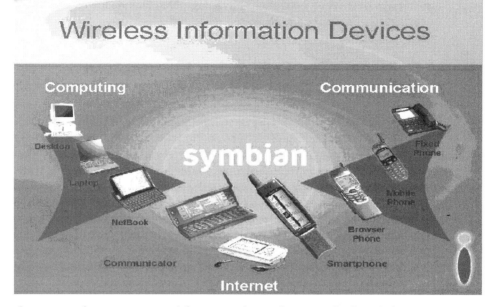

Figure 3.12 The convergence of the computing and communications industries.
(Copyright © 2000, Symbian)

Competition

Businesses are looking for services and applications that differentiate them from the competition. Wireless Internet-based applications and services introduce another way for companies to gain an advantage by forging and extending customer relationships.

Typically, churn rates (the percentages of consumers who switch vendors at any given time) for a majority of consumer-oriented industries range anywhere from 20 to 40 percent. The Internet, being consumer-centric, provides users options—the option of searching and comparing vendors and their offerings. With competition only a click away, businesses need to find new ways to keep their existing customers and find new ones, to build customer loyalty, and to service their customers and partners.

Wireless Internet provides a very powerful medium for reaching customers. Competition is driving businesses to offer services that their customers, partners, and employees alike can access from anywhere, anytime.

Consumer Awareness and Demand

Consumers demand solutions that enhance mobility while connecting them to any information they choose. As we saw in the iMode example earlier in the chapter, people are very excited about the new wireless revolution and will pay for enhanced services. Figure 3.13 shows a sample of consumer interest in common applications.

The same results are reflected in surveys conducted to sense consumer demand for automobile-based wireless Internet services. Figure 3.14 shows results from a survey conducted by evaluations.com for InfoMove. Over half of the survey's respondents were willing to pay more then $10 per month for wireless services such as:

➤ Turn-by-turn driving directions

➤ Live localized traffic incident alerts

➤ Speed alerts

➤ Car diagnostic information

➤ Email

➤ Chat

➤ Games and other services

As we discussed earlier, another surge of interest is coming from corporate users, especially "road warriors." Today's business demands require them to be in touch with their enterprises and have intranet information at their fingertips. IT departments are already having to deal with and plan for deep interest shown by their colleagues. Software and hardware vendors are rising to the challenge by providing solutions that enable enterprises to be mobile. Some of the key drivers in the growth of enterprise mobile computing are as follows:

➤ The need for faster, decentralized decision making

➤ The need to be closer to customers, prospects, and partners

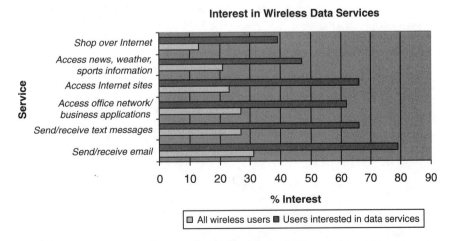

Figure 3.13   Consumer interest in wireless data services.

(Copyright © 2000, *The Wireless Marketplace in 2000,* Peter D. Hart Research Associates)

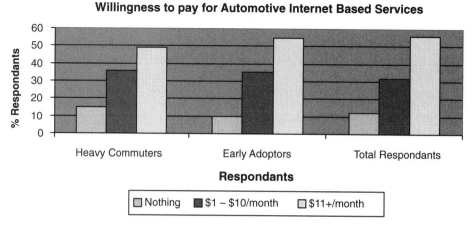

Figure 3.14 Consumers' willingness to pay for automotive Internet-based services.
(Copyright © 2000, *Text 100 InfoMove Study,* Text 100 and InfoMove)

➤ The need for mobile workers who spend more time working and less time commuting

It's evident that consumers and enterprises alike recognize the value of wireless Internet applications and services; the growing interest in these technologies is one of the strongest market drivers for this burgeoning industry.

In this chapter, we reviewed some of the market trends that are enabling the wireless Internet market, technologies that are helping overcome the shortcomings of the mobile environment, and the potential of the mobile economy. In the next chapter, we will take a look at some of the applications and services that have hit the market in the past couple of years.

The Wireless Internet Applications and Services Landscape

● ●

As we established in Chapter 3, innovations in various computing and communications technologies are fueling the rollout of the nascent wireless Internet applications and services market. In this chapter, we evaluate the types of applications and services that are being rolled out in the consumer marketplace. The purpose of this chapter is to provide you with enough examples of the applications and services to give you the flavor of the work being done across various industries.

Consumer Applications

In this section, we look at applications and services that are primarily business-to-consumer (B2C) in nature—for example, stock trading, news, travel, and traffic information. Most consumer applications can also be used by enterprises. Information such as technology news, driving directions, and restaurant guides are as valuable to business users as to consumers.

Wireless Portals

A *portal* is a gateway to the World Wide Web. It's also an aggregation of content from various Internet sources. Portals such as Yahoo! kicked off the Internet boom. Similarly, wireless portals are beginning to leverage the promise of wireless Internet.

Online portals were the first movers in this space. By rapidly reformatting their content, portals want to keep loyal customers coming back to their Web sites from both desktop and wireless devices. Yahoo! acquired Online Anywhere to provide content

Figure 4.1   Yahoo! Mail for a Palm device.

Figure 4.2   People Search for a Palm device.

to handhelds; Excite@Home partnered with Japanese carrier NTT DoCoMo to provide similar service. Infospace acquired a stake in wireless service providers Prio and Saraide to enhance its capabilities in the wireless Internet space. Microsoft and Nextel teamed up to work on MSN Mobile service. The list of companies making the transition from online portal to wireless portal goes on and on. Figures 4.1 and 4.2 show a few examples of some successful providers in this space.

General or Search Portals

Generic portals are aggregators of various types of content sources—news, sports, weather, religion, and so on. Some portals simply provide links to other wireless Web content. Table 4.1 and Figure 4.3 provide some examples of these types of portals.

News

Companies in the news category are existing Web and cable content providers that want to leverage their content by becoming news portals as well as content providers to other portals. Table 4.2 and Figures 4.4–4.6 show some examples.

Table 4.1   Portals and Their Mobile Offerings

COMPANY	MOBILE OFFERINGS
Yahoo!	Yahoo! mail, calendar, address book, news, sports, finance, weather, movies, downloads
Sonera	Zed news, information, events, phone directory, specialty channels
Palm.net	More than thirty-seven content providers supply more than 400 Web clipping applications; InSync is the portal for all things Palm—news, updates, new products, downloads, applications
AT&T	PocketNet premium service for Internet, email, calendar, address book, to-do lists
MSN	Hotmail alerts, news, sports, finance, weather
Phone.com	MyPhone turnkey service for wireless network operators to help them create Internet portals
Pinpoint.com	Wireless search engine for wireless content
Room33.com	Calendar, stocks, short messaging, address book, news, stocks, weather, city guide, chat
Rediff.com	News and information about the Indian subcontinent, astrology, calendar
OracleMobile.com	Driving directions, flight status, traffic information, weather, movie guide, short messaging, yellow pages, news, stocks, food delivery, flowers, eBay auctions
Excite	Stock quotes, news, sports scores, horoscopes, driving directions, movie times, weather forecasts, and email from Excite Mail

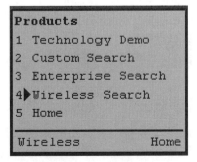

Figure 4.3   A search engine provided by Pinpoint.com for a WAP phone.

Table 4.2   News Sites and Their Mobile Offerings

COMPANY	MOBILE OFFERINGS
CNN	Updated hourly, CNN Mobile offers breaking news, world news, weather, sports, business news, regionalized content
ABCNews	Breaking U.S. and international news, business updates, and technology reports as well as the latest on health, living, entertainment
Newsvendor	Provides links to other news sites such as NV News, ENN News, Examiner News
Reuters	Personalized news and financial data
BBC	News, sports, weather, TV, entertainment
NewsJunkie	Allows access to news sources such as Wired, Fox, BBC, Associated Press, CNet, ZDNN, The New York Times

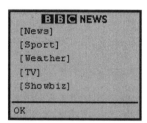

Figure 4.4   BBC News for a WAP phone.

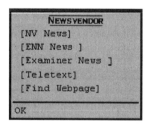

Figure 4.5   News vendor for a WAP phone.

Figure 4.6   ABCNews.com for a Palm device.

Table 4.3   Weather Sites and Their Mobile Offerings

COMPANY	MOBILE OFFERINGS
Accuweather.com	Weather alerts and advisories to pagers
Weather.com	Personalized weather forecast and current condition for a fee
WeatherNet	Live, real-time weather conditions for over 4,000 sites in the United States, in conjunction with 103 local television stations
Marine Weather	National Weather Service forecasts, current conditions at weather stations, and NOAA buoys for most of the northeastern United States

Weather

Web site companies specializing in provision of weather information provide that information by ZIP code, city, state, and country. They also provide weather content to other portals. Table 4.3 summarizes a few of the mobile offerings in this area.

Sports Scores

Sports portals provide live scores as well as sports news, analysis, and statistics. Generally, the nature of sports coverage depends on the country in which these services are offered. Table 4.4 and Figure 4.7 show some examples.

Airline Schedules

Real-time updates of airline schedules is very useful information for busy travelers. Some airlines and airline ticket portals have started offering flight information. The advantage of portals is that they generally cover all major airline schedules. Table 4.5 and Figures 4.8 and 4.9 show some examples.

Table 4.4   Sports Sites and Their Mobile Offerings

COMPANY	MOBILE OFFERINGS
ESPN	News, scores, standings, schedules for major U.S. and international sports: NFL, NBA, college football, baseball, NHL, golf, soccer, auto racing, extreme sports
Sportal	The latest in sports, including football, rugby, and horse racing, on users' mobile phones for multiple European countries

Figure 4.7 ESPN.com for a Palm device.

Figure 4.8 Delta Air Lines for a Palm device.

Figure 4.9 Delta Air Lines for a WAP phone.

Table 4.5 Airline or Travel Sites and Their Mobile Offerings

COMPANY	MOBILE OFFERINGS
Delta Air Lines	Delta flight itineraries; access to up-to-the-minute flight information, including same-day gate information; flight numbers and schedules
Continental Airlines	Flight schedules, flight status, access to OnePass mileage account, specials
American Airlines	Flight lookups, departure time, arrival time, gate and baggage information, AAdvantage, Admiral Club locations, AA Vacation specials
Snakefeet.com	Airport delay information
AirInfo Wireless	Real-time airport status information for all major cities
Biztravel.com	Real-time flight status, including expected departure time, departure terminal, and departure gate information
Travelocity.com	Flight schedules for more than 700 airlines worldwide; up-to-the-minute flight arrival and departure information; existing itineraries and flight paging service
United Airlines	Real-time flight status, flight availability, flight paging, Mileage Plus account summary, upgrade status, award travel availability

Traffic Information

If you have been stuck in traffic, you know the value of real-time traffic information. Online information ranges from live incident reports to bitmaps of city traffic. The site maps' color shading represents various states of traffic congestion. Table 4.6 and Figures 4.10 and 4.11 provide some examples.

Table 4.6 Traffic Information Sites and Their Mobile Offerings

COMPANY	MOBILE OFFERINGS
Webraska.com	Real-time traffic conditions for major European cities
Mapquest.com	Traffic conditions, driving directions, alternate route suggestions
Traffictouch.com	Up-to-the-minute notifications of adverse traffic conditions; define the roadways and areas you travel
Seattle Traffic Viewer	Accepts user queries regarding current Seattle traffic conditions and displays them in graphical format

Figure 4.10 Traffic Touch for a Palm device.

Figure 4.11 Webraska.com for a WAP phone.

(Copyright © 2000, Webraska, All rights Reserved)

Restaurants/City Guides/Locator Information

These virtual guides not only provide information about restaurants and their menu items—they allow users to search by location. For example, you could search for restaurants of your taste within a certain ZIP code, city, or neighborhood in a few keystrokes. Table 4.7 and Figures 4.12 and 4.13 show some illustrations.

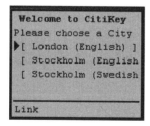

Figure 4.12 CitiKey for a WAP phone.

Figure 4.13 CitiKey for a Palm device.

Table 4.7 City Guide Sites and Their Mobile Offerings

COMPANY	MOBILE OFFERINGS
Telecom Italia	City guides
DigitalCity (a division of AOL)	City guides
TicketMaster Online-CitySearch	City guides
CityKey	City guides with detailed information on restaurants (in multiple languages)
Vindigo	City guides with detailed information on restaurants
Mastercard	Automated teller machine (ATM) locator
Visa	ATM locator
Starbucks	Nearest Starbucks shop locator
Elocal.com	Comprehensive local information on over 30,000 cities across the United States; information ranging from arts and entertainment to travel and lodging

Personal Organizers

Companies such as Wireless Knowledge and Saraide are becoming the application service providers (ASPs) of the wireless world, hooking up employees to corporate networks to provide access to email, calendar, contacts, and intranet content. Some of these providers also host applications. Figure 4.14 shows a typical Web ASP network architecture. Table 4.8 lists some wireless ASPs and their mobile offerings.

Transactional Services

Informational content such as news and sports scores provide value, but the real wireless Internet will specialize in *transactional services* like *banking, stock purchase*, etc. The financial services and banking industries were the first to jump on this bandwagon.

Table 4.8 Wireless ASP Sites and Their Mobile Offerings

COMPANY	MOBILE OFFERINGS
Wireless Knowledge	Connectivity to Microsoft Exchange servers
Saraide	Messaging (synchronizes with Microsoft Outlook and Lotus Schedule), news, travel, financial services
Infinite Mobility	Hosting solutions

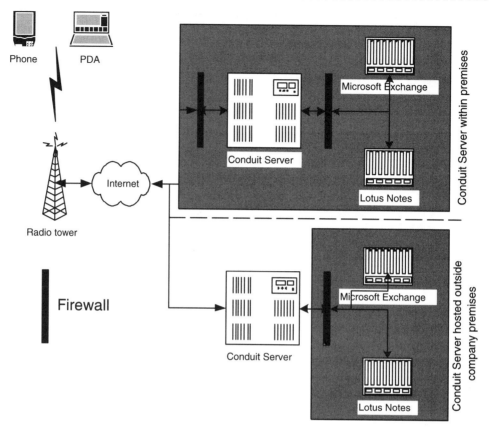

Figure 4.14 A typical Web ASP architecture.

Financial Services

Online financial services companies are traditional financial institutions that extend their online services to the wireless world. Services include stock trading, access to account information, market analysis, alerts, and quotes. Some of the firms also offer some *sticky services* such as horoscopes, news, weather, and the like. Traditional banks initially connected their legacy systems to the Internet and they are now extending the same information to wireless devices. Table 4.9 and Figure 4.15 provide some examples.

Buying/Selling Lottery Tickets

Everything's for sale on the Net, including lottery tickets. Table 4.10 provides information on a couple of lottery sources.

Table 4.9   Financial Sites and Their Mobile Offerings

COMPANY	MOBILE OFFERINGS
Quote.com	Quotes
Bloomberg Online	Quotes, access to account information, view portfolio, news
Schwab	Trades, quotes, alerts, access to account information, view portfolio, news, weather, horoscopes
Ameritrade	Trades, quotes, alerts, access to account information
Bank of Montreal	Trades, quotes, alerts, access to account information, funds transfer and bill payment, view portfolio
DLJdirect	Trades, quotes, alerts, access to account information
Merrill Lynch	Trades, quotes, alerts, access to account information
National Discount Brokers	Trades, quotes, alerts, access to account information, news, weather, horoscopes
Wellsfargo.com	Trades, quotes, alerts, access to account information
Fidelity	Trades, quotes, alerts, access to account information, research
Bank of America	Access to account information
Morgan Stanley Dean Witter	Trades, quotes, alerts, access to account information, research, news, weather, horoscopes
Claritybank.com	Trades, quotes, access to account information, funds transfers and bill payment, news, weather, horoscopes
Suretrade.com	Trades, quotes, view portfolio, research, news, weather, horoscopes
Citibank	Quotes, access to account information, funds transfers and bill payment, news, weather, horoscopes
BOE Securities	News, quotes, and currency information
Eloan	Offers mortgage calculations and rates
StockAlerts.com	Global WAP stock alert system
IOwn.com	Access to mortgage rates, agents, recent home sales and loan information
Prudential	Real Estate program
Oanda.com	Exchange rates

Table 4.10   Lottery Sites and Their Mobile Offerings

COMPANY	MOBILE OFFERINGS
Telecom Italia	Lottery tickets
Genie Internet	Lottery tickets

Figure 4.15 Fidelity Investments for a Palm device.

Ecommerce Services

Ecommerce services relate to buying and selling products and services. Amazon.com was among the first retailers to extend its services to mobile devices. Wireless-based auction services are also becoming commonplace.

Auctions

Auction sites give Web surfers the chance to buy and sell goods themselves to anyone in the world. eBay is a prime example of such a site; that and other auction sites and their mobile offerings are listed in Table 4.11.

Table 4.11 Auction Sites and Their Mobile Offerings

COMPANY	MOBILE OFFERINGS
eBay	Person-to-person online auctions
Amazon.com	Person-to-person online auctions
Xypoint.com	Auctions through voice and messaging
Cat-street.com	Auction site featuring goods and services specifically from Asia
InterAuct	Auction service based in Singapore

Table 4.12   Retail Sites and Their Mobile Offerings

COMPANY	MOBILE OFFERINGS
Amazon.com	Books, music, video, electronics, toys, and games
Barnes and Noble	Books, music

Retail Sales

The number of retail outlets on the Internet is burgeoning; the craze started by Amazon.com has been picked up by retail chains selling everything from home furnishings to CDs. Table 4.12 lists a couple of examples.

Entertainment

Entertainment is the most dynamic and popular segment of wireless applications. In Europe and Japan, wireless entertainment services such as quizzes, puzzles, interactive games, and chat rooms, instead of ecommerce services, are driving up wireless usage. Tables 4.13 and 4.14 give some examples of these services

Table 4.13   Game Sites and Their Mobile Offerings

COMPANY	MOBILE OFFERINGS
Wirelessgames.com	Puzzles, hangman, tic tac toe, mines, quiz, interactive, multi-user games, casino, poker, blackjack
Gameplay.com	News, reviews, and text adventure games
Springtoys.com	Interactive games
Genie Internet	Quizzes and puzzles
PopEx	Music trading game in which players buy and sell shares in bands
w-Trade	Stock-trading game
Gallows	Hangman-type word-guessing game
SFR	Interactive games, horoscopes
AT&T Wireless	Interactive games
Telecom Italia	Interactive games, horoscopes, soap opera updates
Sonera	Interactive games, horoscopes

Table 4.14   Chat Sites and Their Mobile Offerings

COMPANY	MOBILE OFFERINGS
AOL	Mobile messaging, chat
Room33.com	Mobile messaging
Microsoft Network (MSN)	Mobile messaging
Ezoner.com	Mobile messaging, chat, picture messaging
Wireless carriers	SMS chat and messaging

Communications

A number of services available today facilitate email, fax, and event schedule communications. Table 4.15 and Figure 4.16 provide a few examples.

Table 4.15   Event Scheduler Sites and Their Mobile Offerings

COMPANY	MOBILE OFFERINGS
Senada.com	Personal and business event scheduler and tracker
eFax	Receive fax and voicemail notification on your Internet-enabled phone
UniMobile	Unified messaging tool that communicates with cell phones, pagers, PDAs

Location-Based Services

With the advent of position location technologies, the location services market will grow exponentially. However, with the use of some basic and approximate location techniques, some vendors are providing lookup services based on ZIP code or cell site location information. Some of these "yellow pages" services are summarized in Table 4.16.

 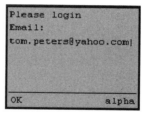 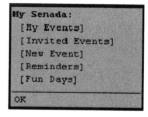

Figure 4.16   Senada.com for a WAP phone.

Table 4.16   Yellow Pages Sites and Their Mobile Offerings

COMPANY	MOBILE OFFERINGS
Whowhere.com	Email and phone searches
Infospace	Phone and email searching, including reverse lookups
Yahoo!	People search by name, address, email
Vicinity Brandfinder	Helps users locate retail stores
WAP411	Provides addresses, phone numbers, and recommendations for local hotels, restaurants, and other travel needs

Corporate Applications

Corporations are increasingly realizing the benefits of wirelessly enabling their customer service applications. The cost savings of doing so are immense because wireless technology reduces operation costs and increases customer satisfaction. Table 4.17 cites a few wireless customer service sites and their mobile offerings.

Table 4.17   Customer Service Sites and Their Mobile Offerings

COMPANY	MOBILE OFFERINGS
Comverse	Service provisioning and customer service
Sprint	Service provisioning and customer service
Lightbridge	Service provisioning and customer service

Voice Portals

Internet content is increasingly becoming accessible by voice. Players such as Tellme are taking advantage of speech-to-text and text-to-speech voice recognition technologies to enable existing content via voice commands. Table 4.18 provides a list of Tellme and other players and their offerings in this arena.

Enterprise Applications

The category of enterprise applications and services is targeted at enterprise users. The motivations behind a majority of these applications are cost savings and productivity gains across various disciplines.

Table 4.18 Voice Portal Sites and Their Mobile Offerings

COMPANY	MOBILE OFFERINGS
Tellme	Theater tickets, restaurant reservations, stock quotes, weather conditions, traffic conditions, soap opera updates, sports scores and news, horoscopes, blackjack, lottery numbers, airline information
BeVocal	Driving directions, traffic conditions, flight information, stock quotes, weather conditions
Webley Systems	Email, fax, phone calls
PhoneRun	News, business reports, weather conditions
Foodline.com	Theater tickets, restaurant reservations
TelSurf Networks	News, weather, sports, stock quotes
UcallNet	News, weather, sports, stock quotes
Onebox.com	Email, voicemail, calendar

Dispatch and Deliver

People in the dispatch and delivery business are almost always on the run. Often times the services they provide need to be accessed on the go. Applications such as ones available from EFX and RateShop (Figures 4.17 and 4.18) allow consumers to do comparison shopping in real-time. There are applications and services available that allow packages and shipments to be tracked throughout the delivery lifecycle. Interactive alerts can also be sent, if something unexpected happens, for example, when a shipment gets delayed or lost. Wireless applications are also being used to do real-time scheduling of tasks and resources.

Figure 4.17 EFX on a Palm device.

Figure 4.18   RateShop on a Palm device.

Field Service

Any organization that deals with field work will benefit from wireless technology. As mentioned in Chapter 1, field service has traditionally required reams of paperwork and inefficient use and scheduling of employees. With the help of wireless devices and technology, the paperwork and workflow can be synchronized.

For example, the Vara Water Works water purification plant in Stockholm, Sweden, is undergoing WAP technology trials to accomplish many day-to-day field activities. With WAP phones, the staff can check water flows, valve openings, and other settings. Armed with this information, the field service personnel can then take action in the event of an accident. Valves and pumps can be controlled directly from the phone. Vara Water Works serves 16,500 municipal residents and an area of about 700 square kilometers. There are ten water works, thirty pumping stations, and five purification plants throughout the municipality. A PC-based system is used for daily monitoring and remote control. The WAP solution complements this system.

Sales Force Automation

The sales force within almost any company needs access to valuable customer and lead-generation data in real time. This real-time access allows managers to make more informed decisions and the sales force to have more meaningful customer engagements. Figure 4.19 shows the site of a sales force automation provider.

Figure 4.19   eBusiness Anywhere on a Palm device.

Figure 4.20 HitBox on a Palm device.

Remote IT Monitoring

Increasingly, information systems (IS) teams must be constantly in touch with their networks. Capabilities that allow them to remotely monitor and diagnose problems and issues will be warmly welcomed in the IS world. Figure 4.20 illustrates one site that specializes in remote IT monitoring.

Remote Access to Intranets

Remote access to intranet-based applications such as project management packages can be very valuable for project managers on the move. It gives them real-time status on their projects on any given day. Figure 4.21 shows a screen of one such service.

Health Care

The health-care industry was among the first to take advantage of the wireless revolution. Wireless technology provides an effective information "glue" to link patient data to doctors and associated entities. Figures 4.22 and 4.23 provide an example of

Figure 4.21 Ask Project Gateway for a Palm device.

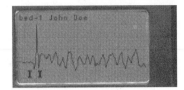

Figure 4.22   Data Critical Solution.
(Copyright © 2000, Data Critical)

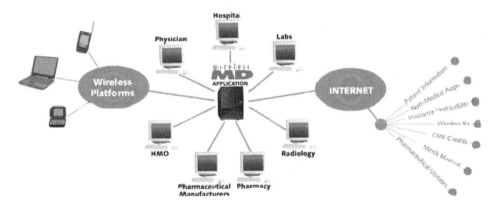

Figure 4.23   WirelessMD product architecture.
(Copyright © 2000, WirelessMD)

how two providers, Data Critical and Wireless MD, are using wireless technology to increase efficiency and improve productivity and decision making.

In this chapter, we looked at a wide range of applications and services used today across various vertical and horizontal industries. In the next chapter, we will learn about the technologies that make all these applications possible, as well as some upcoming advancements in the wireless Internet space.

CHAPTER 5

Technology Landscape

I n Chapter 4, we reviewed some of the applications and services that have been introduced into the wireless marketplace over the past few months. In this chapter, we review some of the technologies that are currently being used and that might be used in the next few years. Chapter 3 outlined some of these emerging technologies. In addition to discussing them in further detail here, we take a look at some of the other important technologies, such as the following:

COMPUTING TECHNOLOGIES

➤ Transcoding and markup languages (MLs)

➤ Wireless Application Protocol (WAP)

➤ Speech recognition

➤ Jini

➤ Moving Picture Experts Group 7 (MPEG7)

➤ IP-based technologies

➤ Compression and encryption

➤ Personalization

➤ Biometrics

➤ Smart Cards

➤ Synchronization

➤ Mobile agents

➤ Smart materials

➤ Micropayments

WIRELESS TECHNOLOGIES

➤ Short Message Service (SMS)

➤ Automatic identification and data capture technologies

➤ Wireless LAN/PAN technologies

➤ 2.5G and 3G wireless technologies

➤ Position location technologies

➤ Satellite technologies

➤ Smart antennas

Computing Technologies

Computing technologies such as the Internet have been at the center stage of technological evolution for the past few years. In addition, advancements in the areas of voice recognition, biometrics, smart materials, and security and the introduction of technologies such as WAP, personalization, and micropayments are fueling the growth of our technology-dependent economy. In this section, we review several of these technologies in further detail.

Transcoding and Markup Languages (MLs)

Transcoding is the transformation and reformatting of online content to match client (device) needs and user preferences. We learned in Chapter 2 that devices are limited by the size of their display screens, memory, processing power, and bandwidth, so it's critical that content delivered to the handset be exactly what the device is expecting and that the user is willing to pay for the delivered services. Remember, communication over the air interface costs users real money. The following are some of the potential approaches to resolving this content conundrum:

➤ *Redesigning the Web site.* Using this approach, content will have to be rewritten and reformatted for every popular markup language (HTML, XML, WML, Web Clipping, cHTML, and so on). This redesign is clearly difficult, tedious, and expensive to maintain and grow, and therefore is unacceptable.

➤ *Scripting.* Using this approach, you can write some scripts that extract information from an existing HTML site and convert the extracted data into the required markup language—for example, WML or VXML. If the Web site changes, the script also must change. The approach is not very flexible and is difficult to support in a fast-moving environment in which Web sites are changed almost daily.

➤ *Markup tags.* Device-specific markup tags can be embedded into existing Web sites so that when a particular (device-specific) browser reads the page, it can extract the information meant for the device. For a complex application, this approach can be a nightmare to support and maintain. Furthermore, with every new markup language, the pages and tags have to be rewritten. This is clearly not an acceptable way of doing things.

➤ *Rendering approach.* This technique allows for selected HTML or XML content on any Web site to convert it into a format that is deliverable to and usable by the mobile device. The rendering tool captures and extracts the underlying logic, rule set, and user interface (UI) elements associated with a particular set of Web content and converts that information into device-specific renderings. This approach has certain benefits. It uses the existing content, and it dynamically generates content for each client.

➤ *Middleware approach.* In this approach, a piece of software called *middleware* resides between database content and the application and devices. Using XSL (depending on the device capability, user preferences, and application), content is formatted dynamically to fit the application, device, user, and network needs.

Let's explore the middleware transcoding approach a bit further. Personalization (see the section called "Personalization" later in this chapter) has become key to any successful Web site implementation. To get a better understanding of transcoding, let's look at the desktop and device personalized communication model. Content consists of video, images, text, and audio; these elements represent the modality dimension of transcoding. The fidelity dimension represents the richness or complexity of the modality. To meet the needs of the devices, content must be transformed and reformatted along the dimensions of modality and fidelity. The translation methods could convert content between modalities, such as text to audio or video to still images. Along the same lines, content conversion could be done within the same modality but of different fidelity. For example, you could compress images, extract relevant text (from a lengthy text document), and extract key video frames, then reanimate them. This framework (termed *Infopyramid* by Smith, Mohan, Li, 1998), as depicted in Figure 5.1, allows for adapting to environmental needs in an efficient manner.

To fully understand the transcoding principle, you must understand how it works in the wireline world. In Internet-based applications, the information exchange between the client and the server takes place as follows (see Figure 5.2):

1. The Web browser requests a URL from the server.

2. The server requests information about the browser and the computer system.

3. The Web browser responds with capability and preference information (encapsulated in the header information).

4. The server (application) recognizing the capabilities, transforms and adapts the content on the fly, and transmits the content back to the browser.

Table 5.1 lists some of the capability and preference information on which an application can act. For example, if the client doesn't have a Shockwave plugin, the server shouldn't send a big Shockwave file, or if the client is connecting to the browser over a slower modem speed, the server should automatically decrease the intensity of the graphics and concentrate on text and streaming content. Content can be transformed to adapt to the device's screen size.

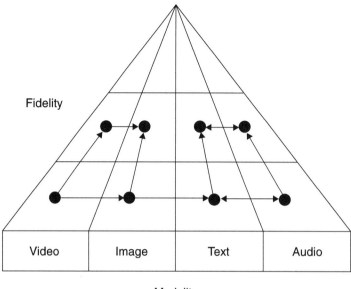

Figure 5.1 The Infopyramid.
(Copyright © 1998, IEEE. Smith, Mohan, Li, *Transcoding Internet Content for Heterogenous Client Devices*)

In the desktop world, there are two dominating browsers—Microsoft's Internet Explorer (IE) and Netscape's Navigator. There are three major operating systems (PC, Macintosh, and Unix. The browser variables that a server needs to track are many but still manageable. In the mobile world, however, there are multiple browsers and hundreds of system platforms (phones, PDAs, information appliances, and so on); each platform, browser, and language has its own intricacies. So, as you can imagine,

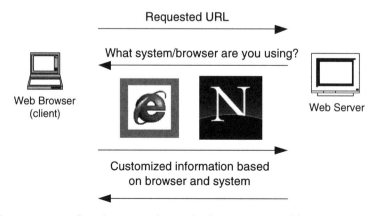

Figure 5.2 A client/server exchange in the Internet world.

Table 5.1   Browser Variables in the Internet World

HEADER INFORMATION
• Browser name, version, security, platform, CPU, connection type
• Component information (for example, language, animation, address book, media player, wallet, text-display support, and so on)
• Plugin information (for example, PDF, Shockwave, VRML, and so on)
• Cookies
• Screen information (size, height, width, pixel and color depth, and so on)
• Window information (size, width, buffering, frame rate, and so on)
• VBScript, Jscript information
• Hardware information (RAM, clock speed, architecture, and so on)
• Profile information
• User preferences
• Document information
• Date, time
• Fonts
• Mime types
• JVM information
• Application foundation classes information
• Internet Protocol (IP) information
• Style sheet information

content creation and management can quickly become a big challenge. Transcoding attempts to solve this very real, practical problem.

Let's discuss how WAP can use device capabilities and user preferences to enhance the user experience in the mobile environment. In WAP, the capability model is divided into the following five general categories:

➢ Hardware platform

➢ Software platform

➢ Network characteristics

➢ WAP capabilities

➢ Browser user agent

Table 5.2 lists some of the variables of these WAP capability categories that can be used to customize the user experience. For example, if the server knows a device's screen size, resolution, number of maximum lines displayed, software capabilities,

Table 5.2 Capability and Preference Variables in WAP

HARDWARE PLATFORM
• Vendor
• Model
• CPU
• User agent media
• Screen size
• Bits/pixel
• Maximum number of screen characters
• Screen size character
• Pointing resolution
• Keyboard
• Color capability
• Text capability
• Sound capability
• Image capability
• SoftKeys capability
• Input character set
• Output character set
• Voice Input (I/P) capability
SOFTWARE PLATFORM
• Recipient application agent
• Operating system vendor
• Software version
• Audio I/P encoder
• Video I/P encoder
• Accept downloadable software
• Java Virtual Machine (JVM) version
• Composite Capability and Preference Profiles (CCPP) Accept Language
• CCPP Accept
• CCPP Accept Charset
• CCPP Accept Encoding
• Mexe Classmark
• Mexe Spec

Table 5.2   *(Continued)*

NETWORK CHARACTERISTICS
• Terminal location
• Location encoding
• Current bearer service
• Supported bearers
• Security support

WAP CAPABILITIES
• WAP version
• WML version
• WMLScript version
• WMLScript libraries
• WTAI libraries
• WTA version
• WML deck size
• WAP device class
• WAP push message size
• WTA repository size
• Push message priority

BROWSER USER AGENT
• HTML version
• Browser version
• XHTML modules
• Browser name
• JavaScript version
• Tables capable
• Frames capable
• Preference for frames
• Downloadable software support

(Source: The WAP Forum)

network speed, user preferences, WAP version support, and location, the content delivered to the device can be customized to both the user as well as the device. If used cleverly, this information can also be used to detect and deter fraud. We will discuss this aspect in more detail in Chapter 8.

So, based on this analysis, the transcoding engine or content transformation engine needs to have the following key components:

➤ Content preference engine (server and client)

➤ Content analysis, selection, and manipulation

➤ Content translation

Transcoding is one of the most important aspects of mobile environments. If it is done incorrectly, even the best of business ideas won't translate into steady revenue streams; rather, they will quickly change into a customer support and churn nightmare. The good news is that relevant tools evolving in the marketplace today are continuously improving (please see Chapter 6 for more information).

The following sections discuss some of the prevalent and upcoming markup languages.

Web Clipping

Web Clipping is the proprietary language for Palm PDAs. Users can access specific content on the Internet over BellSouth's Mobitex network (Palm.net) or use OmniSky's data network (AT&T). Palm also offers email applications for Palm VII.

One of the key differences between Palm.net and WAP is that a WAP user can browse any Web site that handles WAP. Palm.net users, on the other hand, can access only those sites that have been stipulated as readable via a Palm Query Application (PQA), which must be first downloaded to the Palm device. Another main difference is that WAP applications can run over a wide range of networks—CDMA, TDMA, Mobitex, CDPD, GPRS, and so on. Numerous applications can be run on top of the Palm OS, including WAP applications or applications for accessing a corporate LAN.

Figure 5.3 presents a schematic of the Web Clipping network architecture. The two key design principles of Web Clipping are as follows:

➤ Information transfer (user navigation and interaction) is based on simple query and response (rather than hyperlinks). Each client request is in the form of a query back to the server.

➤ An application is partitioned so that the query portion resides on the PDA (PQA).

Synchronized Multimedia Markup Language (SMIL)

SMIL (pronounced *smile*) was created specifically to solve the problems of coordinating the display of a variety of media (multimedia) on Web sites. By using a single time line for all the media on a page, the display can be properly time-coordinated and synchronized (see Figure 5.4).

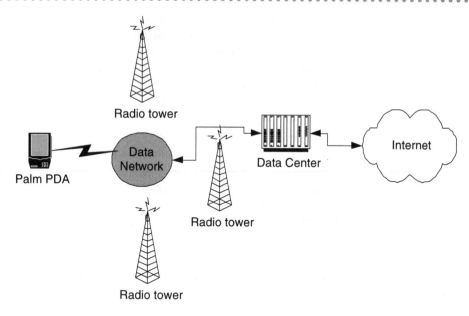

Figure 5.3   The Web Clipping network architecture.

Figure 5.4   SMIL example.

SMIL, which is based on XML, is intended to allow the easy implementation of sophisticated time-based multimedia content on the Web. Multimedia content can include recorded or live video and audio, static and dynamic images, and text—all simultaneously streamed to the client browser in a synchronized fashion (in other words, you can play multiple streams at the same time). Video, images, audio, and text can be available in different formats (AVI, JPG, GIF, AVI, WAV, AIFF, MOV, RAM, Flash, RealAudio, RealVideo, RealPix, RealText, HTML, AU, and so on). SMIL-based systems also take into consideration the network bandwidth and browser requirements and leverage existing Internet technologies.

SMIL provides a more interactive and entertaining user experience through rich media features. It's hard to envision multimedia clips playing on a wireless phone today, but within the next few years, with increased processing power, bandwidth, and network performance and improved battery life, it could be as normal as making a phone call.

The Advanced Television Enhancement Forum (ATVEF) and WebTV

The Advanced Television Enhancement Forum (ATVEF) is an open standards body focused on developing standards that stimulate the evolution of interactive television (ITV). The cross-alliance of industries includes representatives from broadcast and cable networks, cable and satellite service providers, consumer electronics, personal computers, and the software industries. The standards proposed by ATVEF ensure that consumers have a consistent user experience, irrespective of program, communication protocols, and hardware (brand of TV). Internet Protocol (IP) multicast ensures that interactive programming can be delivered over satellite, cable, broadcast, Internet, wireless network, and other technologies. ATVEF uses HTML and ECMAScript (a scripting language supported by all major browsers) from the European Computer Manufacturers Association (ECMA) and ensures that interactive content can be delivered to a wide variety of clients, including PDAs and wireless phones.

WebTV (see Figure 5.5) was designed in accordance with ATVEF standards. Interactive TV has a huge market potential; recognizing that, Microsoft bought WebTV in 1998. SMIL allows for TV-like experience on the Web, and WebTV enables Web-like experience on TV.

User Interface Markup Language (UIML)

UIML is a language for describing user interfaces in a highly device-independent manner. Similar to other markup languages, UIML is based on XML. In order to create a user interface, you can write an UIML document, which includes a presentation style appropriate for devices on which the UI will be deployed. UIML is then automatically mapped to a language used by the target device, such as HTML, WML, VXML, Java, and so on. The concept is very similar to the rendering and transcoding techniques we discussed earlier in this chapter. Figure 5.6 depicts the principle behind UIML.

Figure 5.5   WebTV example.

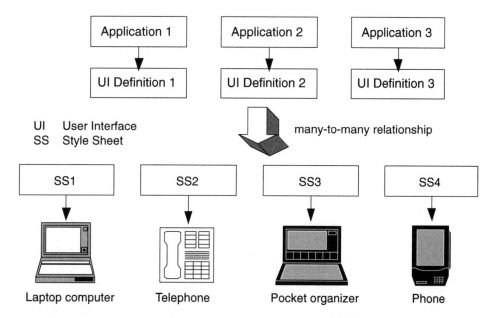

Figure 5.6   UIML architecture.

(Copyright © 2000, Universal Interface Technologies, Inc. www.universalit.com. All rights reserved.)

Voice-Extensible Markup Language (VXML)

VXML, also called VoiceXML, is an XML-based markup language for distributed voice applications, much as HTML is a language for distributed visual applications. VoiceXML is designed for creating audio dialogs that feature synthesized speech, digitized audio, recognition of spoken and dual-tone multifrequency (DTMF) key input, recording of spoken input, telephony, and mixed-initiative conversations. The goal is to provide voice access and interactive voice response (for example, by telephone, PDA, or desktop) to Web-based content and applications.

VoiceXML is being defined by an industry forum, the VoiceXML Forum, founded by AT&T, IBM, Lucent, and Motorola. VoiceXML brings the power of Web development and content delivery to voice response applications and frees the authors of such applications from low-level programming and resource management. It enables integration of voice services with data services using the familiar client/server paradigm, and it gives users the power to seamlessly transition between applications. The dialogs are provided by document servers, which can be external to the browser implementation platform. Figure 5.7 shows high-level VXML architecture.

Let's explore the VXML concept through an example:

```
---------------------
<?xml version="1.0"?>
<vxml version="1.0">

    <form id="login" dtmf="true">
        <field name="account_holder_name" type="digits">
        <dtmf src="builtin:dtmf/digits"/>

            <prompt>
                Hello, and welcome to <emp>Friendly Bank</emp><break
size="small"/>
            </prompt>

            <prompt>
                Please enter your account number <enumerate/>
            </prompt>
        </field>

        <filled>
            <submit next="servlet/verifyaccount"/>
        </filled>

        <field name="pin">
        <dtmf src="builtin:dtmf/digits"/>
        <prompt>
                Welcome Prem Lata Sharma, please enter your pin
        </prompt>
        </field>

        <filled>
```

```
            <submit next="/servlet/login"/>
        </filled>

        <field name="options">

            <prompt>
                You can access your checking or savings account,
                Transfer funds, have a statement emailed, mailed, or
                faxed to you.
                Please say your option
            </prompt>
            <grammar>
                checking [account]| savings [account]| transfer [funds]
                | email [statement]| mail [statement]| fax [statement]
            </grammar>
        </field>

        <filled>
            <submit next="/servlet/options"/>
        </filled>
    </form>
</vxml>
```

The sample computer-human interaction based on the preceding takes place as follows:

```
Computer>>  Hello, and welcome to Friendly Bank.
            Please enter your account number.<<
```

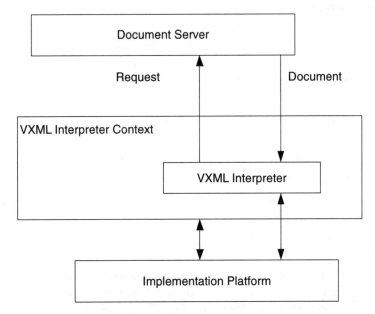

Figure 5.7   VXML architecture.
Courtesy of the VoiceXML Forum (www.voicexml.org)

```
Human>>      1234567890<<
Computer>>   Welcome Prem Lata Sharma, please enter your pin.<<
Human>>      007<<
Computer>>   You can access your checking or savings account, transfer
             funds, have a statement emailed, faxed or mailed to you.
             Please say your option.<<
Human>>      email statement<<
```

The conversation continues to the email_statement of the VXML document.

VXML provides a mechanism to interact with information using the human voice. Voice-based navigation systems are essential in designing good user-experience navigation. When combined with other markup languages such that data drives voice and voice drives data, VXML helps reduce the impact of constraints imposed by wireless devices and networks.

NOTE

Some of the other specialized markup languages include the following:

VML. Vector Markup Language

PGML. Precision Graphics Markup Language

MathML. Mathematical Markup Language

ChemML. Chemical Markup Language

Wireless Application Protocol

Chapter 3 introduced us to WAP and its programming model. In this section, we take a further look at the components that make up WAP (see Figure 5.8). WAP architecture is drawn from Open Systems Interconnection (OSI) was introduced by the International Standards Organization (ISO).

OSI deals with connecting open systems and observes the following principles (Tanenbaum, 1996):

➤ A layer should be created where a different level of abstraction is needed.

➤ Each layer should perform a well-defined function.

➤ The function of each layer should be chosen with an eye toward defining internationally standardized protocols.

➤ The layer boundaries should be chosen to minimize the information flow across the interfaces.

➤ The number of layers should be large enough that distinct functions need be thrown together in the same layer out of necessity and small enough that the architecture does not become unwieldy.

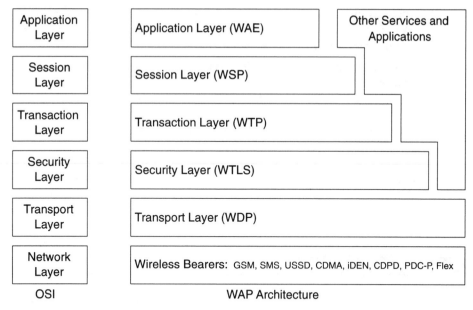

Figure 5.8   WAP architecture.

WAP is made up of the following layers:

➤ *Wireless Application Environment (WAE).* This top layer consists of the following components:

  ➤ A microbrowser specification

  ➤ Wireless Markup Language (WML), based on XML; provides support for text and images and Wireless Bitmap Format (WBMP), user input, user navigation, multiple languages, and state and context management features

  ➤ WMLScript, a scripting language very similar to JavaScript that extends WML's functionality

  ➤ Wireless Telephony Applications (WTA), which provides the framework for accessing telephony commands using WML and WMLScript

➤ *Wireless Session Protocol (WSP).* WSP is very similar to HTTP and is designed specifically for low-bandwidth, high-latency wireless networks. As discussed in Chapter 3, WSP facilitates the transfer of content between WAP client and WAP gateway in a binary format. Additional functionalities include content push and suspension/resumption of connections.

➤ *Wireless Transactional Protocol (WTP).* WTP provides the functionality similar to Transmission Control Protocol/Internet Protocol (TCP/IP) in the Internet model. WTP is a lightweight transactional protocol that allows for reliable request/response transactions and supports unguaranteed and guaranteed push.

➤ *Wireless Transport Layer Security (WTLS).* WTLS is based on Transport Layer Security (TLS, formerly known as Secure Sockets Layer, or SSL). It provides data integrity, privacy, authentication, and denial-of-service protection mechanisms. WTLS can be invoked in a way similar to the way you would invoke HTTPS in the Internet world.

➢ *Wireless Datagram Protocol (WDP).* WDP provides an interface to the bearers of transportation. It supports CDPD, GSM, Integrated Digital Enhanced Network (iDEN), CDMA, TDMA, SMS, and FLEX protocols.

WAP is an important step toward highly interactive multimedia delivered to wireless phones. It's in the early stages of specification and needs more work. Eventually, WAP will either converge into standards such as SMIL and XHTML or evolve to include the functionality of these standards. WAP, combined with technologies such as mobile agents, position location, and voice recognition, can deliver enormous value to business users and consumers alike.

Speech Recognition

By 2001, voice interface will become an expected option in retrieving Internet-based content.

–GARTNER GROUP, NOV 1999

Speech recognition software, equipment, and services will grow to $22.6 billion in 2003.

–SPEECH RECOGNITION UPDATE, 2000

Speech recognition is a computer's ability to receive and understand (process) spoken commands and words. Speech recognition is often confused with *voice recognition,* which is a computer's ability to recognize a specific voice or speaker and is used for security and authentication purposes (see the "Biometrics" section of this chapter for more information).

Speech recognition systems have two functions:

➢ Understanding the words being spoken and then converting them into text for further use

➢ Converting text to speech for the purposes of information access

The second function is easier to do than the first. We discussed the second in more detail in the VXML section earlier in this chapter. Speech recognition is a convenient way for the user to input data. It can be very valuable for people with disabilities or for operating devices under constrained environments (such as interacting with an autoPC or phone while driving car) or with constrained devices (such as phones or PDAs). Speech recognition is often confused with speech or language understanding applications, in which computer programs try to interpret the meaning of spoken words rather than just identifying the words. Language understanding by computing devices is still far from implementation in commercial environments.

There are three basic components of speech recognition:

➤ Capture and preprocessing

➤ Recognition and feature extraction

➤ Communication with other application software and hardware

Figure 5.9 shows a diagram of the speech recognition process. Speech is an analog signal; to be used in computerized systems, this signal needs to be captured and converted into digital format (spectral representation and segmentation). Once the signal is captured, computer algorithms analyze the acoustic signals and recognize common sound patterns, called *phonemes*. Any language, including the sounds of the alphabet themselves and their pairings such as "ao" and "sh," can be broken down into phonemes. Words, phrases, and sentences can be represented digitally as sequences of these phonemes. Once the speech signal is segmented, phoneme probability (that is, the probability that a particular phoneme represents what was spoken) is calculated. Based on this statistical analysis, words are reconstructed by matching the phonetic sounds to the lexical database. Complex neural network programs are used to accurately predict the sequence of the words that make up a conversation or a sentence. After speech input has been identified, it is communicated to the application software or speech-aware applications for further processing.

Speech recognition in and of itself is an extremely powerful tool to enhance usability of input-challenged devices, but when used in concert with technologies such as WAP, it can prove a market shaker and can instantly help create hundreds of new and interesting applications. For example, both speech- and WML-based menus could be used to enhance user navigational experience to locate the desired information in an acceptable number of steps: Instead of clicking through a menu on a device screen,

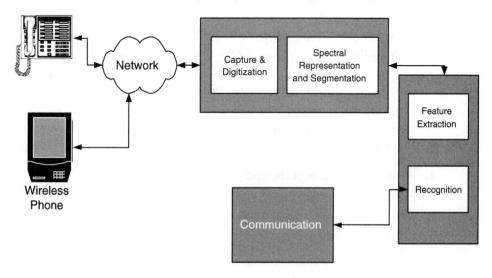

Figure 5.9 The speech recognition process.

you could go directly to the third-level menu item by issuing a simple voice command. The challenge is to design voice and text navigation in such a way that the elements are distinct enough.

NOTE

Speech-based technologies can be classified as the following:

Speech processing. **Conversion of speech into text.**

Speech synthesis. **Conversion of text into speech.**

Machine translation (MT). **Translation from one language into another.**

Natural language processing (NLP). **Understanding of human language and grammar.**

Successful implementation of popular wireless Internet solutions will depend on the seamlessness with which speech technologies can be integrated into the applications and services.

Jini

Jini is the brainchild of Bill Joy, founder and chief scientist of Sun Microsystems. Jini is a distributed computing environment for network plug-and-play capabilities. The concept is similar to the Service Location Protocol (SLP), which helps announce device presence to a network by communicating with the other devices within the network. Some of the scenarios are as follows [source: Newmarch, 2000]:

➤ A new fax machine connected to a network can announce its capabilities. A PDA can then use this fax machine without having to be specially configured to do so.

➤ A digital camera is connected to a network. Its user interface could be aware of the presence of a printer in the vicinity and could automatically present that option without the need for user setup and configuration of the printer.

➤ If new capabilities are added to the hardware, these capabilities can be automatically communicated to the other network devices.

➤ Services can also announce changes in their state. A fax machine could tell a user when it is running out of paper, or a printer could alert the user when its toner is running low.

There are five key concepts behind Jini [source: Edwards, 1999]:

➤ Discovery
➤ Lookup
➤ Leasing
➤ Remote event
➤ Transactions

Discovery is the process by which network devices introduce themselves to the network by announcing their presence and capabilities. Jini supports multiple situations with the use of multicast request, multicast announcement, and unicast discovery protocols. *Lookup* is the ability of devices to find the services and network functionality devices are looking for. Extending our previous example of a printer and a PDA, the PDA would query the network community for a device that is capable of printing.

The network devices together make what is called a *Jini community of devices*. In case of machine crashes and network failures, it's critical for the community to self-heal and come back to its original configuration so that disruption in services is minimal. To get around this disruption problem, Jini uses a technique called *leasing*, in which the access is loaned for a fixed period of time rather than granted for an unlimited amount of time. If there is no interest in services for a given device, the lease expires. This resource allocation expiration helps to avoid stale states of network devices in case of disruption.

Network devices change in state all the time. A printer could need new toner, a fax machine could run out of paper, a new hard disk could be added to a computing device, and so on. State information is communicated to other devices through *remote events*. Finally, *transactions* are a way to allow communications and computations between various devices, such as printing, faxing, and emailing.

The vision of Jini is to enable any device—from toasters to enterprise servers—to be networked smoothly and reliably. A rival technology in this area is Universal Plug and Play from Microsoft.

Motion Picture Experts Group 7 (MPEG7)

MPEG was founded in 1993 to codify noninteractive video compression. Over the years, various MPEG standards have evolved, and their relevance to wireless is increasing. The various MPEG standards and their purposes are listed in Table 5.3.

MPEG7 sets out description standards for content identification. These standards allow automated image searching based on tags. Imagine being able to search twenty years' worth of photographs or a generation of video recordings using an image search engine. You would be able to search movies based on famous lines such as, "I'll be back," or you could simply download a particular favorite scene. This increased volume of audio/visual interactive data can launch the following business and consumer applications [source: MPEG-7 Applications Document, 1999]:

➤ Education

➤ Journalism (for example, searching speeches of a certain politician using his or her name, voice, or face)

➤ Tourist information

➤ Cultural services (history museums, art galleries)

➤ Entertainment (searching a game or a karaoke database)

➤ Investigation services (human characteristics/recognition, forensics)

➤ Geographical information systems

Table 5.3 MPEG Standards

STANDARD	PURPOSE
MPEG1	CD-ROM compression standard
MPEG2	Digital video broadcasting and digital versatile disk compression standard
MPEG3	Officially, MPEG2 Layer 3, but now known as MP3, the audio streaming standard
MPEG4	Audio and video streaming and complex media manipulation
MPEG5	Multimedia hypermedia standard (MPEG4 for set-top boxes)
MPEG7	Standard for content analysis, identification, and description
MPEG21	Network quality, content quality, conditional access rights (multimedia umbrella standard)

(Copyright © 1998, RTT Programmes)

➢ Remote sensing (cartography, ecology, natural resource management)
➢ Surveillance
➢ Biomedical applications
➢ Shopping (searching for clothes you like)
➢ Architecture, real estate, and interior design
➢ Social (clubs and dating services)
➢ Film, video, and radio archives

Rich data available with complex multimedia content will enable this content to be brought closer to wireless devices by on-the-fly transcoding (the transformation of content into different markup language formats). For example, a video can be described by text-to-speech translation rather than shipping the video file to the phone over the wireless network. Both push and pull types of applications will benefit from the MPEG7 standard. In addition, when used in concert with other technologies—for example, multimedia applications working with position location coordinates—MPEG7 information and value delivered to the user can be enormous.

IP-Based Technologies

All servers and devices on the public Internet are identified by a 4-byte numerical value known as an *IP address*. The format is in a series of four 1-byte values separated by periods, such as 207.25.71.23 (the IP address corresponding to www.cnn.com). An

IP address can be assigned to a desktop, a UNIX server, a router, a firewall, even wireless phones. IP address assignment can be permanent or temporary. IP-based communication has become the key building block of the Internet economy. Here we discuss some of the new technologies in the IP space.

Mobile IP

Mobile IP provides IP-based routing for the mobile environment. This enhancement to IP allows for devices such as laptops to "talk" to their networks even though their point of attachment might change from one subnet to another. Essentially, mobile IP enables all information (packets) to be routed to the original IP address.

Internet Protocol Version 6 (IPv6)

IPv6, or IPng (for IP next generation), is the next version of the current IPv4 protocol and is designed to solve the problem of running out of IP addresses. IPv4 uses 32-bit numbers, which allows for only 4 billion distinct network addresses. Due to the proliferation of the Internet, we are quickly running out of those addresses. IPv6 uses 128-bit addresses, which allow for about 340 trillion trillion trillion unique addresses, enough to assign every known thing on earth an IP address. IPv6 also allows for QoS and strong packet-level encryption features.

IPsec

IP is at the heart of Internet traffic. However, one thing that IP doesn't provide is security. IPsecurity (IPsec) is a suite of protocols designed with security in mind. IPsec integrates security into IP and provides data source authentication, data integrity, confidentiality, and protection against replay attacks.

VoIP/FoIP

Since voice calls can be broken up into small packets for transmission purposes, the Internet can be used for transporting and reassembling these packets, thus providing an effective way to relay voice calls over the Internet. Internet call routing can be done by completely or partially bypassing the existing Public Switched Telephone Network (PSTN). The voice-over-IP (VoIP) process works as follows:

1. First, the voice calls are converted from analog into digital format by a *codec*. This can be done using software or hardware, depending on the implementation.

NOTE
A *codec* (compression/decompression) is the software that compresses audio and video for sending the content to a destination and then decompresses at the destination for recovery of the content.

2. The digitally encoded voice is then encapsulated within small IP packets to be carried over the IP network.

3. The IP packets are decoded on the other end and converted back into analog voice format.

The same process is applicable to fax over IP (FoIP) because the system doesn't distinguish between data and voice. VoIP can interface with the PSTN using VoIP-to-PSTN gateways, which allow for conversion of the packets into an applicable format. Figure 5.10 shows a high-level VoIP/FoIP network architecture.

VoIP can provide significant savings for corporations, especially companies with multiple geographically dispersed offices. If you have already invested in connecting your staff over a common IP network, you can utilize the investment by allocating some percentage of processing time to voice-based traffic. So, if your sales, marketing, technical, and executive staff travel from office to office, instead of paying roaming and long distance phone charges, they can connect over the corporation's IP network.

HTTP-NG

HTTP/1.X is the underlying protocol used in a majority of Web communications. However, it's not very modular. For example, with HTTP1.0, if an HTML document contains text and twenty embedded images, it will take twenty-one exchanges between server and browser to construct the document at the user end. This problem was fixed with HTTP/1.1, but the specification is still fairly complex and inefficient in

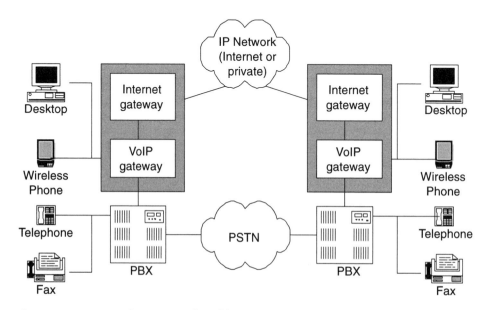

Figure 5.10   A VoIP/FoIP network architecture.

terms of accomplishing simple tasks. There is still a lot of protocol overhead that can be improved upon by making the HTTP protocol more modular. Doing so will lead to better caching, connection management, scalability, and network efficiency.

The HTTP-NG activity is proposing a new architecture for the Web infrastructure based on an approach in which HTTP is split into layers, as depicted in Figure 5.11.

The basic design goal for the new work is to separate HTTP into three distinct layers:

➤ Message transport

➤ Remote invocation

➤ Web application

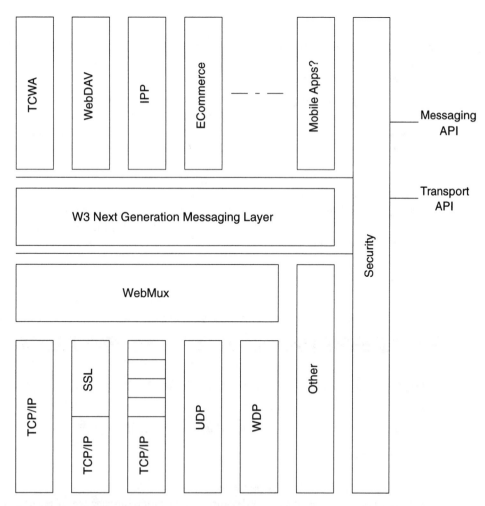

Figure 5.11 The HTTP-NG architecture.

Copyright © 1998 W3C (MIT, INRIA, Keio), All Rights Reserved.

HTTP-NG is a significant step forward in the W3C's pursuit of realizing the full potential of the Web. Today there are many applications people would like to see on the Web that either cannot be implemented or are simply too complex to deploy in the current infrastructure; HTTP-NG could make those applications possible.

Compression and Encryption

Compression of data (or content, which can be audio, text, image, or video) is necessary to optimize its transmission, storage, and latency. The more you can compress the data, the higher the possible data transmission speed. Increased compression also means that if errors occur, recovery costs are higher. Typical compression rates for various kinds of content are given in Table 5.4.

Today's encryption options are as follows:

Data Encryption Standard (DES). One of the most common encryption techniques, DES uses the same key for both encryption as well as decryption (a symmetric cipher). Both parties need to know the key.

Asymmetric cipher. RSA (after Rivest, Shamir, and Adelman) requires different keys for encryption and decryption (an asymmetric cipher). It is used in cases in which sender and recipient don't have any prearrangement. The security of RSA is based on the difficulty in factoring the product of two very large prime numbers. Since different keys are used for encryption and decryption, you can encrypt a message using your private key and someone can decrypt the message using your public key. The drawback of RSA is that it is slow and can operate only on data up to the size of the modulus of its key. A 1024-bit RSA public key can only encrypt data that is less than or equal to that size. So, RSA is unsuitable for bulk data encryption. RSA patents expire in 2000.

Table 5.4 Compression Rates for Various Types of Content

CONTENT	COMPRESSION
Voice	8:1 (GSM) to 20:1 (TETRA)
Image	Lossless 3:1, lossy 40:1
Text	4:1
Video	500:1 (fractal compression)

(Source: RTT Programmes)

Notes:

Lossy means the transmission doesn't preserve the original data.

Lossless transmission preserves the original data (necessary for medical imaging and image archiving such as that done in museums).

Compression can also be used for encryption.

Pretty Good Privacy (PGP). PGP is the encryption program developed by Phil Zimmerman and is freely available on the Internet. RSA and PGP, when implemented with extended key lengths, are computationally secure.

Public key cryptography. This technique can be used for authentication purposes by constructing a digital signature.

Steganography. Steganography is the technique of hiding one format of data inside another. For example, you might hide or embed audio files in an image or hide text information within a video file. Unlike encryption, which hides the content of a message, steganography hides the mere fact that anything is hidden.

Personalization

Personalization is person-specific content. Personalized content can be advertising, items for sale, a screen layout, menus, news articles, applications, or anything else we see via the Internet. In addition, personalization also refers to a user's customized navigational and interactional experience.

Personalization is the result of technology integrated into a Web site that allows the server to dynamically modify what is presented to each viewer. With personalization technology, two individuals accessing the same Web site simultaneously could see two completely different sets of information based on their profiles and preferences.

Personalization takes a variety of forms, identified here as two major categories. From simplest to most complex, they are:

➤ Customization by name

➤ Implicit customization:

    ➤ Configuration

    ➤ Segmentation and rules-based customization

➤ Explicit customization

These methods can coexist. Each type has a specific purpose, and two or more can be blended to produce a seamless, comprehensive personalized experience at a Web site.

Customization by Name and Address

Name recognition, such as "junk" email addressed to John Rivers, is familiar to anyone who receives unsolicited printed material in the mail. This sort of mass personalization is similar to three-dimensional junk mail addressed to "Dear Homeowner at 123 Main Street." However, a few years ago this type of email marked a turning point in mass-marketing techniques. Name recognition continues to be used because it still has value; most people like to be acknowledged by name.

Implicit Personalization

Implicit personalization uses the personal information provided by the user, such as name, address, telephone number, personal preferences, hobbies, age, and so on. Based on this personal information, the server dynamically generates user-specific content. Essentially, the whole user population is divided into classes that are defined by some characteristics. For example, a bank could classify its Web site users as one of the following:

➢ High income, low-risk investments

➢ High income, high-risk investments

➢ Low income, low-risk investments

➢ Low income, high-risk investments

Based on the category a user falls into, customized content is displayed to each user. Customized content could include news items, stock tips, investment ideas and techniques, portfolio recommendations, and so on. This customization is very useful for the consumer because he or she is presented with targeted information and avoids the hassle of having to search for it on his or her own and avoids being sent unwanted, useless information.

Configuration or Check-Box Personalization

Check box is the short name for user-provided information. *Configuration-based personalization* is gathered from questionnaires, surveys, registration forms, and other solicitations in which the user answers specific questions. An example is the Web site registration page for a software purchase. Registration forms often ask for information about the program you just bought as well as additional information, such as store location, whether the purchase is for home or business use, whether you're the head of household, your annual income, and so on. You check the box beside the appropriate answers. A Web site using check-box personalization presents ongoing content based on your answers.

Segmentation and Rules

Segmentation and *rules-based personalization* use demographic, geographic, interest profile, or other information to divide or segment large populations into smaller groups. Data such as income level, geographic location, and buying history is aggregated to identify groups of people. Web sites using these types of personalization systems deliver content based on *if this, then that* rules processing.

Explicit Personalization, or Almost Real-Time Personalization

Explicit personalization refers to personalization based on click-stream data collected from the user. Click-stream data gives information about a user's interaction with Web content (including flashy advertisements). So, if a user has already read the content or if the user doesn't read or respond to the content even after several iterations of display, the content is either taken off future displays or recustomized for the next time the user visits the page or the site.

Some preference-based personalization systems are learning systems that become more precise over time. A news Web site using preference-based personalization might follow this sequence for content delivery: *Repeat visitor Hilary Shodack clicked on Seattle weather for 2 seconds, then clicked on the Seattle Mariners advertisement banner and searched for Microsoft's stock quotes during her previous visit. Therefore, the Web page will load Seattle's weather forecast, Mariners season performance and ticketing information for upcoming games, and the analyst report and news on Boeing at the top of the page on her next visit.*

We have increasingly seen almost all the major Web sites using personalization to attract and retain customers and partners. As you can imagine, serving personalized content becomes even more important for wireless devices. Future personalization technologies will have to adapt to displaying content onto multiple devices owned by the same user.

As displayed in Figure 5.12, personalization essentially amounts to data mining and business intelligence from the sources of server logs, user preferences, device preferences, click-stream data, and ecommerce history. Business rules need to be applied to the analysis of data to produce personalized content.

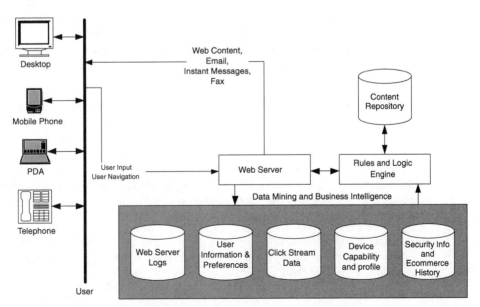

Figure 5.12   A personalization framework.

NOTE

Data mining is the analysis of data for relationships that have not previously been discovered. For example, the sales records for a particular brand of a wireless phone, if sufficiently analyzed and related to other market data, reveal a correlation of age groups of customers.

Business intelligence (BI) is a broad category of applications and technologies for gathering, storing, analyzing, and providing access to data to help enterprise users make intelligent business decisions. Sample applications include data mining, statistical analysis, online transactional processing, and knowledge management.

Biometrics

Biometrics is the science of using a unique, measurable characteristic or trait of a human being to automatically recognize or verify identity. As an illustration of this concept, Let's take a look at the types of security techniques available:

➤ What do you have? (ID, photo, and so on)

➤ What do you know? (Passwords and personal identification numbers, or PINs)

➤ Who are you? (Biometrics)

Individual humans are unique, and so are their physical and behavioral traits. By successfully extracting the measurable information from these traits, we can map an individual using that extracted information for verification and identification purposes. Although biometrics has been around for a while, it has only recently started gaining some traction with the computing and communications industry for consumer applications.

Figure 5.13 shows the operation of a typical biometric system. All biometric systems essentially operate in the same fashion. First, a biometric system captures a sample of the biometric characteristic. Then unique features are extracted and converted into mathematical code. Depending on the needs and technology, multiple samples can be taken to build the confidence level of the initial data. This data is stored as the biometric template for that person. When identity needs to be checked, the person interacts with the biometric system. Data on the person's features is extracted and compared with the stored information for validation.

Types of biometric identification systems available today can be classified as face recognition, finger scanning, hand geometry, finger geometry, iris recognition, and palm, retina, signature, and voice biometrics.

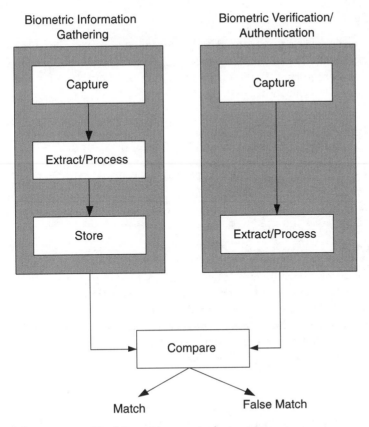

Figure 5.13   The biometrics comparison process.

Face Recognition

Face recognition technologies analyze the unique shape, pattern, and positioning of facial features. This technology is fairly complex and is mostly software based. Capture is done using video or thermal means. The latter is more expensive because it requires expensive infrared cameras. The main advantage of this thermal technique is that it is hands-free. This approach could be preferable in situations in which human/machine interaction needs to be minimal—for example, under dangerous or harsh climatic conditions.

Finger Scanning

Finger scanning is one of the most commonly used biometric technologies. It uses analysis of minute points such as finger image ridge endings, or *bifurcations* (branches made by ridges). Automated fingerprint identification systems (AFIS) are already being installed on a variety of devices such as desktop PCs and wireless phones from Sagem.

Hand Geometry

The three-dimensional images captured by hand geometry systems are unique and can be highly accurate. This technique has been used with considerable success at high-profile events requiring strict security, such as the Olympics, and in security-intensive places such as airports.

Finger Geometry

Finger geometry is much less a dominant market force than finger imaging but is particularly well proven in the area of physical access control, regulating the movement of people within a secure area. This technique is suited to large-scale, high-volume applications such as secure areas or airport check-in.

Iris Recognition

Iris recognition is one of two biometric techniques that focus on the eye; the other is retina scanning. The iris is the colored ring of textured tissue that surrounds the pupil of the eye. Because of the unique characteristics found in the iris, capture of information about it provides over 200 independent variables that can be compared, making it a highly accurate biometric system. Because of this accuracy, iris recognition is a good candidate for network access authentication.

Palm Biometrics

Palm biometrics is similar to finger scanning. An abundance of minute data is found in the human palm, making this technology useful for criminal and civil applications. Palm systems are often integrated with AFIS technology to provide law enforcement with a complete crime detection kit.

Retina Biometrics

The retina is the layer of blood vessels situated at the back of the eye. The biometric technique used to capture data from the retina is often thought to be the most convenient for end users. An end user must focus on a green dot while the system uses a harmless beam of light to capture the unique retina characteristics. Retina biometric systems are often considered some of the most unbeatable security systems.

Signature Biometrics

Signature biometrics are primarily concerned with the study of dynamic characteristics—the movement of the pen during the signing process rather than the static image of the signature. Experts can study many aspects of the signature in motion, such as pen pressure, the sound the pen makes against paper, or the angle of the pen. This study of signatures is very much a behavioral biometric. Tablet-based systems are widely deployed in the United States and elsewhere.

Voice Biometrics

Voice biometrics combine the physical and behavioral characteristics of an individual. This technology is different from speech recognition. Voice biometrics goes beyond speech and identifies the speaker of the words. Techniques such as measuring change of frequency between phonemes can be used. Voice-based speaker verification has applications in wireless networks, voicemail, interactive voice response (IVR), calling cards, and so on.

Figure 5.14 compares accuracy of various biometric technologies.

False Rejection and False Acceptance

The efficiency of a biometric system is measured by its accuracy for identifying authorized individuals and rejecting unauthorized people. The *false rejection rate (FRR)* is the number of instances that an authorized individual is falsely rejected by the system. The *false acceptance rate* (FAR) refers to the number of instances a nonauthorized individual is falsely accepted by the system. Often biometric systems allow you to configure the FRR and FAR variables. Typical values of FRR and FAR are close to 1 percent.

In March 1999, the Human Authentication API, Biometric API (BAPI), and BioAPI specification groups joined to combine their efforts into a BioAPI organization. This organization consists of representatives from various technology, health care, finance, and government sectors.

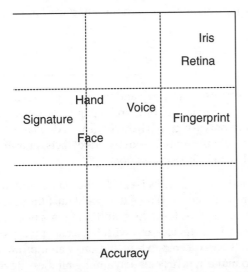

Figure 5.14   Accuracy of various biometric technologies.

Smart Cards

The popularity of smart cards emerged from the successful implementation and proliferation of the GSM wireless standard in Europe and elsewhere. Smart cards are essentially integrated circuit cards containing memory and microprocessor processing power that can be used for a variety of applications: from simple telephone cards to storage devices for patient data. Since you can store encrypted data on them, they also find a use in many user authentication schemes. In GSM, for example, smart cards were and are being used for authentication and security purposes. A unique secret key is stored in the smart card, which interacts with the wireless network authentication center to validate the card's ownership and rightful services.

Smart cards can also contain biometric information such as a voiceprint or fingerprint for providing highly secure procedures. With advances in semiconductor and processing technologies, it's possible to put more and more memory and processing power into the thin smart cards—they are literally their own computers. Smart cards will become increasingly multipurpose, and a variety of applications will reside on them. Smart cards can be used to authenticate network users (on corporate, private, banking, and public networks) and for storing personal data such as address books or personal memos. The cards can even be used in cars to store vehicle information that can be transmitted to the driver's auto shop to facilitate repairs. Smart cards, in concert with wireless technology, can be a highly effective means of storing and transferring information.

Depending on the type of applications and data that need to go onto the smart card, smart cards can be built to be tamper-resistant. If a crook tries to break into the card for data or secret keys, the card will destroy the data residing there. Due to low costs and high functionality, smart cards have been and will continue to be an important part of both the computing and communications technology landscapes. Figure 5.15 shows the processing and memory requirements for various smart card applications.

Synchronization

In the pervasive computing world, one user can carry and use multiple devices: a computer at home and work, a PDA, a wireless phone, and a pager elsewhere. Once information appliances become more pervasive, this list will grow. An *information appliance* is an appliance specializing in information—knowledge, facts, graphics, audio, video—and that has the ability to share information.

One obvious problem facing information appliances is *synchronization*. Standards such as Bluetooth and SyncML were initiated to resolve this problem. Simple things such as address book, phone numbers, emails, to-do lists, and calendars need to be synchronized continuously among various devices and with the least amount of inconvenience to the user. Users can't be expected to buy and carry an inordinate number of connectors and cables to make synchronization among all these devices possible. If pervasive computing is to be embraced as widely as predicted by industry pundits, synchronization is absolutely the key to wide acceptance. We will discuss some of the synchronization product offerings in the next chapter.

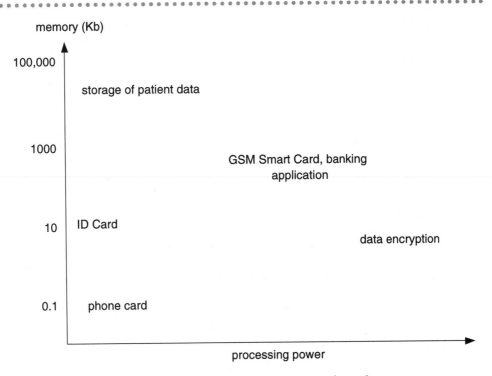

Figure 5.15   Processing power and memory requirements for various smart card applications.

(Copyright © 1997, Rankl, Effing. *Smart Card Handbook*, John Wiley & Sons, Limited)

Mobile Agents

Mobile agents are software programs that can move through a network and autonomously execute tasks on behalf of users. These devices are useful due to the quantity of information content on the Internet, which is exploding at a breathtaking pace. Hundreds of Web sites are created every minute; countless documents are loaded onto intranets and extranets. Furthermore, seemingly useful information resides in disparate databases. Hence we need intelligent information agents that can act like secretaries and help do the legwork that is often required in information mining. *Information agents* can go even further than mobile agents and can accomplish a sequence of tasks.

We have already begun to see some form of mobile agents being implemented by various online businesses. For example, many online comparison engines utilize agents that go out into cyberspace and bring back pricing and item availability information in real time or on a predetermined frequent basis. Mobile agents are also used for discovering, updating, and indexing content for various search engines. These mobile agents are also referred to as *bots* or derivatives (such as *shopbots*), a term related to *robots*. According to a survey conducted by Neilsen NetRatings, shopbots were the second-fastest growing ecommerce market segment during the 1999 holiday shopping season. Agents are also used for personalizing Web content. Software agents can mine the plethora of user- and device-specific databases and quickly generate a dynamic page as the user clicks through the site.

These mobile agents are generally based on fuzzy logic or artificial intelligence algorithms that train the agents to behave in a certain way, depending on the request or input they receive from the user's navigation patterns. In some of the more sophisticated setups, mobile agents of one system can interact with mobile agents of another system (even systems belonging to different companies) to negotiate for the best rates or deals on products or services. In the future, mobile agents will be able to handle much more complex transactions. So far, agent technology has been limited to the desktop environment, but agent technology is gradually moving in its natural progression to wireless devices.

In this section we consider an example to further explain the migration of intelligent agents to wireless devices. MySimon.com is a Web site that helps users comparison shop. A user enters the name of a product he or she wants to explore, and the mobile agents go to merchants' sites for the real-time pricing and availability information. This way, the user doesn't have to travel to multiple merchant sites to figure out the best rates available. Similarly, mobile agents can be used to search multiple enterprise information sources using a single user interface. Figure 5.16 shows a search done for Palm V handhelds at mySimon.com.

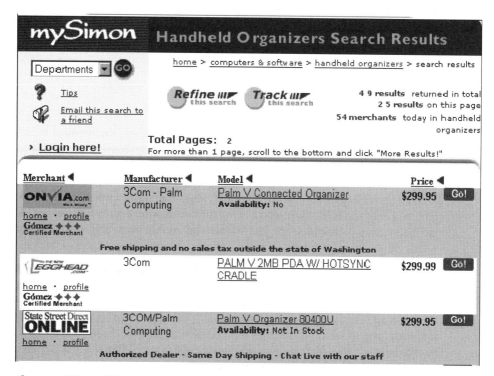

Figure 5.16   mySimon.com, a site that uses mobile agents.

The mobile agent concept can be further expanded to the execution of multiple tasks and, more interestingly, to coordination and negotiation among the various tasks.

Smart Materials

With miniaturization of computing processors, it's possible to embed small processors in materials. *Electronic ink*, or *Eink*, is one example of this technology.

Eink

Electronic ink is a new material that will have far-reaching impact on how we receive and process information online. Eink technology is essentially an electronic paper technology in which Eink microcapsules are coated on a surface. These microcapsules can be controlled remotely to display a message of your choice. Electronic paper and Eink look and feel just like real paper and ink. The difference is that the electronic paper could change, much like the characters on a computer screen can change. If you bind 200 such pages of electronic paper coated with Eink, you have a book that never needs to be thrown away. Any time there are updates to the book's information or if you want to replace the content, you merely plug it into a phone line or wireless receiver and the entire content of the book could be changed in an instant. So, you could distribute product brochures and manuals to your employees, customers, and partners once, and all the updates and changes could be managed remotely, all at the same time. Or, you can buy a single copy of an Eink-enabled newspaper or book and use that copy to upload customized content on demand, over and over again. This technology could have far-reaching effects on the publishing and media industry.

The ink itself is a liquid that can be printed onto nearly any surface (paper, plastic, or metal). Within the liquid are millions of tiny microcapsules, each one containing white particles suspended in a dark dye. When an electric field is applied, the white particles move to one end of the microcapsule where they become visible. This movement makes the surface appear white at that spot. An opposite electric field pulls the particles to the other end of the microcapsules, where they are hidden by the dye. This movement makes the surface appear dark at that spot.

To form an electronic display, the ink is printed onto a sheet of plastic film that is laminated to a layer of circuitry. The circuitry forms a pattern of pixels that can then be controlled by a standard display driver.

Electronic ink moves information display to a new dynamic level, with dramatic benefits over traditional media. The advantages of such a material are numerous.

Because it's made from the same basic materials as regular ink and paper, electronic ink retains the superior viewing characteristics of paper, including high contrast, wide viewing angle (180 degrees), and bright, paper-white background, thus overcoming user complaints about reading lengthy material on a computer screen. Electronic ink can be printed on almost any surface, from plastic to metal to paper. Furthermore, it can be coated over large areas cheaply. Electronic ink consumes low

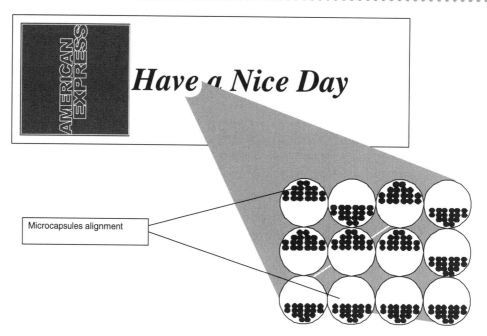

Figure 5.17   An example of Eink.

power (0.1 W). It can display an image even when the power is turned off, and it's legible in low light, thus reducing the need for a backlight. This power conservation can significantly extend battery life for portable devices. Due to all these factors, Eink's electronic ink process is highly scalable.

This technology is available today for big boards (see Figure 5.17), but by 2003 or 2004, it should be available for newspaper and books.

Micropayments

In the wireless Internet world, a majority of the transactions are at a micro level, compared with the desktop Web-browsing world. One of the problems that businesses will have to face is figuring out the billing model for their services. How do you collect for your services in a way that is both convenient and secure? Traditional payment methods such as credit cards involve too much transaction fee activity and delay to be useful under these conditions. In this section, we examine the concept of *micropayments*, which allow consumers to pay at the *cents-per-click* or transaction level.

Let's consider a few scenarios in which micropayment technology could be applied:

➤ You have a Web portal containing regular free content and premium content for which you would like users to pay. This premium content is not pages and pages of documents, but brief blurbs of useful text. You would like to charge every time a user accesses that content.

➤ You are an entertainment services provider and you would like to charge every time a user checks his or her horoscope or when the user plays a game at your site.

➤ You run a confectionery shop and you would like to automatically deduct the cost of your services from a user account. So, instead of spending time and energy billing customers on a *point-of-sale* (POS) terminal, you could be servicing more customers and in less time. Similarly, you might want to charge for streaming music, headline news, real-time sports scores, and so on. If the payment mechanisms were convenient, more people would buy and use your services.

Micropayments can be done in two ways:

➤ A user downloads electronic cash or some equivalent to a device (phone, Smart Card, PDA), and every time the user purchases something, whether online content or goods, the amount of the transaction is deducted from that electronic cash pool. Electronic cash could be paid for by traditional methods such as checks, credit cards, and so on.

➤ Another way of doing things is to account for every transaction, add them up, and send the user a bill toward the end of the billing cycle to collect payment.

For the iMode service in Japan, NTT DoCoMo has successfully used these micropayment methods for collecting payments for the services they and their partners offer. W3C has a group focusing on micropayment markup specifications.

Wireless Technologies

Over the past few years, wireless technologies have improved significantly. Additionally, many new advances, such as position location and Bluetooth, have been introduced. In this section, we review some of the predominant wireless technologies.

Short Message Service (SMS)

SMS became popular with second-generation digital systems, especially GSM. It is a packet-based architecture that sends data over the control channel. SMS messages are limited to 160 characters in GSM, 256 bytes in TDMA and 255 characters in CDMA. SMS-based services are very popular in Europe, where the use of simple applications such as weather, email, and instant messaging has skyrocketed in the past few years. However, due to the size limitations of these messages, SMS cannot be used for content-rich applications.

Wireless Local and Personal Area Networks (LAN and PAN)

Wireless LAN and PAN technologies eliminate the need to use expensive wireless wide area network (WAN) technologies such as CDMA and GSM for short-range wireless networking. In this section, we discuss short- to medium-range wireless networking technologies such as Bluetooth, HomeRF, and IEEE 802.11.

Bluetooth

Bluetooth is a low-power radio technology that replaces the cables and infrared links for distances up to 10 meters. More than 1000 companies worldwide support and/or are working on standardizing the technology. Key applications are synchronization of information among various types of equipment, data exchange, ticketing, or electronic cash/wallet applications. The throughput available is about 1Mbps.

How Does Bluetooth Work?

Let's consider a scenario that is applicable to both home and office environments. Figure 5.18 shows a Bluetooth-enabled desktop, PDA, and laser printer. These devices would work in tandem as follows:

1. A Bluetooth-based Internet desktop "listens" to other Bluetooth radios in its vicinity. On finding none, it configures itself as the master device. Then it configures its radio to a randomly selected frequency and broadcasts the same (say, Pattern 5).

2. Later, another Bluetooth-enabled device, a laser printer, is turned on. It listens to the other Bluetooth radio in its vicinity and finds the desktop as the master broadcasting on Pattern 5. The printer turns its transmitter to Pattern 5 and identifies itself to the desktop.

3. The laser printer and the desktop PC exchange information regarding their capabilities and privileges. The printer becomes the "slave" of the desktop piconet.

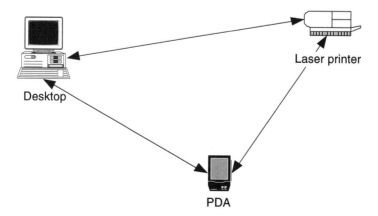

Figure 5.18   A Bluetooth-enabled desktop, PDA, and laser printer.

NOTE A *piconet* is a collection of devices connected in an ad hoc fashion using Bluetooth technology.

4. A user walks into the room carrying a Bluetooth-equipped PDA and hears the broadcast "I'm here on Pattern 5." The PDA tunes its transmitter to Pattern 5 and identifies itself to the desktop PC and becomes a slave to the desktop.

5. The three devices exchange information on each other's capabilities and access privileges. So, the PDA can access both the desktop and the printer.

6. The user decides to print a large document residing on the desktop PC. The PDA communicates directly to the desktop over Pattern 5. The printer, in turn, communicates over Pattern 5 with the printer to print the file. Once the print job is done, the printer sends a notification to the PDA.

HomeRF

From an enterprise perspective, *home radio frequency* (HomeRF) technology is useful for telecommuting. For example, it could allow employees to access the corporate network from home using a wireless modem.

The Home Radio Frequency Working Group has produced a specification called Shared Wireless Application Protocol (SWAP) that allows a variety of devices such as PCs, wireless phones, and consumer devices to share voice and data in and around the home environment. Some of its features are as follows [source: HomeRF.org FAQ, 2000]:

➤ The current available data rates range from 1Mbps to 2Mbps.

➤ Range is up to 150 feet.

➤ It can network up to ten PCs.

➤ It can work through walls and floors.

➤ It can work with DSL, modems, and cable modems.

➤ Data is secured through a unique network ID.

➤ It includes support for near-line-quality voice and telephony.

➤ It minimizes radio interference.

Clearly, HomeRF and Bluetooth are quite similar; they even operate within the same frequency range. The main difference is that HomeRF is optimized for the home environment. The industry also supports interoperability between the two protocols so that devices with these protocols can work together. It's also possible to implement both protocols within the same device.

Some examples of what users will be able to do with products that adhere to the SWAP specification include these:

➤ Set up a wireless home network to share voice and data between PCs, peripherals, PC-enhanced cordless phones, and new devices such as portable, remote display pads

➤ Access the Internet from anywhere in and around the home from portable display devices

➤ Share an ISP connection between PCs and other new devices

➤ Share files, modems, and printers in multi-PC homes

➤ Intelligently forward incoming telephone calls to multiple cordless handsets, fax machines, and voice mailboxes

➤ Review incoming voice, fax, and email messages from a small, PC-enhanced cordless telephone handset

➤ Activate other home electronic systems by simply speaking a command into a PC-enhanced cordless handset

➤ Play multiplayer games and/or toys based on PC or Internet resources

IEEE 802.11 Wireless LAN Standard

The Institute of Electrical and Electronics Engineers (IEEE) 802.11 standard for wireless LANs is aimed at medium-range, higher data rate applications. Available data rates are up to 11Mbps. This technology can be used in shop-floor areas in factory environments or other enterprises in which the wireless interaction is confined within a limited range.

Automatic Identification and Data Capture (AIDC) Technologies

AIDC technologies include technologies such as barcode, machine vision, optical systems, and mechanical and inductive flags. Businesses in the supply chain, logistics, transportation, and shipping benefit from AIDC technologies. Barcode technologies have been used extensively in the past for capturing the information related to an item, whether a box, a document, or a truck—just about anything. However, this approach is highly mechanized and is prone to error. A worker still has to point the scanner at the right place (called the *line of sight*), and barcode scanners often suffer from optical problems. Barcode information cannot be changed and is prone to counterfeiting.

Two technologies in this area have become prominent: Inductive Radio Frequency ID (RFID) and the recently introduced BiStatix technology from Motorola:

Inductive RFID works on the principle that as soon as the tag enters the magnetic field of the reader, the reader receives the data transmission, which it can process for further use. This way, the tag data can be automatically read and requires no human intervention, so operating costs are lowered (though RFID tags are more expensive than barcode labels). Read/write RFID provides the ability to change data (unlike barcoded information, which can't be changed). RFID also eliminates the common problems with barcode, such as ink bleeding, stray marks, label tearing, and so on, and is resistant to counterfeiting due to encryption. Despite its many advantages, RFID hasn't been that widely deployed due to high costs, especially for large applications.

BiStatix is a technology developed and promoted by Motorola that not only enhances RFID technology, but the design enables much lower costs in manufacturing. BiStatix works on a capacitive coupling principle. Electric fields are capacitively coupled to and from a reader and a tag. Similar to the inductive system, the BiStatix reader/writer generates a field, which serves as tag's source of power, and its master clock. The reader converts and decodes the data signal and provides a formatted data packet to the host computer for further processing. It's a fairly simple and cost-effective tag design suitable for large-volume and disposable applications. The tag can hold up to 900 bits of useful information.

As you can see, AIDC, coupled with wireless technologies, can provide a very effective means to track and trace shipments, equipment, and information.

2.5G and 3G Wireless Technologies

As discussed in Chapter 2, next-generation wireless technologies promise much-improved bandwidths. With bigger pipes, more complex content can be pushed to the devices and enhance the user experience and the value proposition. HSCSD, GPRS, and EDGE are referred to as the 2.5-generation technologies.

High-Speed Circuit-Switched Data (HSCSD)

HSCSD is a circuit-switched protocol based on GSM. It can use four control channels simultaneously and provide up to four times the speed available in GSM (14.4kbps). Some of the European carriers have already started to offer HSCSD services, but the technology lacks wide support. It's considered an interim technology before the arrival of GPRS, which offers instant connectivity at higher speeds.

General Packet Radio Service (GPRS)

GPRS is a packet-switched wireless protocol that allows for burst transmission speeds up to 115kbps (the theoretical limit is 171kbps). GPRS introduces the novel concept of the device being *always connected* to the network, meaning that the device and terminal can get instant IP connectivity. The network capacity is used only when data is actually transmitted. Due to high available speeds, GPRS, along with EDGE, provides a nice transition for operators who are not keen on investing in 3G infrastructure up front.

Enhanced Data Rates for Global Evolution (EDGE)

EDGE is a higher-bandwidth version of GPRS and has transmission speeds up to 384kbps. Such high speeds will allow for wireless multimedia applications.

3G Technologies

Third-generation wireless technologies is a term generally used for technologies that promise to provide unprecedented transmission speeds and performance. The formal standard for 3G is IMT-2000, which is being pushed by different developer communities. Wideband CDMA (WCDMA) is being backed by Ericsson, Nokia, and Japanese handset manufacturers. CDMA2000 is supported by QUALCOMM and Lucent. The first 3G network is expected to be operational by NTT DoCoMo in 2001.

The following are the key goals of IMT-2000:

➢ Increased efficiency and capacity

➢ New services, such as WANs for PCs and multimedia

➢ Bandwidth on demand—the ability to dynamically allocate the required spectrum depending on the application-sensitive data rate requirement

➢ Increased flexibility—multiple standards, frequency bands, environments, and backward compatibility

➢ Seamless roaming across dissimilar networks

➢ Integration of satellite services and fixed wireless access services with the cellular network

➢ Higher data rate services (384kbps mobile, 2Mbps fixed in the early phase, increasing to 20Mbps in the later stages)

Position Location Technologies

On December 23, 1997, the FCC released the mandate (FCC 97-402) that requires that by October 1, 2001, carriers must have the capability to identify the latitude and longitude of mobile units making 911 calls within a radius of 100 meters RMS 67 percent of the time and 300 meters RMS 95 percent of the time for network-based technologies. For handset-based technologies, the accuracy requirement is within 50 meters 67 percent of the time and 100 meters 95 percent of the time.

This marriage of location with wireless communication services has opened up a huge market for position location services. This section discusses the position location market and its various technologies and lists the status and progress of various position location providers.

The position location techniques can basically be categorized into network-centric and handset-centric approaches. We discuss both network-based and handset-based technologies in this section. Handset-centric techniques require modifications to the mobile terminal; network-centric approaches confine changes to the network infrastructure, thus ensuring that existing unmodified telephones can be located.

Network-centric Approaches

Although several network-based techniques exist for locating an unmodified hand-set, three have become most useful and popular: time difference of arrival (TDOA), angle of arrival (AOA), and location pattern matching.

Figure 5.19 depicts as to how the position location technology fits into the wireless infrastructure architecture.

Time Difference of Arrival (TDOA)

A TDOA system works by situating location receivers at three sites, with each site having an accurate timing source. When a signal is transmitted from a mobile terminal, it

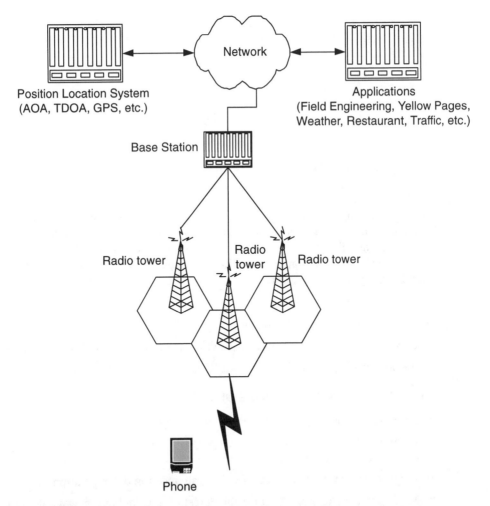

Figure 5.19 A typical wireless position location architecture.

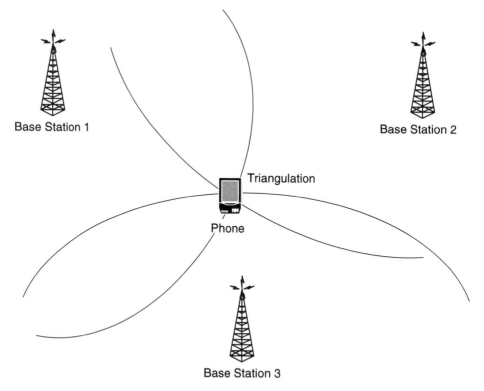

Figure 5.20   Time difference of arrival (TDOA).

propagates at approximately 300m/μs to each antenna site. When the cell site receives the signal, it is time stamped. By examining the differences in time stamps, TDOA can determine a mobile terminal's location by computing intersecting hyperbolic lines. To work correctly, the base stations must be time-synchronized to better than 100ns. Figure 5.20 illustrates this concept.

ADVANTAGES OF TDOA

➤ Provides location for all handsets

➤ Can utilize the RF information to provide network design and monitoring services

➤ Indoor coverage is similar to indoor RF coverage

CHALLENGES AND LIMITATIONS OF TDOA

➤ Requires extremely precise time synchronization

➤ Requires TDOA systems at 80 to 100 percent of the cell sites, thus increasing the overall cost of the system

➤ Requires at least three cell sites for accurate location determination

➤ Multipath propagation effect (problem resulting from bouncing wireless signals) deteriorates the accuracy of the system

> Only able to track location at the start of the call

> No privacy; the carrier can track the user all the time (when the phone is on)

> For CDMA systems, due to the near-far problem, the signal-to-noise ratio (SNR) at the neighboring base stations decreases and leads to inaccuracies in position location estimation

NOTE The term *near-far problem* refers to the fact that, under this power control scheme, when a mobile unit's received power level increases as it moves in closer proximity to the base station, the mobile unit is directed to reduce its transmitting power. In this situation, the signal power levels of neighboring base stations will be lower because of the reduced transmitting power and increased transmitter/receiver distance.

Angle of Arrival (AOA)

Also called *direction of arrival,* AOA has several versions. Small-aperture direction finding is the most common version and requires a complex antenna array at two or more cell site locations. The array consists of four to twelve antennas in a horizontal line. The antennas work together to determine the angle (relative to the cell site) from which a cellular call originated. When at least two sites can determine the angles of arrival of a given call, the caller's location can be determined from the point of intersection of projected lines drawn out from the cell sites. This concept is illustrated in Figure 5.21.

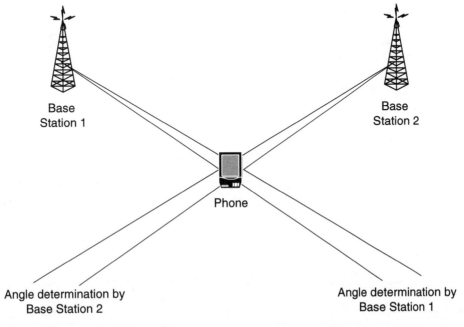

Figure 5.21 Angle of arrival (AOA).

ADVANTAGES OF AOA

➤ Provides location for all handsets

➤ Antennas could be used to improve capacity, reduce interference, and better system performance

➤ Indoor coverage similar to indoor RF coverage

➤ Can track the call in progress

CHALLENGES AND LIMITATIONS OF AOA

➤ Requires at least two cell sites for accurate position location determination

➤ Requires AOA systems at about 100 percent of the cell sites, thus increasing overall cost of the system

➤ Requires highly expensive antenna beams that need to be kept in a calibrated state all the time

➤ Since AOA tracks on the voice channel, additional processing is required to query the mobile switching center (MSC) to get information about the user (MIN)

➤ No privacy; carrier can track user all the time (when the phone is on)

➤ For CDMA systems, suffers from the same near-far problem as discussed in the TDOA section

Location Pattern Matching

Multipath is a phenomenon in which the wireless RF signal bounces off solid objects such as buildings, towers, and so on. While multipath deteriorates TDOA and AOA accuracy in locating handsets, this technique utilizes the multipath characteristics (measures the phase, the timing, and the amplitude path of all the RF signals from a single caller) of an RF environment to locate a handset. Multipath characteristic patterns within a block are analyzed and stored as fingerprints or patterns in the database. When a handset transmits its RF waveforms, algorithms try to match these RF characteristics to the fingerprints or patterns in a database, thus identifying the block from which the call came. Figure 5.22 illustrates this concept. This technique is also referred as multipath fingerprinting.

ADVANTAGES OF LOCATION PATTERN MATCHING

➤ Single cell site can be used to locate and track multipath rays from a handset, thus decreasing the capital and operating costs (compared with TDOA and AOA solutions)

➤ RF characteristics analysis could be used for network design and optimization

➤ Works very well in urban and densely populated areas

➤ Can track the call in progress if on the same voice channel (no handoffs)

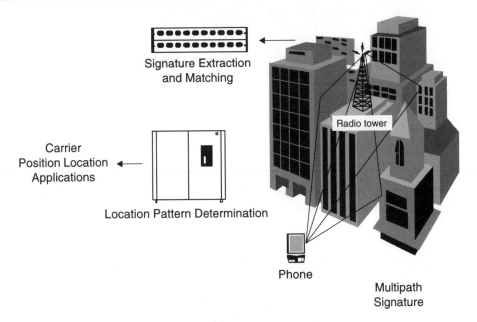

Figure 5.22   Location Pattern Matching.

CHALLENGES AND LIMITATIONS OF LOCATION PATTERN MATCHING

➤ Requires several iterations to build the fingerprint database; the fingerprints would change with weather or construction layout

➤ Antenna beams need to be kept calibrated

➤ Difficulty in tracking hard handoffs

➤ Stationary handsets harder to track (in comparison to moving handsets)

➤ Performance degrades in rural areas

➤ No privacy; carrier can track the user all the time (when the phone is on)

Handset-centric Approach: The Global Positioning System

The most commonly considered handset-centric option is the global positioning system (GPS). It takes advantage of the multibillion-dollar investment the U.S. government has made to establish a satellite infrastructure for location determination. For several years, twenty-four satellites have been operational, and they have provided accurate, continuous, worldwide, three-dimensional position and velocity information at no charge.

The basis of GPS is triangulation from satellites (see Figure 5.23). To triangulate, a GPS receiver in the handset measures distance using the travel time of radio signals from the satellites. Since satellites already "know" their location, a precise location of the GPS

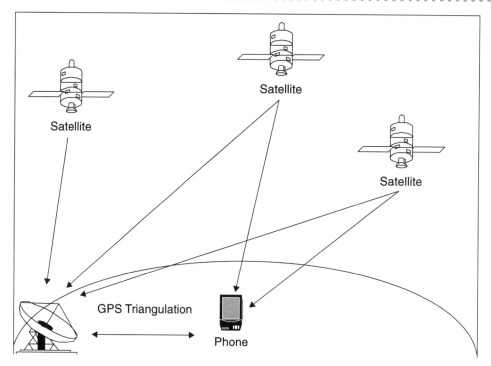

Figure 5.23   GPS triangulation.

receiver can be computed. Mathematically, four satellites are needed to determine exact position, but using some error correction and digital signal-processing techniques, the number of satellites required for accurate measurements can be reduced to as few as one (three satellites are required initially, one or two thereafter).

There are two types of solutions available in this category: network-driven GPS and autonomous GPS.

Network-Driven GPS

The *network-driven GPS* method places a minimal GPS front end in the handset and lets the wireless infrastructure equipment handle all the calculation and position determination.

Autonomous GPS

Autonomous GPS technology is based on placing a complete GPS subsystem in a handset. Wireless carriers and handset vendors could place all location-determination functionality inside the phone, making virtually no changes in wireless infrastructure.

ADVANTAGES OF GPS

➤ Doesn't require expensive network modifications and infrastructure; the cost of putting GPS in a phone is declining fast, thus making it a very attractive long-term solution for carriers

➤ Much higher accuracy possible

➤ Provides privacy; location could be available on demand

CHALLENGES AND LIMITATIONS OF GPS

➤ No location of unmodified phones (FCC mandate requires location to be provided for all handsets, and there are over 61 million handsets without GPS capability)

➤ GPS-enabled phones will affect battery consumption

➤ Up to two or three minutes of initial warmup time

➤ Poor location determination in buildings and other shadowed environments

Satellite Technologies

Satellites augment and provide essential communication network links for radio, TV, and telephones across the globe. With the spiraling down of the Iridium project (Iridium was an international consortium which included players like Motorola and Sprint, operated and marketed global satellite communications services), the hard reality of having a sound business plan has become even more apparent. The cost for launch, implementation, and maintenance of satellite-based systems is very high. So, it's even more important for these technologies to provide value and benefits to the business and consumer community.

There are essentially three types of satellites:

➤ *Geostationary Earth orbit (GEO).* These types of satellites rotate about 22.3K miles above Earth. Their speed of rotation is the same as the rotational speed of Earth, so they always appear to be at the same spot from Earth. Four satellites are required to cover Earth.

➤ *Low Earth orbit (LEO).* These types of satellites rotate 180 to 1000 miles above Earth, and their speed is much lower than the rotational speed of Earth. Fifty satellites are required to cover Earth.

➤ *Medium Earth orbit (MEO).* These types of satellites rotate at about 6.25K to 10K miles above Earth, and their speed is between that of GEO and LEO satellites. Twelve satellites are required to cover Earth.

Satellites have been used very successfully over the past few decades for position location applications. Satellites can also be used for augmenting the existing wireless, cable, telephony, and Internet infrastructure. Especially in rural areas where it is cost prohibitive to install wireless or fiber equipment for just a few residents, satellite technologies can provide the necessary link between the rural area and the rest of the world. Satellite technologies are also useful in providing access from airborne computers (for instance, Internet and corporate access from airplane personal video monitors). Recently, two prominent satellite services-based companies, ICO and Globalstar, decided to combine their operations.

Smart Antennas

Antennas are a key component of the wireless network infrastructure. Their role is to establish radio transmission between base stations and wireless devices. These antennas can be configured such that one antenna can serve a geographical radius (360 degrees) or it can also be sectorized to serve two or more segments within the same geographical radius. This helps in optimization, interference reduction, spectrum utilization, capacity enhancements, and performance improvement.

In recent years, with the help of *smart antennas*, performance of wireless systems has further improved. The better the utilization of spectrum, the higher number of users can be served within the same geography with less interference. Recently, Arraycomm—a company that pioneered the concept of smart antennas—has demonstrated the use of smart antennas for improved wireless Internet access.

Smart antennas use sophisticated signal processing and computing techniques to rapidly optimize reception of and transmission from multiple users at the same time. This results in the wireless systems' ability to serve up many more connections in any given area and with a given amount of radio spectrum. Arraycomm claims that its I-Burst technology can provide up to forty times more capacity than 3G systems will provide in the future.

Since 1998, Kyocera, in its PHS wireless network, has used Arraycomm's technology successfully in thousands of base stations. The technology has resulted in improved coverage and network capacity.

Technology Ecosystem

Throughout this chapter, we have discussed different types of computing and communications technologies that are and will be impacting the pervasive computing era. However, you might wonder how these things fit together. Figure 5.24 shows the *technology ecosystem* and how various technologies will fit together. In Chapter 6, we will take a look at the solution providers of the technologies discussed in this chapter.

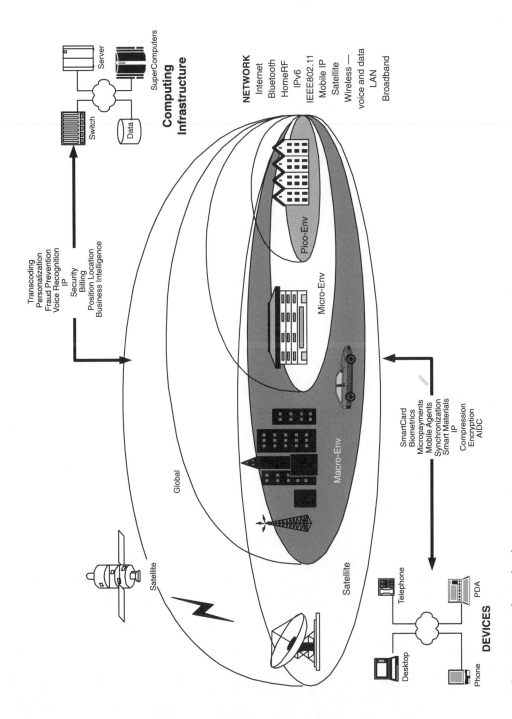

Figure 5.24 The technology ecosystem.

Players

In the last two chapters, we looked at the types of applications that are emerging in the wireless Internet market and the key technologies that are driving them. In this chapter, we review the various segments that make up the value chain of the wireless Internet market and present some of the key players in each of those segments.

The list of industry players described in this chapter is by no means a comprehensive one. The main objective of this chapter is to give you a feel for the main innovators in specific areas.

The Value Chain

As is true with any industry, the wireless Internet industry is made up of several players. The value chain, as shown in Figure 6.1, consists of the following:

➢ Content providers:
  ➢ Corporate: intranet, extranet
  ➢ Internet
➢ Aggregators:
  ➢ Mobile portals
  ➢ Internet portals
➢ Middleware software providers
➢ System developers and service providers:
  ➢ Mobile service providers

> ➢ Application developers
> ➢ System integrators
➢ Infrastructure providers:
> ➢ Communications infrastructure providers
> ➢ Computing infrastructure providers
➢ Network operators and wireless service providers
➢ Device providers:
> ➢ Technology platform providers
> ➢ Device manufacturers
➢ Consumers

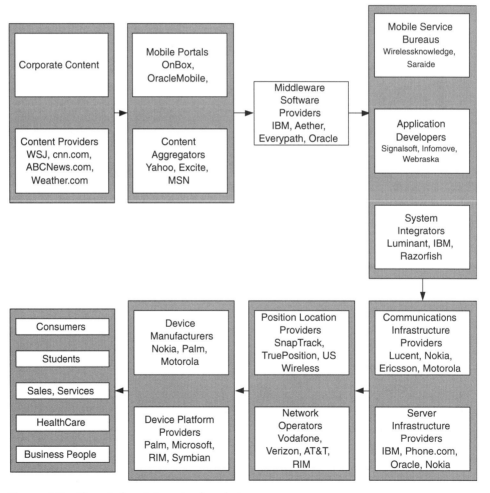

Figure 6.1   The wireless Internet value chain.

Content Providers

Content can be of two types:

➤ *Corporate content.* This content consists of email, calendar, address book, access to corporate intranets (business-to-employee, or B2E). It can also include content meant for partners who can access the content through extranets (B2B).

➤ *Consumer content.* Consumer content consists of B2C content such as news, sports, entertainment, weather, and traffic information from Web sources.

Content providers are very quickly moving into the mobile space to benefit from the wireless Internet revolution. Content, or information, is still king in the mobile world. Actually, due to the constraints of the wireless environment, distribution of this content becomes even more important. Many B2C sites, especially the news organizations, want to leverage the content they have to extend their brands and relationships with new and existing consumers. Similarly, corporations are realizing the need and demand for providing access to corporate data to employees and partners on the move and hence have already implemented or are preparing to set up the right infrastructure and partnerships to deliver the data to mobile devices.

Some household names in the content provider space include *The Wall Street Journal,* CNN, ABCNews, the BBC, and Reuters. Some of the other pioneers in this space were listed in Chapter 4.

Aggregators

Aggregators are essentially service providers that collect content from a variety of sources and repackage available data from a single source. Via this method, users don't have to browse from site to site. In addition, thanks to personalization, the user is presented with only the content from various information types and sources that interest him or her. The portal information can be stored or collected in real time. Portals from the Internet world were among the first movers in this space. Firms such as Yahoo!, Lycos, Excite@Home, and MSN are partnering with or buying firms that have expertise in wireless delivery to extend their valuable content to mobile devices.

Some new players, such as Iobox.com and mobileID.com, are emerging to take advantage of the wireless Internet revolution. Aggregators can either specialize in one or more content categories or they can be generalists. Some aggregators, such as DLJDirect, provide content related to business and financial markets; others, such as CNN.com, specialize in providing news across multiple disciplines and sectors. Some mobile portals also provide personal information management applications such as email, calendar, instant messaging, and so on. The key to successful delivery of content is personalization and localization.

Sensing the growing market opportunity, many mobile operators are also jumping in the mix to become content aggregators. They have partnered with some top-tier content providers and aggregators to build their own wireless portals. BT Cellnet with its

Genie, Telia with its MyDOF (My Department of the Future), Sonera with its Zed, and Deutsche Telekom's T-Mobil with its T-D1@T-Online were among the first movers in Europe. In the United States, AT&T and Sprint PCS were among the first movers, and in Japan, NTT DoCoMo's iMode service has been a big hit with consumers.

Middleware Software Providers

One of the biggest challenges in the wireless Internet arena is taking advantage of aggregated content and transforming it for disparate devices that have different capabilities for different users who have differing preferences and needs. Middleware software is the glue that binds the communication and computing worlds together and thus is a very important component of the value chain.

Some players that have introduced products to address this market segment are listed in Table 6.1. IBM's Transcoding Publisher is part of the Websphere Everyplace Suite, a development platform for building wireless Internet-based applications. Middleware software is generally based on XML at its core for doing transcoding of existing or new content into a variety of formats such as WML, VxML, HDML, HTML, Web Clipping, and so on. These products connect to application servers, databases, and various gateways, such as WAP, UPLink, Palm.Net, SMS, and VXML to push the content onto the devices.

Table 6.1   Middleware Solution Providers

PRODUCT	COMPANY	DEVICE AND LANGUAGE SUPPORT
Transcoding Publisher/ Websphere Suite	IBM	Smart phones, Windows CE, Palm, VxML
Portal-to-Go	Oracle	Smart phones, Windows CE, Palm, VxML
Ianywhere	Sybase	NA
Gatewave	Passcall	Smart phones, VxML
Microstrategy 6/Infocenter	MicroStrategy	Smart phones, Blackberry, Skytel, Metrocall, Pagenet pagers, voice
Avantgo Server	Avantgo, Inc.	Smart phones, Windows CE, Palm
Premion Server+	Geoworks	Smart phones, pagers
ScoutWare/Aether Intelligent Messaging Platform	Aether Software	Windows CE, Palm, pagers
Everypath Server	Everypath	Uses Dialogic as voice engine; smart phones, Palm, Windows CE, pagers, Psion Revo, VxML

System Developers and Service Providers

System integrators or developers build the applications and integrate them with the infrastructure. They use middleware and other tools to put it all together. They typically partner with a wide variety of players in the value chain to provide services. Due to the lucrative nature of this emerging market, a majority of middleware software providers have also taken up the role of mobile ASPs. Companies such as Wireless Knowledge provide integration services (including email, calendar, contact list, and company intranets and extranets) for employees to be connected to the corporate LAN. Furthermore, some middleware software firms offer mobile services ranging from simple content and notification to complete wireless Internet solutions. Some mobile wireless ASPs are listed in Table 6.2. Some of the system integrator companies in this area are IBM, Andersen Consulting, Luminant Worldwide, and Razorfish.

This category of the value chain also includes other application and product developers that specialize in certain aspects of the whole puzzle—voice recognition, application servers, caching, synchronization software, and so on.

Table 6.2   Wireless ASPs

COMPANY	AREA OF SPECIALIZATION
Wireless Knowledge (joint venture between Microsoft and QUALCOMM)	Connecting devices to corporate Microsoft Exchange servers
Saraide (bought by InfoSpace)	Messaging (synchronizes with Microsoft Outlook and Lotus Schedule), news, travel, financial
724Solutions	Targeted toward financial institutions
Aether Software	ScoutWare and Aether Intelligent Messaging (AIM) enable real-time transactions and communications with wireless devices
Everypath	Development and hosting solutions to enable existing Web sites to go wireles
AirFlash	ASP for position location applications
Aspective	Ecommerce, eCRM solutions
SmartServ Online	SmartServ platform for transaction-based applications
Wysdom, Inc	Applications enable sites to deliver content, advertisements, and ecommerce solutions
Geoworks	Mobile ASP server enables sites to deliver relevant, time-sensitive information to customers on wireless devices
Oz.com	Messaging, mcommerce, mservices (mPresence service platform)

Table 6.3   Voice Recognition Vendors

TECHNOLOGY	COMPANY AND PRODUCT
Continuous speech recognition	• IBM ViaVoice • Dragon Systems Naturally Speaking • L&H Voice Xpress • Philips Free Speech
Speech processing—command and control	• Conversa TalkRadio, Conversa Web • Nuance Voyager, BetterBanking, Brokerage Suite • Philips SpeechWare
Text to speech (TTS)	• Elan TTS Speech Engine • L&H RealSpeak • Lucent text-to-speech engine • SoftVoice TTS • Willow Pond WillowTalk
Unassisted machine translation	• IBM Speech Server • L&H iTranslator • MultiLingual Media GlobalTV
Assisted machine translation	• IBM Translation Manager 2 • L&H Power Translator Pro • Logos Translator Pro
Natural language processing (NLP)—querying	• NLP front ends • Inference k-Commerce Web • Microsoft English Query • Question-answering systems • AnswerLogic Inc. Answerlogic • EasyAsk Inc. EasyAsk
NLP—email response	• Brightware Automated Answer • Egain Mail • Kana Response
NLP—Commonsense Knowledge Base	• Cycorp Cyc Knowledge Server

(Source: Wired)

Voice Recognition

As discussed in Chapter 5, voice recognition will be very important for navigation by users who require constrained devices. Some of the leading players in this arena are listed in Table 6.3.

Synchronization

Synchronization is another area key to wireless Internet technology, since information existing on disparate devices needs to be synchronized to be useful. Some players that offer synchronization solutions are listed in Table 6.4.

Table 6.4   Synchronization Product Vendors

PRODUCT	VENDOR	PARTNERS
ActiveSync	Microsoft	Wireless Knowledge
Enterprise Harmony	Extended Systems	AnyDay.com (Palm), SixDegrees, Lotus Organizer
FusionOne	FusionOne	HP, Sun Microsystems, EMC
FoneSync	Phone.com	
Synctalk	Synctalk	Clarion, Microsoft, Psion
IntelliSync	Puma Technology	AOL, PlanetAll, Visto
TrueSync	Starfish (Motorola)	Yahoo!, Excite@Home
Mobile Connect	IBM	
MQ Series	IBM	
Synchrologic	Synchrologic	Palm, Oracle, Microsoft

Infrastructure Providers

Infrastructure providers furnish the necessary components to complete the big picture. These providers range from suppliers of the wireless base and switching stations (Nokia, Ericsson, Motorola, and Lucent) to providers of public-key infrastructure for encryption and security (VeriSign and Certicom). Some players specialize in niches such as personalization, performance measurement, business intelligence, and so on. The major players in this space are listed in Table 6.5 by area of specialization.

Table 6.5   Infrastructure Providers

SPECIALIZATION	VENDOR
Communications— wireless specific	• Nokia • Alcatel • Ericsson • Motorola • Lucent • Qualcomm • Nortel • Siemens
Communications— gateways	• Phone.com • Nokia • CMG • Siemens • IBM • Ericsson

Continues

Table 6.5   Infrastructure Providers *(Continued)*

SPECIALIZATION	VENDOR
	• Dr. Materna • Alcatel • Palm • Infinite Mobility
Computing	• Oracle • Microsoft • Sybase • HP • SUN • Netscape (AOL) • IBM
Smart Cards	• Schlumberger • GemPlus • Mondex
Caching	• Akamai • Inktomi
Business intelligence	• Business Objects • Cognos • Brio • IBM • Oracle • Microsoft
Personalization	• Art Technology Group • Broadvision • Yodlee • Net Perceptions • Blaze Software
Others	• Cisco (networking equipment) • VeriSign (digital certificates) • F-Secure (antivirus) • Keynote (performance measurement) • Speedwise (content compression) • Surfnotes (content customization for wireless devices) • Certicom (digital certificates) • Visa, MasterCard (online payment) • Roku (peer-to-peer communication) • Categoric (alerts)

Network Operators and Wireless Service Providers

Network operators are the wireless carriers that provide and manage the link between an application and the device or user through their networks. Network operators are always looking for ways to increase the *average revenue per user* (ARPU), and the advent of wireless Internet will benefit them the most. Figure 6.2 illustrates the increase in ARPU over time with the introduction of mcommerce services. Some of the early adopters of the technology are using wireless Internet applications and services to differentiate themselves from the competition and enter new markets with new business models. Wireless Internet provides them with the opportunity to continually expand and improve their networks and provide a wide range of services to their customers.

In addition, *wireless service providers*—such as vendors that provide position location technology and infrastructure, billing, and antifraud solutions—are important in the value chain. They enhance the value proposition offered by network operators.

Table 6.6 lists, by country, some network operators that are actively pursuing the wireless Internet marketplace through infrastructure investments and partnerships. Every month, new players jump into the fray.

In Chapter 5, we reviewed some of the predominant position location technologies and how they interact with the wireless infrastructure. Table 6.7 lists the major players in this space, along with the technology they bring to market.

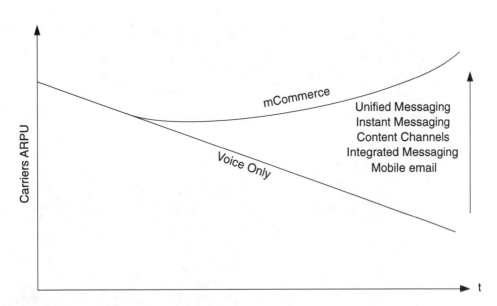

Figure 6.2   Carrier ARPU over time.
(Copyright © 2000, Microsoft)

Table 6.6 Network Operators by Selected Country (Early Adopters of Wireless Internet Technology)

COUNTRY	OPERATOR
Australia	• C & W Optus • Telstra
Czech Republic	• Oskar Mobil
France	• Itineris • SFR
Finland	• Radiolinja • Sonera • Telia
Germany	• E-Plus • Viag Interkom • Mannesmann Mobilfunk
Hong Kong	• Smar Tone • Hutchinson • Peoples Phone
Ireland	• Eircell • Esat Digifone
Italy	• Omnitel Pronto Italia
Japan	• NTT DoCoMo • IDO • DDI
Korea	• Shinsegi Telecom
Netherlands	• KPN Telecom • Libertel
Norway	• Telenor Mobile
Philippines	• Smart
Portugal	• Telecel
Singapore	• Moblie One
Spain	• Airtel Movil • Telefonica Moviles
Sweden	• Europolitan • Telia Mobile
Taiwan	• Taiwan Cellular
United Kingdom	• One 2 One • Vodafone • Orange

Continues

Table 6.6   *(Continued)*

COUNTRY	OPERATOR
United States	• AT&T Wireless • Sprint PCS • Bell Atlantic Mobile • BellSouth • US WEST

Table 6.7   Position Location Technology Providers

COMPANY	TECHNOLOGY
Accucom	AOA
Grayson Wireless	TDOA, AOA
Arraycomm	AOA
Cambridge Positioning Systems, Ltd.	Time of Arrival (TOA)
Cell-Loc, Inc.	TDOA
Corsair	TDOA, AOA
Ericsson	TDOA, AOA, network-assisted GPS
Harris Communication	TDOA, AOA; requires chip in the phone
Hazeltine	Intelligent Antenna Arrays
Integrated Data Communications	GPS
Lockheed Sanders	TDOA
Locus Corp	Enhanced Signal Strength
Lucent	Forward Link Triangulation (FLT), Integrated Wireless Assisted GPS (WAG), AOA, pattern matching, statistical modeling
Nokia	Observed time of arrival (OTA), Enhanced observed time of arrival (EOTA), network-assisted GPS
Nortel	EOTD
Radix Technologies	TDOA, AOA
SigmaOne	TDOA, AOA
SiRF	GPS chip
SnapTrack (QUALCOMM)	Network-assisted GPS
TruePosition	TDOA, AOA
US Wireless	Location Pattern Matching

Device Manufacturers

Device manufacturers and technology platform (operating system, or OS) providers are critical in the value chain. Consumers generally identify very well with a particular handset brand rather than a particular network operator. These devices are very personal in nature and in many cultures—Japan, for instance—have become equivalent to fashion accessories, especially among teens.

Devices come in various form factors and functionalities. Figure 6.3 provides a glimpse of the wide range of devices on the market today. The handheld market is dominated by Palm-based devices (Palm, Handspring, IBM, Symbol, Sony) followed distantly by Windows CE (Hewlett-Packard, Compaq, Casio) and EPOC-based devices (Psion). The handset (or phone) market is dominated by the big three: Ericsson, Nokia, and Motorola. Some other popular handset manufacturers are Siemens, Kyocera, Sagem, Sony, QUALCOMM, Samsung, Mitsubishi, and Philips. Table 6.8 lists manufacturers and their OSs for the devices shown in Figures 6.3 and 6.4. As you can see, a wide variety of devices with pretty sophisticated feature sets are available. They range from handheld PDAs from Palm, HP, IBM, and Casio to innovative videophones such as the VP 210 from Kyocera, which has videoconferencing capability with users on other videophones or PCs.

To give you a feel for the extensive feature set available in these devices, Table 6.9 lists the main features and specifications for various types of devices.

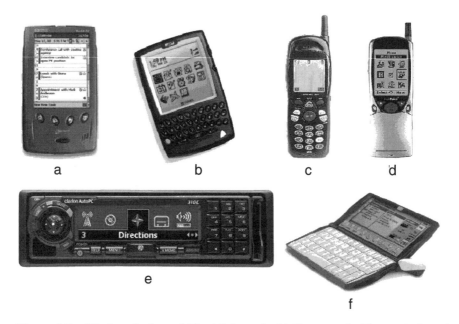

Figure 6.3   Wireless devices. a) The HP Jornada. b) The RIM Blackberry. c) The Mitsubishi T250. d) The NeoPoint N1000. e) The Clarion AutoPC. f) The Psion Revo.
(Sources: Hewlett-Packard, RIM, Mitsubishi, NeoPoint, Clarion, and Psion)

Table 6.8   Devices and Their Manufacturers and Operating Systems

DEVICE	MANUFACTURER	OS
Jornada	Hewlett-Packard	Windows CE
Blackberry	Research in Motion (RIM)	RIM OS
T250	Mitsubishi	Phone.com microbrowser
NeoPoint 1000	NeoPoint	Phone.com microbrowser
AutoPC 310c	Clarion	Windows CE
Revo	Psion	EPOC
Visor	Handspring	Palm OS
Communicator	Nokia	GEOS
MediaMaster (future-concept device)	Nokia	Linux
Timeport P30	Motorola	Reflex
Videophone VP210	Kyocera	NA

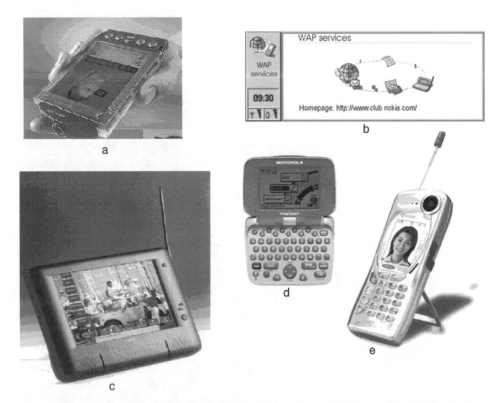

Figure 6.4   a) The Handspring Visor. b) The Nokia Communicator. c) The Nokia Media-master. d) The Motorola Timeport. e) The Kyocera Videophone.

(Sources: Handspring, Nokia, Motorola, and Kyocera)

Table 6.9 Device Features and Specifications

DEVICE	FEATURES AND SPECIFICATIONS
Kyocera Videophone (available only in Japan's PHS network) VP-210	**Display** • Two-inch reflective TFT color LCD • Six letters, seven lines • Camera—CMOS image sensor with approximately 110,000 pixels **Videophone functions** • Approx. 60 min. (hands-free mode) • Approx. 2 frames/sec. • Twenty (JPEG files) • Max. four (one image/call plus 15 sec. of audio) • Available if account numbers are set on both sides **PHS function** • Approx. 120 min. (power-saver mode, LCD off, nonhands-free mode) • Approx. 200 hrs. (power saver mode, LCD off) • Two hundred entries (with images) • Outgoing: 30 mail messages, incoming: 30 mail messages • Outgoing five messages, incoming: max. 63 messages • Hands-free function available • Four (can sort into four different groups: visual phone, pay phone, telephone book registered numbers, house phones) • Max. of ten 15-sec. messages, including the number of incoming answering machine messages that can be stored in memory • Time alarm, time alarm with message • Single phrase • Available when not using the hands-free function • Vibration function available
Clarion AutoPC	**Audio features** • Ten AM/ FM presets with title memory • Audio CD/CD-ROM drive • Four-channel line-level output • Ten-band Graphic Equalizer with three presets • 140W (35W x four) • Eight-color TFT Active Matrix LCD **Display** • Detachable control panel **Computing features** • Windows CE operating system • Voice-activated control and response • Text-to-speech read-back • Hitachi SH3 processor • A 16MB DRAM/8MB ROM • Type 2 Compact Flash slot • IrDA and USB interface *Continues*

Table 6.9   *(Continued)*

DEVICE	FEATURES AND SPECIFICATIONS
	Included applications • Voice memo • Address book
Motorola Timeport P390 two-way pager	**Display** • Nine-line display • Twenty-nine characters total or selectable larger font • EL backlighting • Lighted QWERTY keyboard • High-resolution graphics **Indicators/alert features** • Graphic battery gauge • Message transmission status indicator • Personal alarm clock • Service indicators • User-selectable alerts **Messaging features** • Address book with nine fields of information • Automatic signature capability • Confirmed message delivery (01) • In-box clean-up functions • 4.5MB total Flash memory (04) • Full two-way messaging capability • Message management • Message time and date stamping • Saves messages when off • Smart enough to communicate wirelessly with pagers, Internet email (01), telephones, and fax machines **Technology** • Customizable Features • EL backlighting display is user friendly • FLEX capable for advanced paging reliability • Information services capable (01) • IR data port • PC compatible and upgradable • QWERTY keyboard for easy text entry **Control features** • Font size selection • Private time • Volume

(Sources: Kyocera, Clarion, and Motorola)

In the future, with advances in semiconductor, wireless, and computing technologies, these feature sets will only become more diverse. No single form factor will dominate the market; instead multiple form factors and feature sets will coexist due to diversity in consumer and business consumer population. However, certain devices will become popular in certain niche market segments. For example, teens will most likely continue to prefer slim, attractive handsets that give them convenient messaging and information access features, whereas business people on the run will buy the devices that offer them PDA and phone features in a single device so that they don't have to carry multiple devices on business trips. Current market dynamics demand phone manufacturers come up with new phone models every six to nine months or so. Because of this constant demand for innovation, we will continue to see new and exciting products in the near and distant future.

Consumers

Users, or consumers, are at the end of the value chain and basically define the entire market. If the value proposition for users is not attractive enough, even the most technologically advanced and sophisticated solution will not be successful in the marketplace. Therefore, it is critical for manufacturers to understand consumer demand and acceptance profiles by geographic region and class before any major initiative is launched. According to a Nokia study on mobile value-added services, the primary targets for mcommerce consumer services are as follows:

➤ Teens (eighteen years and under)

➤ Students (nineteen to twenty-five years old)

➤ Young business people (twenty-five to thirty-six years old)

The business market is divided into three major categories:

➤ Sales staff in any type of organization

➤ Services staff in organizations such as banks and system integrators

➤ Logistics-driven organizations such as courier and taxi services

In order for any technology or service to be pervasive, it's essential that the value proposition is carried across the entire value chain. If somebody in the chain is not benefiting from the technology, most likely the overall value proposition to the consumer will stumble. For the same reason, it's critical for market players to understand the value chain and the various players in it.

In this chapter, we took a look at the various components of the wireless Internet value chain, from content providers to users, and discussed some of the major players in each of those segments. In the next chapter, we will evaluate various solutions available for implementing wireless Internet services.

Evaluating Wireless Internet Solutions

So far we have taken a look at various technologies and players in the wireless Internet industry. In this chapter, we evaluate some of these technologies based on the needs of a typical organization. We also discuss some of the developer tools available to develop, simulate, and test wireless Internet based applications and services.

Wireless Internet development projects can range from simple phone directory or email access to more comprehensive, enterprisewide planning and implementation of custom-developed, mission-critical applications across different geographic regions supporting a multitude of device types. Wireless Internet projects can be broadly divided into the following three categories:

➤ Extending the email platform (constitutes email, address book, and calendar)

➤ Extending existing Web-based applications to wireless devices

➤ Building fresh ebusiness solutions for your employees, partners, and suppliers

We discuss each of these in further detail in this chapter.

If we revisit the value chain described in Figure 6.1, depending upon the type of solution you are building, you will need to consider and pick solution offerings from players in different segments.

It's very important to understand end users' needs both now and projected for the future before you make any major decisions about technology, vendors, or partners. Depending on the mobility of the user and his or her information needs (such as how often up-to-date information will be needed), you might need to select different wireless technologies and partners. Sometimes it might be necessary to support more than one technology because of the distinct segmentation of the users within your company. For example, an energy company has at least two distinct user sets:

➤ Users who are not mobile a majority of the time but have a need to access email, address book, and calendar while mobile within a metropolitan area

➤ Users who work in remote areas all the time, such as the field workers who must get readings from the field in order to file reports

Users in the second group require better wireless network coverage, more ruggedized and feature-rich devices, and different application requirements from users in the first group.

Mobile applications requiring wireless networking include those that depend on real-time access to data that is usually stored in centralized databases. If your application requires mobile users to be immediately aware of changes made to data, or if information put into the system must immediately be available to others, you have a definite need for wireless networking. Not all mobile applications, however, require wireless networking. Sometimes the business case doesn't require mobile, real-time access to information. If the application's data can be stored on the user's device and changes to the data are not significant, additional wireless network hardware might not provide enough benefit to justify the additional expense. Keep in mind, though, that other needs for wireless networks could still exist. Network choice is generally mandated by the nature of an application and the mobility of the user in question. After doing a cost/benefit analysis of a network technology, relevant devices can be selected based on corporate preferences, existing device availability, application demand, robustness of the operating system, and other factors.

Some of the major wireless data network technologies are discussed in Table 7.1. For a majority of applications today, latency is more important than bandwidth. Figure 7.1 shows typical network coverage for wireless data technologies (most of the time, wireless data is available in metropolitan areas only).

Extending the Email Platform

For a majority of corporations, daily-use applications such as electronic email, calendar, and address book are the first applications that they would like to extend to their remote users. Email is the killer application for wireless. If a service allows users to seamlessly receive and send emails from wherever they are, the value is paramount. In addition, the ability to view and act on calendar items and search an address book is highly valuable to the mobile user. Two groupware packages, Microsoft Exchange and Lotus Notes, pretty much dominate the market, and good support is available for both.

Microsoft Exchange

Microsoft Exchange is one of the predominant corporate electronic mail packages available today. Wireless Knowledge's Workstyle Server allows corporations to connect multiple Exchange servers with wireless handhelds and phones, so that the corporate users can read email, check their calendars, or look up phone numbers using wireless devices. Some of the features available from Wireless Knowledge's Workstyle Server are listed in Table 7.2, on page 139.

Table 7.1 Capabilities of Various Wireless Networks (in U.S.)

NETWORK TECHNOLOGY	DESCRIPTION	BEST APPLICATIONS	GEOGRAPHIC COVERAGE	SPEED AND PERFORMANCE	PROS	CONS
Circuit-switched cellular	Data is sent over circuit-switched cellular network via special modems	Voice/data: Paging and short messages for dispatch	Nationwide	4.8–14.4kbps	Good coverage; economical for file transfer, fax	Expensive for short messages
Packet Radio (ARDIS or RAM)	Radio network designed specifically for packet data	Short bursts (POS, database queries, fleet dispatch, telemetry)	Nationwide	4.8–128kbps	Nationwide coverage	Expensive for long files
Narrowband Personal Communication Service (PCS)	Two-way PCS based network	Short messages with brief interaction	Regional to national	25.6kbps on Skytel	Two-way messaging cost is attractive	Limited messaging protocol
Wireless (CDMA, TDMA, GSM, etc.)	Two-way circuit-switched/packet-switched network		Regional to national	9.6–19.2kbps with 2G, up to 144kbps with 2.5G, and up to 2Mbps with 3G	Higher speeds are attractive	Depending on the pricing model, could turn out to be expensive, spotty coverage in certain areas, interference problems
CDPD	Packet-based digital data over cellular infrastructure	Short, bursty data	Metropolitan areas	19.2kbps	Can leverage existing infrastructure	Higher priority is given to voice, thus affecting the availability for data
Satellite	Data sent over low Earth-orbit satellites	High-speed file transfer	National and international	9.6kbps	Great coverage except for "urban canyons" (such as downtowns)	Expensive

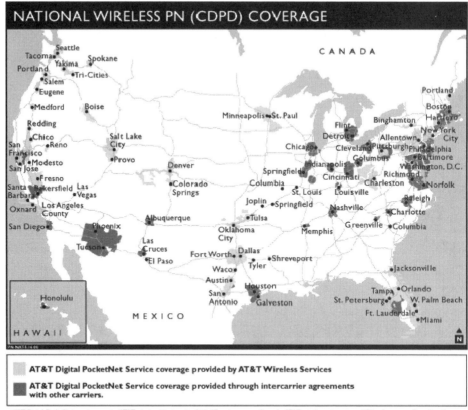

Figure 7.1 AT&T's CDPD network coverage.

(Copyright © 2000, AT&T)

Another service bureau company (A service bureau company, in this context, is one which provides software solutions, services, and hosting for these solutions and services) called Saraide provides a similar feature set with its Spring technology. In addition, groupware services are available from emerging wireless ASPs such as IoBox.com and MobileID.com and from carriers such as AT&T and Sprint PCS. Most of the time, any corporation would like its users to directly hook into a corporate intranet using technology and services from companies such as Wireless Knowledge that work with carriers such as AT&T to provide a service to corporations.

Recently, Research in Motion (RIM) launched its innovative Blackberry service. The highlights of this service offering are as follows:

Table 7.2 Functionality and Features of Wireless Knowledge's Workstyle Server

FUNCTIONALITY	FEATURES
Browser support	HDML, WML, XML, HTML, Microsoft Microbrowser, dual-mode HTML/WML microbrowsers
Airlinks	GSM, CDPD, Mobitex, CDMA
Email	• Read, reply, forward, compose email messages • Filter and manage in-box • Navigation to in-box folders • Search global address list and contact list by email • Accept/decline meeting invitations
Calendar	• Create, edit, view meeting appointments • Send meeting invitations to people in the global contacts list • Cancel meetings and send notifications to attendees • Compose meeting notes
Contacts	• Create, view, edit contacts • Search personal and global contacts lists • Initiate phone calls from the interface without typing in phone numbers

➤ Seamless single mailbox integration of Microsoft Exchange (Lotus Notes to follow shortly)

➤ Personal information management (PIM) functions available with synchronization (such as Puma Intellisync)

➤ End-to-end security

➤ Flat-rate pricing

➤ Filtering software

The service runs over BellSouth's data network and has over 90 percent coverage of U.S. metropolitan areas.

Lotus Notes

Lotus mobile service for Domino software package from Lotus allows mobile users to connect to their Lotus Notes applications like email, calendar, address book, discussion databases etc. Figure 7.2 shows the service using AT&T on Mitsubishi T250 phones.

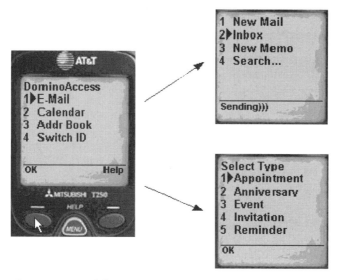

Figure 7.2   Mobile services for Domino from AT&T.

Extending Existing Web-Based Applications to Wireless Devices

Depending on the devices—WAP phones, Palm PDAs, WinCE PDAs, Blackberry handhelds—the solution sets differ.

HTML Sites

Both HDML and WML are languages supported by smart phones. The term *smart phone* is industry lingo for a specific type of cellular phone. To qualify as "smart," the digital phone must include a multiline display and a microbrowser such as WAP.

HDML is a proprietary language from Phone.com that is supported in most WAP phones today (mostly in U.S.). WML is a more open language that supports WAP browsers from Phone.com as well as other vendors such as Ericsson. WML is not supported by today's phones but will be the protocol of choice on the next generation of smart phones.

It takes a handset manufacturer about six to nine months to manufacture a new phone, so even though phones that support WML are few and far between today, it is important that a Web site support both HDML and WML to be accessible on the wireless Web.

There are two approaches a company can take to place existing content on WML and/or HDML devices:

➤ Rewrite all or sections of the Web site into WML or HDML.

➤ Use rendering/extraction techniques to transfer existing content and then apply transcoding to produce the content into multiple formats such as WML, HDML, HTML, cHTML, and VxML.

Clearly, the first choice is not a recommended way of doing things because the process is cumbersome, difficult to manage, and difficult to maintain and doesn't leave room for growth as the need for multiple formats grows. The extraction and transcoding techniques are becoming increasingly popular for content providers because they allow them to leverage their existing investments. A number of companies offer such services. Although Everypath had an early mover advantage, companies such as Isovia and Databites are making inroads with their service offerings as well. These companies generally handle extraction, maintenance, and hosting of wireless services.

There is also an option of using transcoding server products such as IBM's Transcoding publisher. It consists of the following base transcoding technologies:

➤ HTML reduction

➤ HTML reformatting

➤ Image reduction, modification, and elimination

➤ XML to XML variants

➤ XML to WML

➤ HTML to WML

➤ Extensible framework for "pluggable" transcoders

Transcoding Publisher supports handhelds, both WinCE and PalmOS, and WAP phones. Microbrowsers from Nokia and Phone.com are also supported.

AvantGo

AvantGo is a leading provider of solutions for PDAs. It is available for both Microsoft Windows CE and the Palm Computing Platform. One of the advantages of using AvantGo's solution is that it is agnostic regarding network connection. It can work in both network-connected and network-disconnected conditions. Content can be synchronized by either wireless or wired (PC) network connection. The deployment architecture of AvantGo's solution is shown in Figure 7.3.

Creating content for the AvantGo service is similar to creating wireless Web pages with HTML. It relies on the notion of *channels*, which are essentially groups of related pages. A user can select or create a channel using a desktop Web browser. The handheld platform's desktop synchronization interface (Palm or WinCE) uses the information in a channel in conjunction with the desktop application to synchronize Web pages between the channel's original server and the handheld.

AvantGo Enterprise Server is a two-way gateway that runs on Windows NT, Solaris, and Linux. It integrates with NT domain services and LDAP directories and employs

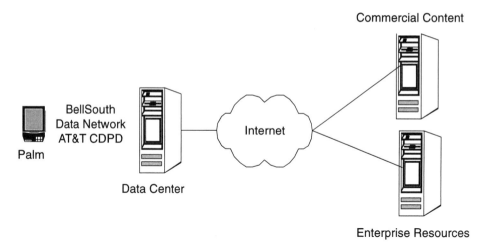

Figure 7.3   AvantGo architecture.

128-bit SSL encryption. It also allows administrators to have control over users and groups via the ability to channel content and access to applications based on user profiles—a much-needed feature in a corporate environment.

Palm

Palm OS-based handhelds pretty much own the market with over 80 percent market share worldwide. Wireless services on Palm VII use BellSouth's Data Network (Palm.net); Palm V uses AT&T's CDPD network (marketed as OmniSky service). The Web Clipping proxy server at Palm.Net converts HTML pages into versions that are more optimized for wireless device usage. These pages—called Web clippings—are formatted in a subset of HTML 3.2 with a handful of special Web Clipping extensions.

Figure 7.4 illustrates the Palm.net architecture.

Palm uses User Datagram Protocol (UDP) instead of the more computationally intensive TCP/IP. The main difference between Palm VII and Palm V wireless service is that with Palm VII, users can only browse preconfigured Web site content using client-installed Web Clipping Palm Query Applications (PQAs)(unless they install special browsers such as DP Web). However, with Palm V and OmniSky Service, users can go to almost any Web site, although formatting doesn't work that well at some sites.

Figure 7.5 shows an example of wireless Web access using OmniSky service.

So, it's easy to convert existing Web applications for Palm devices. We will review some Palm-based applications in the last chapter. Palm.Net provides security measures, including data encryption and SSL, as well as server-only access from Palm.Net through your firewall.

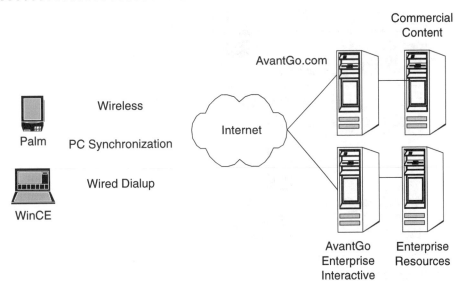

Figure 7.4   Palm architecture.

Windows CE

Windows CE devices come with Microsoft's microbrowser (Mobile Explorer), which is richer in functionality. It also uses a subset of HTML. Some of its features are as follows:

➢ It supports both WML and HTML as well as cookies, bookmarks, and forms

➢ Access to corporate email (Microsoft Exchange)

➢ Access to Internet email via POP3

Figure 7.5   OmniSky service for Palm devices.

(Source: OmniSky)

Figure 7.6   PocketPC microbrowser.

> No real-time operating system (RTOS) required; Mobile Explorer can run directly on the target hardware, or can run in conjunction with any existing phone RTOS

> Supports industry-standard networking protocols, including WTP, HTTP, Point-to-Point Protocol (PPP), and TCP/IP

> Supports all major airlinks, which include GSM, GPRS, 3G networks, CDMA, (Personal Handy Phone System) PHS, PDC, TDMA, and so on

Figure 7.6 shows an example of rich content browsing on a Windows CE-based device.

Mobile Explorer can be upgraded over the air to add new features to handsets that are already in use (a feature that might not be enabled in all implementations). This actually is a big advantage over some of the other implementations for which users need to replace the hardware in order to go to the next version of browser software.

Building New Ebusiness Solutions

Reprinted with permission from Website Architectures for a Wireless World

COLIN HENDRICKS, 2000

If you are looking to build a fresh new site, it's important to make some key architecture decisions. One common mistake in many projects is separating the online and wireless development efforts with separate teams and architecture in the hope that it will all work together at the very end. Although online and wireless are two development environments, they should be built on the same architectural foundation. This is critical for the following reasons:

➤ Reuse of content for multiple formats and languages

➤ Ongoing maintenance and support

➤ Scalability and reliability

➤ Better control of content—hence important services such as personalization for multiple devices (for the same user) are possible

For years, software developers have been preaching the many virtues of object-oriented software development. Object-oriented development simply means that instead of writing procedural code that is always executed from top to bottom, software developers create objects that model real-world entities. The software consists of interactions between these objects. An object encapsulates all the data and all the methods that represent the behavior of the object. One of the biggest benefits of this approach is that this behavior is isolated in one object rather than recoded in lots of places throughout a procedural program.

The encapsulation achieved via object-oriented programming allows software engineers to partition programs into logical layers of objects. A common approach is to create three tiers: a presentation layer, a business logic layer, and a data services layer. This approach allows for flexibility such as having several different presentation layers use the same business logic layer or switching out the data services layer to support a different database platform.

This sort of multitiered, object-oriented programming takes longer than traditional two-tier approaches in which visual elements of the interface are mapped directly to data elements in the database. However, the benefits of increased maintainability, scalability, and flexibility of loosely coupled layers of software are supposed to outweigh the extra development costs.

In practice, this doesn't always happen. Rarely do organizations find a good reason to slap a whole different presentation layer on a desktop PC program or find that they need to switch database vendors. However, the multitude of wireless interfaces in the Web world is changing that. Now, sites really do need to support many different interfaces, and an investment in a presentation-independent middle tier of business objects can really pay off. The following sections discuss each of the distinct software layers in such architecture.

The Presentation Layer: The User Interface

The functional design phase of the wireless interface often determines the success or failure of the wireless project. Two factors constrain the wireless interface: bandwidth and screen real estate. If restraint is not employed in determining the contents of the wireless interface and the reasonable bounds of these two constraints are exceeded, the platform will be unusable. In practice, this means that the interface should be limited to just a few pages, probably fewer than three that deliver a very focused collection of possible actions.

The Business Logic Layer

As mentioned, the most practical way to support different interfaces and to build a system that is flexible enough to support unforeseen interfaces in the future is to decouple the business logic form the presentation logic. In other words, if you're building an auction system, don't write the auction rules into the Java servlets or Active Server Pages themselves; write them in an independent middle layer that is ignorant of how the information is displayed.

The business logic layer consists of objects that model the business rules that apply to real-world objects. For instance, it might contain a "user" object that represents a user of the site. The object would have fields such as first name, last name, and password and contain business rules such as a requirement that the password be more than eight letters. This object could be reused every time the site interacts with a user. For example, this same object can be used when a user logs in to the regular site and when they log in using a Palm VII.

The objects in the middle tier can be created in almost any technology. They could be based on Sun's Enterprise JavaBean (EJB) architecture, Microsoft's Component Object Model (COM) technology, the Object Management Group's (OMG) Common Object Request Broker Architecture (CORBA), or just plain Java or C++ classes.

One important thing to consider is that the centralized nature of Web server architectures actually obviates complex distributed object architectures such as EJB, DCOM, and CORBA. Those technologies allow clients on remote machines to use objects on the server as though they were local to the client. In the Web world, especially in the wireless Web world, the client is actually the presentation layer of the site, not another device. The browser on the remote device is just a dumb terminal that does close to nothing. This means that the presentation layer will most likely be on the same machine as the business object layer. Therefore, the complexities of distributed objects can be dispensed with in favor of simple Java or C++ classes.

However, a valid argument could be made that using distributed objects in the middle layer increases the scalability of the site because it allows for the separation of the software layers between physical machines. The presentation layer could run on one machine while the all the business objects containing the business logic reside on a completely separate box.

The Services Layer

The services layer is the abstraction layer that decouples the business objects from the database (the persistence layer). This decoupling allows the business objects to contain nothing but business logic code, rendering this logic portable to other persistence mechanisms. The services contain things such as all the Structured Query Language (SQL) for storing the business objects in the database.

In addition to providing services to the business objects, the services layer can also provide services to the presentation layer. Different interfaces have different basic requirements in addition to merely presenting a user interface. Session management is a good example.

Session Management for Wireless Platforms

Web sites that provide business functionality typically need to store user session information between page requests (such as items in a shopping cart). This information is usually stored in a session object in memory on the Web server.

Different interfaces have different ways of dealing with sessions. For instance, conventional Web browsers often use memory cookies. *Cookies* are tokens that are passed along with every page request and contain a small bit of data—in this case, a unique session ID. The Web server uses the session ID to match session objects in memory on the server with requests from each Web browser client it is serving.

Wireless devices, on the other hand, typically do not support cookies. This means site developers have to create their own services for managing wireless sessions. A common way of doing this on the Palm VII platform is to take advantage of the unique device ID of the Palm device. This ID can be passed to the Web server with every request from the device. The Web server can then use this unique ID to match each request with any session information it is storing in memory for that user.

Application servers automatically do this kind of session management for conventional browsers, but managing wireless sessions requires the developers of the site to write some extra code to manage these sessions and the mapping of them to device IDs. Code must be written to grab the incoming device IDs and to store session information keyed to those values.

A sample Web architecture is shown in Figure 7.7. Among the Web application servers available today, IBM's Websphere platform provides the widest range of functionality in terms of features, including synchronization, transcoding, security, load optimization, caching, LDAP, network and device management, log analysis, and personalization.

Some of the other vendors in this application server space are BEA Systems, Oracle, iPlanet (Sun and Netscape), Sybase, Silverstream, Allaire, Art Group Technology (ATG), Microsoft, Persistence, and Inprise.

HDML or WML?

HDML is Phone.com's proprietary language that predates WAP. If you are developing applications and services for the U.S. market, you unfortunately have to deal with this legacy browser markup language, since there are a fair number of cell phones (sold by Sprint PCS Wireless Web and AT&T–PocketNet) still in use that run older browser software that understands only HDML and not WAP's WML. Phone.com's solution to the problem is to convert WML content from WAP sites to HDML before it is served up to the phones. However, the translation isn't perfect, since no one-to-one mapping of features is available from HDML and WML. So, if a significant portion of your user population is using HDML-only phones, it's worth considering publishing content in HDML as well. The translation functionality is available only with Phone.com's gateway server, so work with carriers to figure out the optimal solution for your applications.

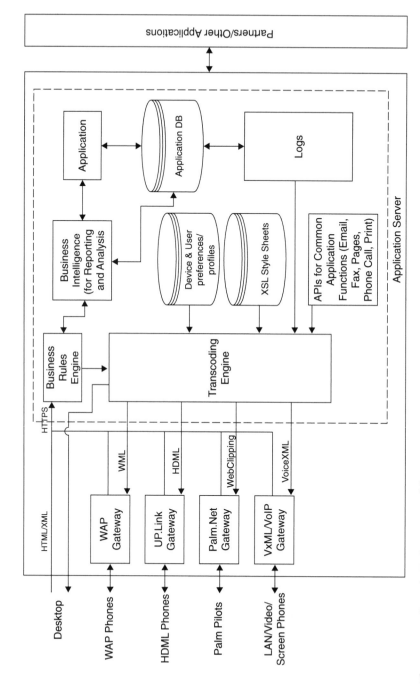

Figure 7.7 Sample Web server architecture.

Additionally, developers working on WAP applications can check their HTTP headers to retrieve the version of the WAP browser and the version of the WAP gateway that a cellular handset is using. Depending on these versions, a somewhat different content syntax will need to be sent back to the handset. This is an unfortunate situation, but developers who create applications and content for the Internet are used to doing the same thing for the various versions of Netscape and Internet Explorer browsers.

This interoperability problem primarily exists in the United States and Canada. In contrast, most of Europe and Asia support the WAP 1.1 standard in both handsets and gateways. In these markets, applications written using HDML might or might not work, depending on the type of WAP gateway used. However, if your WAP application will be deployed in the United States, using Phone.com's UP.SDK 3.2 is almost essential to ensure that your application will work properly across Phone.com's version 3.x gateways. If you choose to code in HDML 3.0, this toolkit is your only choice.

Although any application server is capable of serving up WML pages, the most productive approach is to generate WML pages using XML. Web content is stored in XML format, and then XML style sheets can be applied to generate WML. Cocoon, a set of open-source tools offered by the Apache XML project, is Java servlet technology that can easily transform XML-encoded Web content into WML using XML Style Sheet technology. If you're interested in this approach to generating WML content, Cocoon is a good place to study how these transformations can be accomplished.

Developer Tools

In this section, developer toolkit resources are provided for various technology standards. If you are planning to build applications using these standards, it's important that the application and service be tested using the simulators provided by various manufacturers, because the implementation varies from player to player. For example, even though Phone.com, Nokia, Ericsson, and Motorola are fiercely working on standardizing WAP and resolve interoperability issues, there are differences in their UI implementations that could give unexpected results. Therefore, developers and testers should identify the phone distribution for target consumers and simulate and test their work on the corresponding simulators.

The following sections contain tables listing URLs from which toolkits can be downloaded. Some other helpful URLs are listed in Appendix A, "Useful URLs."

WAP

Several developer toolkits are available from all major WAP infrastructure providers, namely Phone.com, Nokia, Ericsson, and Motorola. The WAP Software Development Kit (SDK) also includes simulators for multiple phones of varying form factors. Table 7.3 lists the URLs for toolkits provided by selected companies. Figure 7.8 shows Motorola's (Mobile Internet Exchange) MIX development platform that allows for both WML and Voice Application development. Voice development environment is

Table 7.3 WAP Toolkits

COMPANY	TOOLKIT DOWNLOAD URL
Phone.com	www.phone.com/developers/index.html
Nokia	www.nokia.com/wap/development.html
Ericsson	www.ericsson.com/developerszone/
Motorola	http://mix.motorola.com/audiences/developers/ dev_main.asp

on ly available in Motorola's proprietary VoXML Language which is different form Voice XML.

Palm

Handspring, Palm, Sony, and Symbol provide toolkits for their respective handhelds, which are based on Palm OS. Table 7.4 lists the URLs for these toolkits.

WinCE

Microsoft recently relaunched Windows CE, its entry into the handheld market. The simulator and development toolkit are available for a small fee. More information is available at the Microsoft site listed in Table 7.5.

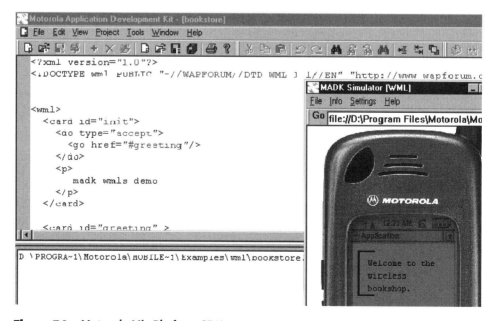

Figure 7.8 Motorola Mix Platform SDK.

Table 7.4 Palm Simulator Toolkits

COMPANY	TOOLKIT DOWNLOAD URL
Palm	www.palmos.com/dev/tech/webclipping/
Symbol	www.symbol.com/products/mobile_computers/ mobile_palm_developers_zone.html
Handspring	www.handspring.com/developers/index.asp
Sony	www.sonypdadev.com

Table 7.5 WinCE Toolkit

COMPANY	TOOLKIT DOWNLOAD URL
Microsoft	www.microsoft.com/mobile/developer/default.asp

EPOC

Symbian is a joint venture among Ericsson, Nokia, Motorola, and Psion. Symbian's EPOC technology is used for both phones and handhelds; the URL for the toolkit is shown in Table 7.6.

Table 7.6 EPOC Toolkit

COMPANY	TOOLKIT DOWNLOAD URL
Symbian	www.symbiandevnet.com/

ATVEF

Advanced Television Enforcement Forum (ATVEF) is a standards body for WebTV. A browser, tools, and tips for WebTV developers are available at the URL listed in Table 7.7.

Table 7.7 WebTV Toolkit

COMPANY	TOOLKIT DOWNLOAD URL
WebTV	http://developer.webtv.net/

VoiceXML

VxML is a fairly new technology. IBM and Tellme have provided some development and simulation toolkits at the URLs listed in Table 7.8.

Table 7.8   VxML Toolkits

COMPANY	TOOLKIT DOWNLOAD URL
IBM	www.alphaworks.ibm.com/tech/voicexml
Tellme	http://studio.tellme.com

XML

As we discussed in Chapters 3 and 5, XML is a core technology that developers should consider using whenever the requirement is to publish content into multiple markup-language formats such as HTML and WML. Table 7.9 lists some of the prominent developer resources for XML.

Table 7.9   XML Toolkits

DEVELOPER	TOOLKIT DOWNLOAD URL
XML.org resources	www.xml.org/xmlorg_resources/index.shtml
The Apache XML project	http://xml.apache.org/cocoon/
IBM XML resources	www.ibm.com/developer/xml/
Oasis XML Cover Pages	www.oasis-open.org/cover/publicSW.htmls
MSDN XML Developer Center	http://msdn.microsoft.com/xml/default.asp

Definition and Implementation Checklist

Once you have identified your high-level project and figured out its strategic direction, next comes the job of implementing the chosen wireless Internet solution. Like any other Internet implementation project, these tasks can be divided into two broad categories: requirements and implementation. The requirements phase is used to gather the creative, usability, technology, and test requirements. It is highly recommended that you build some quick prototypes to help you further define requirements. Focus group sessions, during which actual or simulated users get to interact with prototypes, are also very helpful. This section presents checklists for the requirements and implementation phases. Depending on the needs of the project, items could be combined into one action item or milestone.

Requirements

The following is a sample requirements checklist. The steps on this list can serve as milestones for the requirements phase of the project. The requirements phase is critical to the eventual success of the project. Like any other project, it is critical to define and assemble requirements as clearly as possible up front. Furthermore, it's highly recommended that some proof-of-concept and prototype work be done for both functional and usability design. Since usability is a big success factor for wireless Internet projects, it's wise to conduct usability reviews and focus groups with actual users at regular intervals throughout the project. Prototypes in these cases are fairly easy to build.

Here is a checklist for the requirements phase:

1. Develop the initial proof of concept and/or prototype
2. Build the detailed business plan(s)
3. Analyze the marketing situation
4. Update competitive assessment
5. Research customer wants and needs
6. Perform user analysis
7. Define creative strategy
8. Perform technical assessment
9. Define technical strategy
10. Hold focus groups
11. Predict user acceptance and impact
12. Detail business requirements
13. Define functional requirements
14. Update the return-on-investment (ROI) business case or financial pro forma
15. Define high-level content requirements
16. Develop conceptual technical architecture
17. Define user interaction
18. Build technical feasibility prototype
19. Define software and technical requirements
20. Build test cases
21. Define performance requirements
22. Design business processes

Implementation

Once the requirements have been solidified and agreed on, it's time for implementation. Good project management mandates minimal high-level requirement changes once the implementation project begins. Testing is often the most neglected phase of Internet projects. Due to tight schedules and limited time, teams often tend to ship code without thorough regression and stress testing. For wireless Internet projects, depending on the number of markup language formats and family of devices the team is targeting, the testing requirements can get fairly complex and cumbersome.

Automated testing tools can be used to ease the pain. Software should be tested using multiple software development toolkits, and there is no substitute for testing with actual physical devices. Due to discrepancies in implementation and realities of real-world operating environments, it's critical that multiple users on multiple actual physical devices test the applications and services. Remember that with wireless environments, users have low tolerance for buggy code or unusable interfaces. Unlike the desktop environment, they can't multitask while they wait for content to appear on their devices.

Here is the checklist for the implementation phase:

1. Begin high-level design
2. Build site map
3. Conceptualize the visual design
4. Build navigation map
5. Develop content matrix
6. Define test approach and tools
7. Create content delivery plan
8. Engage in development
9. Engage in regular unit testing
10. Conduct midpoint reviews and usability analysis
11. Freeze code
12. Perform stress testing
13. Fix bugs
14. Conduct limited launch
15. Conduct full-scale launch

In this chapter we learned how to select various wireless and computing solutions, depending on the needs of a project and the type of application you are trying to build. In the next chapter, we will discuss the critical success factors and guiding principles for three successful wireless Internet implementations.

CHAPTER 8

Wireless Internet Strategy: Critical Success Factors and Guiding Principles

So far we have taken a look at various wireless technologies, players, and solutions. In this chapter, we review some of the critical success factors and guiding principles required for successful wireless Internet projects.

The success factors and guiding principles covered in this chapter are as follows:

➢ Have a clear strategy and goal

➢ Do competitive analysis

➢ Perform affinity of device and services analysis

➢ Aggregate content

➢ Ensure usability

➢ Be in touch with specifications and emerging technologies

➢ Ensure interoperability

➢ Ensure internationalization

➢ Create prototypes and do testing

➢ Ensure personalization

➢ Ensure security

➢ Engage in strategic and synergetic partnerships

➢ Learn and leverage from Web experience

➤ Consider billing and pricing

➤ Ensure QoS and put in place SLA

➤ Ensure detection and prevention of fraud

➤ Keep it simple

➤ Ensure consumer privacy

➤ Ensure existing infrastructure and backward compatibility

➤ Monitor the network

Now let's take a look at each of these points in detail.

Clear Strategy and Goal

Changing times have made it necessary for any high-tech company to consider wireless Internet in its overall strategy and business goals. This strategy involves a thorough understanding of the competitive marketplace and viable technologies that will make realization of the strategic vision and goals possible, as well as a detailed knowledge of major players that are potential partners and are critical to successful execution of any strategy. Often, companies respond to market buzz and hype instead of real market demands and opportunities. Some technology companies also get ahead of the game by bringing solutions to market for which there is no demand. Every idea, every application and service needs to be well thought out from a strategic point of view. If it's not something that enhances the core business values (revenues, productivity, customer loyalty) that the company delivers or can deliver, the application probably needs to be thought through some more.

For any good idea to succeed, some significant effort should be put in up front in gathering information about the following:

➤ Business model

➤ Market demand

➤ ROI (time, revenue, profits) and revenue model

➤ Partnerships

➤ Targeted customer and industry segment(s)

➤ Capability (what you can really deliver)

➤ Marketing, education, and branding campaigns

➤ Executive buy-in

Once you have identified the end goal, a clear and a well thought out strategy is critical in implementing the plan.

Competitive Analysis

Corporations need agility to be successful in an ever-changing environment. They need to avoid being obliterated or playing catch-up with the competition. They must keep a finger on the pulse of their potential customer base as well as that of their competitors—traditional as well as nontraditional. A thorough, constant competitive analysis helps companies foster growth, solutions, and success.

For any organization thinking about playing in the wireless Internet field, it's important to understand the value chain and to figure out its place in the whole mix. Gaining this insight will help the company understand the competitive landscape in the real world. More often than not, it's the nontraditional competitors that the firms need to worry about. The strength of the online revolution is that anyone with an idea for doing things better can very quickly launch applications and services online and go global instantly. So, it's critical to understand the dynamics of the market and gauge its next step.

Key competitive pulse points are as follows:

➤ Type of industry

➤ Type of information/application

➤ Type of partnership, vendor relationship

➤ Customers categorization

For example, financial institutions were the first to jump on the wireless Internet bandwagon. So, today wireless financial services are no longer considered a feature; users have come to expect them from their brokerages. Companies that don't get their acts together in time are most likely to see increases in customer churn rates.

Affinity of Service and Devices Analysis

Right now, companies are rushing to deliver all possible content to all possible devices [source: Forrester Research, 1999]. Such strategies are bound to fail. To get a sense of any particular service's success on a given device, research and analysis should be undertaken to determine the suitability of a service to the device.

Let's consider an example to further illustrate this key point. As discussed in Chapters 1 and 4, field engineers and service staff can greatly benefit from wireless applications that allow them to input and retrieve information as it relates to their day-to-day work. The cost savings can be immense. If we break down this application, it could have the components listed in Table 8.1.

The best types of devices suited for field workers are Palm Pilot-type handhelds that have 160 x 160 screen resolution, have enough memory to run a compact application, and can operate in both connected (wireline, wireless) and disconnected setups. There is really no need to publish this content on a WebTV, a kiosk, small display

Table 8.1   Affinity of Applications to Devices

NATURE OF APPLICATION	USER	SUITABLE DEVICE
Data entry (filing report) and summary analysis in the field	Field engineers	Handhelds, large-screen smart phones
Business intelligence and detailed analysis/reports	Analysts, supervisor	PCs
Work assignment	Supervisor	PCs, PDAs
Alert notification	Field engineers, supervisor	Pagers, phones, wireless handhelds

phones, autoPCs, or the like. For the analysts and supervisors who need to evaluate the data and read the reports, and because they are in their offices most of the time, desktop PCs are more suited to their needs. Therefore, it's critical to analyze application-to-device suitability. Applications should be evaluated from the point of view of conformance to standards and protocols, usability, network bandwidth, purpose, and target audience. Devices should be evaluated from the point of view of form factors, user interface, usability, limitations, and conformance to standards. If the suitability of the application doesn't match the capability of the device, most likely the application will not succeed on that device.

Aggregation of Content

The vision that transcends the next generation of applications is that of device independence. Wherever it makes sense, consumers will demand content delivery, irrespective of the devices they use: desktop PCs (HTML, XML, XHTML), mobile phones and PDAs (WML), telephones (VxML), screen phones, televisions (ATVEF, TVHTML), pagers (SMS), watches, kiosks, airline seats, Web-enabled Sega games, and so on. Developing and maintaining separate content for specific devices will be nearly impossible. Companies need to move toward a model in which different templates are used to serve the same content to different devices. This model will help in content reuse (for example, providing weather information across multiple devices) and make content easier to manage.

Aggregation of content and transcoding strategies depends a great deal on your business objectives and goals. If you have already built an online presence and it's not based on an XML architecture at its core and the content is pretty static without much personalization, it's worth considering solutions from wireless ASPs such as Everypath, Aether Software, and the like. If, however, your ebusiness site generates dynamic pages with unique content for a majority of the users, it's wiser to rethink your Web architecture. Having an XML-based core allows you to not only react to today's needs but prepare for the next few years. XML provides more control of the formatting of the content based on device and network capability and user preferences. Furthermore, since you have more control over content, the personalization model is much more scalable to your subscriber growth.

For the content management aspects of the project, it's crucial to understand these two points:

➤ Wireline and wireless projects should be part of the same initiative.

➤ Wireline and wireless development environments are quite different.

As we will learn in the next few sections, usability and personalization are absolute keys to successful pervasive computing solutions. If a solution is not designed with the user in mind, it's bound to fail—it's that simple. Research shows that a majority of consumers, especially the business population, will carry more than two devices, whether pagers, phones, laptops, PDAs, or something else. This means that they will access the same information from multiple devices. However, the user experience on each of these devices needs to be different and customized to user preferences and device capabilities.

Usability

Reprinted with permission from Usability–WAP

CASEY KRUB, 2000.

Usability is important for any application or device, but it's even more important for capability-constrained devices—those with limited display or input. Ease of use is critical to provide a positive user experience with wireless Internet applications. Usability analysis should encompass any wireless Internet project from start to finish. Even the best application will fail to take off if it is designed without investing enough resources in usability studies. Since usability is such key to success for applications and services, here we discuss some of the things you can do to make your site more usable and user friendly.

People tend to think of computers as "new" technology and telephones as "old" technology, but as one has evolved, so has the other. Now you can access the Internet over a cordless, mobile, or Web-enabled phone, or you can buy a Webphone, such as the em@iler or iPhone, which are traditional phones with a screen for viewing email or surfing the Web.

Most people in North America who access the Internet do so via home computers, but not everyone can afford the costs associated with owning one. Furthermore, the majority of the world does not share the same telecommunications infrastructure as North America. Cheaper and easier to access, the wireless Web is a viable option for people who cannot afford personal computers or who lack the infrastructure necessary to use them to access the Internet.

Non-PC Devices

Many companies that provide wireless Web services or pages erroneously assume that users can use a wired device, a desktop or laptop computer, to set up, configure, and maintain the accounts they will access on their handhelds. This is a large assumption, because as we just noted, not all users have access to desktop computers. In Finland, for example, a mobile phone is called a *kännykkä* or a *känny*—"extension of the hand"—and it is estimated that nearly 70 percent of the population own them. These users clearly do not view mobile phones and handheld devices as adjuncts or peripherals of personal computers.

Know Your Users

Don't assume your users are all upwardly mobile, tech-savvy Americans. Nearly 90 percent of teenagers in Finland, for example, have wireless phones. Of the 2 million wireless Web users in Japan, teenagers are gaining ground as the largest audience in the wireless arena. So, although the small screen of a wireless device lends itself to accessing information such as stock quotes and golf scores, these uses hold little appeal for these audiences.

Remember too that people use handheld devices to fulfill specific information needs, not to browse the Web or create new data. Browsing and data creations are functional strengths of the personal computer.

> *The Usability Group* is a research and consulting firm specializing in managing the customer experience with interactive products

The unforgiving nature of the wireless environment and its users is the one thing that most differentiates WAP applications from Web and desktop applications, notes Jim Berney of the Usability Group. (The Usability Group is a research and consulting firm specializing in managing the customer experience with interactive products) Disciplined structure and design are vital to the success of your application. "Cowboy coding and off-the-cuff design decisions" are amplified in the WAP environment and can be much more expensive than mistakes made in the HTML world. In the telecommunications world, where WAP applications exist, users expect things to work the first time and every time. Functional prototypes, usability testing, and rigorous quality assurance (QA) procedures are essential.

Interfaces for Handheld Devices

Imagine a window on your computer screen that is approximately 4 inches by 3 inches and what it would take to navigate through a Web site or the files on your hard drive on such a screen. It wouldn't be easy, even with access to a mouse and a full-size keyboard—the two input devices most common to the desktop computer.

Input devices on handheld devices vary. Some use a stylus, others have touch screens, and others have tiny keyboards; the possibilities and combinations are endless. Since screen space is limited on handhelds, designers must focus on meeting user needs and goals while minimizing user interaction in a manner that does not affect the quantity of information displayed. Table 8.2 shows the disparity in screen resolution and screen size for the devices available today; this is just the beginning. In the coming years, devices with varying features and capabilities will continue to evolve. In the future, the majority of new PDAs, phones, and appliances will be Web

Table 8.2   Screen Resolution and Size for Various Devices

DEVICE	SCREEN RESOLUTION AND SIZE
PDAs	
Helio	160×160; 59mm $\times$ 59 mm
Palm	160×160; 8 bit
Cassiopeia E-115	240×320 [5 1/8" $\times$ 3 1/4"]
HP Jornada 430 range	240×320 [5.1" $\times$ 3.2"]
HP Jornada 540 range	240×320; [5.2" $\times$ 3.1"]
Symbol PPT 2700 Series	240×320
Compaq iPaq	240×320; 2.26" $\times$ 3.02" viewable
Compaq Aero	240×320; 2.4" $\times$ 3.2" viewable
Matsucom OnHand PDA	102×64; 20 characters $\times$ 5 lines; 1.1" $\times$ 0.75"
Franklin Rex	160×98; 9 lines or 30 characters of text [3-3/8" $\times$ 2-1/8"]
Sharp Zaurus	320×240; 65 characters $\times$ 20 lines; 4.0" $\times$ 2.6"
Web-Enabled Mobile Phones	
QUALCOMM QCP products	12 characters $\times$ 4 lines + 1 line for icons
QUALCOMM pdQ products	160×240 [6.2" $\times$ 2.6"]
Nokia 9000il Communicator	640×200 [6.5" $\times$ 2.5"]
NeoPoint Smart Phones	160×120; 1.5" $\times$ 2.0"
Motorola StarTrac	240×136; 55mm $\times$ 33.8mm
Webphones and Email Appliances	
ICL TeamPad 7100	128×240; 16 characters $\times$ 13 lines [5.9" h $\times$ 2.4" w]
ICL TeamPad 7200	192×240; 24 characters $\times$ 15 lines [8.3" h $\times$ 3.4" w]
ICL TeamPad 7500	800×600; 8.4" diagonal [10" $\times$ 7"]
ICL TeamPad 7600	640×480; 7.2" diagonal [8.4" $\times$ 6"]
MailBug	79 characters $\times$ 6 lines [10.6" $\times$ 7']
iPhone	640×480; 7.4" screen
I-opener	800×600; 10" flat panel
e-Mail Postbox	240×80; 40 characters $\times$ 8 lines [12.4" $\times$ 8.2"]; screen is very small
e-Mail express	240×50; 40 characters $\times$ 5 lines [6.3" $\times$ 3.5"]; screen is very small
e-Mail Traveler	160×160; 2.1" $\times$ 2.1" (PDA screen that fits into docking station)
eMailBox	640×240; 8" $\times$ 2.5"
JVC HC-E100	240×64; 40 characters $\times$ 8 lines [6.25" $\times$ 3.24"]

Note: Measurements in brackets indicate device size rather than screen size.

enabled. That means that content will have to be generated on the fly based on the capabilities of the device and preferences of the user.

Simplify

Simple navigation is important due to the limitations of small screens. If your content is displayed over several screens, navigation and context become critical. Clear navigational signals enable the user to move through your site easily, and plenty of feedback keeps the user from feeling lost.

Try using an inverted pyramid approach when designing content: Put the most important information at the beginning of a WAP page, which is called a *card*. The WAP metaphor is a deck of cards; the site is a deck, and each page is a card. Needless to say, you should be wary of falling into the standard HTML layout and display assumptions. Since a wide variety of devices support WAP applications, the browser must be allowed to format the display for optimal use on various devices.

Keep Text Concise

Although this idea may seem obvious, it is easily overlooked in the effort to add more features. Keep content brief and to the point. Use short, significant words, especially for navigation links. Here are some other tips:

➤ Precode options to avoid text entry.

➤ Offer lists of words, numbered menu items, check boxes, and radio buttons to minimize text entry.

➤ Use images to enhance text, not replace it. Many browsers do not support images, or users might turn off images.

➤ Provide image text descriptions using the <ALT> tag, especially if images are used as hyperlinks.

➤ Use alert boxes to push information, in moderation.

Additional Usability Tips

Here are a few more ways you can increase the usability of WAP applications:

➤ Use flat menu structures; users are more likely to get lost when they go deeper than two levels. A complex menu system can make your site seem slower than it is.

➤ Keep information clear and logical, and use standard layout techniques available within your schema. In WML, for example, use <ALIGN>, <STRONG>, <BIG>, <BOLD>, and other tags.

➤ Use tables to present data in rows and columns, *not* to place text and graphics in a specific location, as in HTML.

➤ Use optional elements such as headers and titles; many browsers display these elements to enhance navigation.

Because the field of handheld and mobile devices is so young, it does not yet have standards for studying application designs and their uses. This makes user-centered design and testing even more important. As the wireless Web continues to grow, a greater variety of devices will become readily available. The more designers become aware of device variations and limitations—and their users—the more effective the applications will be. Soon, this "new" technology will evolve into becoming the standard we could never imagine living without.

All the limitations of the handheld, such as the struggle to get data through that tiny on-screen keyboard and a tricky pen interface, could be overcome with speech technology. Theoretically, with voice control, anyone who can use a telephone can use a handheld device.

Issues in Developing Speech Recognition-Based Applications

TECHNICAL OBSTACLES THAT BAR WIDESPREAD ADOPTION

➤ Speech recognition averages one error per second.

➤ Background noise further confuses recognition systems.

HUMAN FACTORS ISSUES

➤ Short-term memory restricts choice; when users must rely on a speech interface for complex instructions or content, the interface breaks down.

➤ Privacy concerns limit transactions; users will reject voice input/output for personal information such as credit card numbers, PINs, and so on.

➤ Weak technologies require users to adjust speech habits; it is estimated that for at least the next ten years, automated voice applications will force users to change the way they speak in order to compensate for the technology's inadequacies.

Specifications and Emerging Technologies

The wireless Internet world is in warp-speed mode. Needless to say, it's important to keep up with the specifications, to look out for technologies from which you can leverage your applications, and to be aware of their impact on consumers. Enhancements in other technologies will indirectly improve applications. For example, improvement in compression techniques of graphic images (GIF to PNG) will lead to faster loading, richer graphics, and a better user experience. Improvements in bandwidth technologies (ISDN to DSL to fiber optics) will allow richer interactive applications. Furthermore, the technologies and platforms should be picked with an eye toward long-term viability and flexibility.

Interoperability

The world of wireless Internet technology is changing rapidly. Keep in mind issues regarding interoperability of various devices, server software and hardware, applications and services. The user should not be forced to upgrade or buy a new device just to access a new site. However, due to the nature of the competitive landscape, companies often engage in these interoperability wars until consumer demands force them to cooperate and interoperate. During the early phases of WAP deployment, phone microbrowsers and WAP gateways from different vendors such as Phone.com, Nokia, and Ericsson simply didn't interoperate. Applications designed using an SDK from one vendor wouldn't work well on other vendors' phones.

Some of these issues are being resolved in the WAP Forum, but still there are issues with standardization on some of the key elements such as UI navigation and size of information transfer. Developers need to be aware of such issues because ignorance can easily lead to unhappy customers. Therefore, it's critical for businesses to understand the distribution of devices in the customer base and understand the variances and nuances among the devices. Designing an effective XML-based system can help alleviate some of this pain, but there is no substitute for a thorough market analysis.

Internationalization

Thirty-seven percent of the Fortune 100 support their Web sites in a language other than English.

—FORRESTER RESEARCH, JUNE 2000

By 2004, 50 percent of online transactions will occur outside the United States.

—FORRESTER RESEARCH, 2000

With shrinking global boundaries, adequate attention must be paid to internationalization issues for applications and services to be successful around the globe. Companies must design sites that have character-encoding support for multiple languages, especially some of the Asian languages, which have over 6000 characters. Other intricacies are the way these sites are displayed. User experience is different for each language, so it's important to understand how different cultures interact with information.

Workflow applications and software need to take into account localization. As the number of non-English-speaking users increases, internationalization will be absolutely critical for successful operations—for customers, clients, and partners alike. Don't go for multiple languages at once; it ties back into the business strategy. Set your goals, design a strategy road map, and finally, execute and take into account cultural nuances.

Prototypes and Trials

The key to good application design is iteration: design, develop, learn, and iterate. Any given wireless Internet project needs to go through the rigors of prototype testing and trials for successful acceptance. These prototypes and trials should also address performance, caching, and scalability issues. As discussed earlier, it is imperative that information architects and usability experts be involved in the project from the start.

Personalization and Configuration

Our experience in the Internet space has shown that a well-implemented personalization strategy is key to an effective user experience and to creating loyal customers. Users who consistently have a customized navigational experience tend to come back often. Personalization information can be collected via explicit and implicit means.

NOTE

Explicit information is what the customer provides, such as name, address, and preferences. Implicit information is collected without user input and is based on the user's site navigation.

Real estate on a handheld device is scarce. Personalized content is the key to success in the Web world, and it's also critical in the wireless Internet space. Content, service, and application providers should thoroughly understand the consumer and his or her likes and dislikes before serving up information. Airtime costs money, so it's imperative that the content provided is of value to each consumer. With competitors only a click away, businesses need every possible advantage to keep the consumer from going elsewhere.

Analysis of server logs is an excellent source of information that can expedite understanding of consumer behaviors and demands, helping customize services and information to individual consumers. The concepts of "on-the-fly" menu hierarchy and content based on past history and preferences allow an application to not only conform to user expectations but exceed them.

Security

Internet access is cheap in the United States; mobile access is not. The coalescence of the computing and communications industries creates outstanding opportunities. However, any breach of information is potentially more harmful in the wireless world, where information is now interconnected and interdependent. Having strong security procedures and algorithms in place at various intermediary steps ensures that consumers feel comfortable embracing the information evolution.

Forging Synergetic Relationships

Content providers, device manufacturers, wireless carriers, and application developers need each other. The device manufacturers benefit if application developers build exciting applications that enable new services and meet new content/information demands. This in turn benefits wireless carriers, which are the benefactors of airtime usage. These partnerships not only reduce design and development costs, but they also help the various players better understand consumer demands. Cooperation and partnerships across traditional boundaries of industry and location can now create opportunities for players that offer the right mix of services.

No single company can do it all, from providing content to system integration to running and maintaining computing and communications infrastructures. For successful execution of projects, it is critical to have the right players in the mix. The core strength of Yahoo! is aggregation of content; Nokia's strength lies in communication technologies and handsets, while AT&T's bread and butter is its ability to run and maintain a complex communications network. In order to bring Yahoo! content onto Nokia handsets on the AT&T wireless network, it is essential for the three players to work together to provide maximum value to the consumer. Companies that try to extend themselves beyond the realm of their expertise and capabilities are setting themselves up for failure.

Learning from Web Site Building Experience

Wireless Internet applications and services development follows a model similar to the wired Internet. Consequently, lessons in the importance of usability, personalization, information architecture, configuration options, and the like can be learned from Internet applications development.

Billing and Pricing

The issue of pricing in the electronic commerce arena is one of unlimited potential as well as complications. While currently there is a need for human interface in negotiation and transaction of pricing, the future proves to extend electronic capabilities with agents that seek best pricing options.

—THE BIG IDEA, PERSPECTIVES ON BUSINESS INNOVATION: ISSUE 3, ERNST & YOUNG, 2000

Billing is still a conundrum in the wireless Internet world. Old pricing models don't make sense in the new landscape, but multiple new options of charging for services are possible. Billing is important for enterprise application suppliers and partners.

Basically, two things can be charged for: airtime and content. The wireless networks are either circuit-switched or packet-switched networks. If the network is circuit switched, the number of minutes are counted for billing purposes; for packet-switched networks, the number of packets goes toward billing for services. Content-based billing can be a service that provides preset content, or a consumer could be charged for small content transactions. For example, if the user simply wants to read a *Wall Street Journal* story, she pays for that particular story only (content). Some billing models also incorporate both airtime- and content-based pricing.

The broad range of billing models can be divided as follows:

➤ *Transaction-based billing*. In this model, both airtime and content are bundled to provide certain services. The difficult thing in this case is to come up with the right pricing model based on transactions. Transaction-based billing can be further categorized as follows:

  ➤ Performance

  ➤ Volume

  ➤ Quality

  ➤ Per use

  ➤ Per application/service/feature

  ➤ Flat rate

➤ *Monthly fee billing*. Users could be charged a flat rate based on either airtime or content.

➤ *Free services*. Depending on the packaging of services, certain partners could be offered free services.

➤ *Combination billing*. This model is based on the combination of a transaction-based and a fixed-price model.

Whatever the business pricing model, a new critical component of QoS and *service level agreements* (SLAs) is significant. Without having a solid grasp on these two elements, performance of applications and services will suffer. Standards for billing future wireless data services are also being formed.

QoS and SLA

Quality of service is the measure of guarantees that can be made in meeting certain performance requirements in advance as opposed to "best effort" services provided today. Using some advances in network and computing technologies, a company or user preselects a level of quality in terms of service. QoS can be measured and guaranteed in terms of the average delay at a gateway, the variation in delay in a group of bit losses, and transmission error rates. Increasingly, partners and suppliers want to get SLAs for QoS that meet their requirements and needs.

A *service level agreement* is a contract between a network service provider and a customer that specifies, usually in measurable terms, the services that the network service provider will furnish. Some of the metrics for SLAs could be as follows:

➤ Percentage of uptime

➤ Number of concurrent users

➤ Peak-time performance

➤ Response times in case of outage

➤ Reports on usage statistics and outages

Increasingly, corporations work with multiple partners to provide aggregated services under one umbrella. In order to provide quality and guaranteed services to their partners and suppliers, firms need to secure and solidify SLAs with their application, content, and service providers.

Detection and Prevention of Fraud

Fraud write-off by Visa and MasterCard in 1999: $26.01 billion.

—NILSON REPORT, 2000

Wireless fraud was about $1.7 million a day in 1999.

—LIGHTBRIDGE, 2000

Fraudulent Internet and ecommerce transactions account for $16 billion annually.

—PRICEWATERHOUSECOOPERS, 1999

As some research shows, fraud is a major problem in the ecommerce world. It's a problem not often talked about at meetings and conferences. Companies seldom admit how much they are losing because they are getting defrauded by hackers and fraudsters, yet it's a serious issue that needs to be dealt with.

As depicted in Figure 8.1, the mcommerce world combines good and bad components of the wireless, Internet, and credit card industries. For the following reasons, there is more potential for fraud:

➤ Mcommerce: more reward for risk

➤ More information available

➤ Stolen credit cards

➤ Over-the-air activation of mobile account and services

➤ Stolen identity

➤ New technologies, new security holes

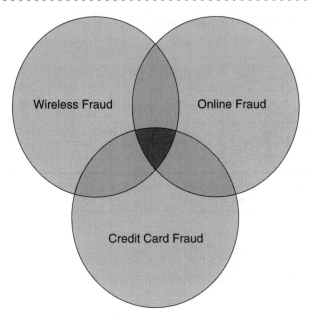

Figure 8.1 Fraud in the mcommerce world.

➤ Authentication for each session
➤ Latency in authentication
➤ Intermediary Gateway architecture

Types of Wireless Fraud

The following are wireless fraud mechanisms that have been prevalent over the past five years or so:

➤ Cloning (the United States still has millions of analog phones, which are very easy to clone)
➤ Tumbling
➤ Subscription [70 percent of a multimillion-dollar pie (source: Lightbridge Inc. as quoted in Wireless Week, June 2000]
➤ Theft

Although revenue losses due to technical fraud are dropping, losses due to subscription fraud have kept the overall losses due to fraud on the rise (see Figure 8.2).

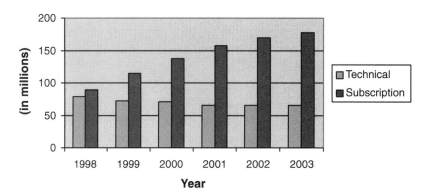

Figure 8.2 Losses due to various types of wireless fraud.
(Source: Wireless Week)

Solutions to Wireless Fraud

Some solutions have been used, with varying degree of success, to thwart the rise of fraud in the wireless industry:

➤ Profiling

➤ RF fingerprint analysis

➤ Authentication

➤ Fraud databases

➤ Voice verification

➤ PIN/SIM

Credit Card Fraud and Solutions

The credit card industry writes off billions of dollars each year due to credit card fraud. Table 8.3 lists the various ways the credit card industry has been duped.

Some credit card fraud solutions are:

➤ Profiling

➤ Simple rules-based solution

➤ More complex neural network-based solution

Table 8.3   Credit Card Fraud by Type

FRAUD TYPE	PERCENTAGE SHARE (%)
Stolen credit cards	28
Identity theft	20
Card generators	10
Other	7
Don't know	35

(Source: Mindwave Research, commissioned by Cybersource)

Mcommerce Fraud and Solutions

It's likely that with the rise in mcommerce solutions, fraudulent activities will also rise. For hackers, pranksters, and organized criminals, mcommerce provides more reward for the risk. Not only can they steal airtime, but they can also perform financial transactions on your behalf.

To put up a unified front against mcommerce fraud, all the players (carriers, application developers, infrastructure providers, handset manufacturers) need to work together to fend off this emerging yet unacknowledged threat. The following data sources already exist and can be used intelligently to create profiles of users that can help in detecting and preventing fraud as it happens:

➢ Subscriber data

➢ Server logs

➢ Wireless billing records

➢ Wireless usage records

➢ Online history

➢ Behavior patterns and personalization data

➢ Device transactions

➢ User profile, device capabilities

➢ Location

Fuzzy logic or artificial intelligence (AI) engines can be used to dynamically analyze and approve transactions. Figure 8.3 provides an example of how existing data can be used to detect and prevent fraud. In addition, gateway architecture introduces another point of failure. You should either have pretty tight SLAs or, for confidential data, host gateways within your corporation.

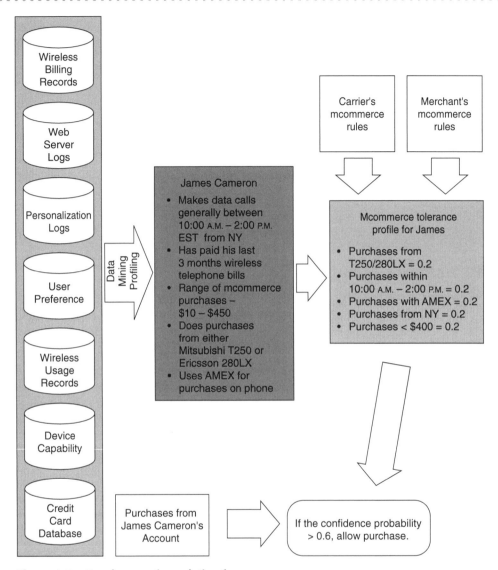

Figure 8.3   Fraud prevention solution for mcommerce.

Keep It Simple

Simplicity often wins. Although there were various incarnations of handhelds, it took a simple Palm Pilot to capture consumer imaginations. This truism holds for applications and services as well. Yahoo! didn't win the portal wars by creating a complicated user interface. It found its user loyalty with a simple design and quick access to content. Wireless Internet technology, by its very nature, mandates simplicity. The process of providing content and information needs to be simple and fast. For example, users shouldn't be expected to remember different sets of user IDs and passwords simply because they are accessing the same content from different devices. Authentication procedures should be integrated with other applications using a standard such as Lightweight Directory Access Protocol (LDAP).

Respect Consumer Privacy

Web servers and gateways can collect an awesome amount of data based on user interaction with a Web site. Greedy corporations tend to sell this data for money. This practice is not only unethical; it is also an abuse of the user's trust. Companies should not distribute user data unless permission has been obtained explicitly from the user.

Existing Infrastructure and Backward Compatibility

Often, when companies rush to offer services, they tend to forget the investment that has been made in the existing infrastructure. Even though the system might be legacy and old, it's highly unlikely to disappear overnight. More often than not, companies look for migration strategies that take advantage of their existing investments by extending the functionality of legacy systems and infrastructure. It's not always possible to leverage old technology, but an effort should be made to analyze the possibilities. In addition, solution providers should always consider providing backward compatibility for their applications and services.

Monitor the Network

Often times web applications and services are launched without keeping ongoing maintenance and monitoring in mind. It's not uncommon for a company to underestimate consumer demand or intelligence. Very few companies go through the effort of setting up monitoring infrastructure from the start, it's only when things start to crash and burn that the issue of proactive network monitoring comes to mind. Network monitoring can not only be used to ensure scaleable performance and minimum outages but also to continuously improve applications and services based on how the users interact with them. Companies should strive to make their applications the most usable and useful they can be to the target audience.

In this chapter, we reviewed the critical success factors for implementing robust and useful wireless Internet solutions. In the next chapter, we will discuss the future of wireless Internet.

CHAPTER 9

Wireless Internet Tomorrow

I t's always risky to predict the future. Over the last decade or so, technologies have changed so fast that the future, beyond a one- to two-year time frame, has essentially become unpredictable. Technologies that hold a lot of promise sometimes fail due to lack of consumer demand, poor business plans, and reasonable service offerings. On the other hand, innovations in one sector can have a ripple effect on the entire economy.

It has become increasingly clear that technologies and trends are heavily interrelated. A breakthrough in one area can lead to innovations in others. For example, progress in semiconductor, storage, and display technologies have a profound impact on both computing and communications industries. At the end of the day, it's the applications and services that win the hearts of consumers.

So far we have discussed the wireless Internet landscape in terms of applications and services, primarily focusing on things as they stand today or as they will be in the next couple of years. In this chapter, we attempt to stretch our imaginations and wander into the next five to ten years. We discuss the following areas of technology that will have the maximum impact on wireless Internet in the future:

➢ Semiconductor technology

➢ Displays and devices

➢ Biometrics

➢ Networks

➢ The Napster model

➢ Wireless Internet as an interface to different technologies

Semiconductor Technology

Moore's Law has been at the center stage of the technology revolution for the past few decades. Gordon Moore, cofounder of Intel, predicted in the mid-1960s that the number of transistors on a silicon chip would double every eighteen to twenty-four months. The more transistors on a chip, the more processing power the chip has and hence the higher performance it achieves. The Semiconductor Industry Association's International Technology Roadmap for Semiconductors (ITRS), produced in 1999, predicts continued advances for the next decade or so (see Figure 9.1).

Advances in some futuristic computing technologies will be watched with considerable interest, because even a slight breakthrough can lead to revolutionary impact on computing as we understand it today. Some of these technology areas are as follows:

> Molecular computing

> Quantum computing

> Biological computing

> DNA computing

Whatever the predominant technologies, the processing power for these building blocks of technology will continuously increase over the foreseeable future. This increase in processing power will lead to the proliferation of devices, networks, and technologies discussed in the next few sections of this chapter.

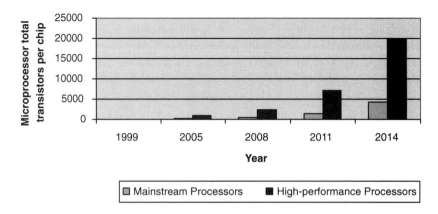

Figure 9.1   The semiconductor manufacturing road map.

(Copyright ©, 1999, The Semiconductor Industry Association, *International Technology Roadmap for Semiconductors*,)

Displays and Devices

The display is a key component of any device. A majority of the time it's also the most expensive component of the device. Thus far we have mentioned fixed displays that come in different forms, shapes, and sizes. At one end of the spectrum are high-definition TVs (HDTVs); at the other end are small communication devices such as pagers with a couple of lines of display and poor resolution. Functionality of the device is generally limited by the size of its display. But what if you could have flexible displays—displays that you can just roll out from the device? Or even displays that can interface with any device—desktops, phones, PDAs? If that were possible, a consistent user interface could be provided. These displays would, of course, be wirelessly enabled so you could access your information from anywhere. Figures 9.2 and 9.3 depict such conceptual displays.

A number of companies are working on flexible display technologies. This development could fundamentally change the way we interact with devices. With the use of smart materials like Eink, you would buy a display once and use it for reading daily newspapers, books, and magazines of your choice from wherever you are. Your personal mobile agent, which knows your preferences, calendar, and credit card information, could carry out a multitude of mundane tasks even before you open up the display. For example, in the morning before you even get up, your mobile agent

Figure 9.2 Conceptual displays.
(Copyright © 2000, Business Week)

Figure 9.3   Flexible display concept.
(Copyright © 2000, Business Week)

could download sections of *The New York Times* and *The Wall Street Journal* that suit your interests.

Wearable computers will also start to enter the consumer market in the next few years. With enhanced bandwidths and battery life, devices will be able to videoconference, stream video, and establish a phone call all at once. Figure 9.4 shows some of the future conceptual devices from various manufacturers.

Flexible displays would have impact on areas beyond our wildest imagination. For example, a slim GPS receiver with an Eink display could wirelessly download a topographical map and be able to pinpoint your coordinates in real time. Figure 9.5 shows such a prototype.

Biometrics

Biometrics will become an accepted way of authentication and verification, not only for computers and networks but also for opening house doors, arming alarm systems, and more. As discussed in Chapter 5, biometrics provides a very powerful authentication means to simplify the verification process, which today involves multiple passwords, PIN codes, mother's maiden name, and the like. Figure 9.6 shows a biometric prototype for opening doors using fingerprint recognition.

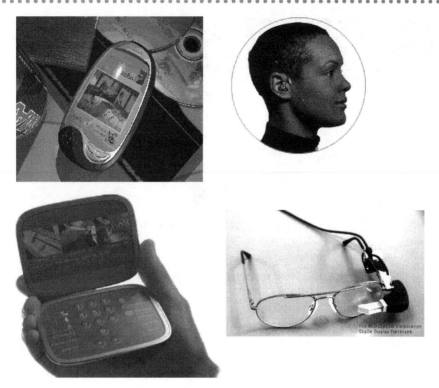

Figure 9.4 Future conceptual Internet-enabled devices from various vendors. a) Nokia. b) IDEO Design. c) Compaq. d) MicroOptical.

(Sources: Nokia, Business Week, Compaq, and MicroOptical respectively)

(Copyright © 2000)

Figure 9.5 Conceptual GPS device.

(Copyright © 2000, Business Week)

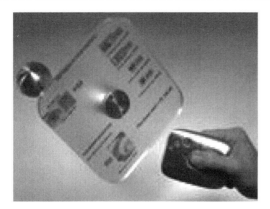

Figure 9.6   Fingerprint recognition for authentication and verification.
(Copyright © 2000, Business Week)

Networks

The evolution of next-generation network technologies is the key to the development of innovative applications and services. We discussed some of the next-generation wireless network technologies (specifically, 2.5G and 3G) in Chapter 5. In addition, many companies and research groups are working on technologies that go beyond 3G. Mobile Broadband Systems (MBS) and Wireless Local Area Network (WLAN) provide the ability to restrict radio coverage to small areas such as airports, sports stadiums, conferences, and museums. The network speeds for MBS mobile terminals go up to 155Mbps (see Figure 9.7).

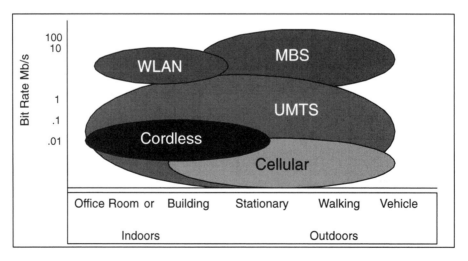

Figure 9.7   Mobility versus bit rates for various technologies.
(Source: Glisic, Leppanen, 1997)

The Napster Model

Napster is an Internet startup that is stirring up the music industry. At the time of this book going to press, it's uncertain if Napster as a company is going to survive or not but its innovative technology has huge implications, not only for the music industry, but in the way we view and use Internet architecture in general. The Napster model (peer-to-peer) works as shown in the following example:

1. Tom stores MP3-formatted songs on his hard drive at home.

2. Napster.com maintains a central directory to keep track of users who are logged on and the available songs by title, artists, and users.

3. Jennifer wants to listen to a specific song, so she searches the Napster database and finds that it is stored on Tom's hard drive. She then downloads the song to her computer, then decodes and plays the music.

Traditionally on the Internet, we are used to the client/server model. Generally, a back-end server has access to legacy systems, databases, and other servers. These servers communicate with the clients that can reside on different devices such as phones, PDAs, or Web-enabled TV. Napster's model empowers the client/server paradigm in a powerful way by allowing any client (such as Tom in the preceding example) to become a server, depending on the situation.

For example, let's say I have a Word document residing on my home computer and I am with a client demonstrating my company's capability. The client unexpectedly requests that particular Word document. Using Napster's architecture, I would be able to go to the Internet and fetch that document wirelessly from my home computer into my PDA or laptop computer. The document doesn't have to reside on a centralized server for it to be accessed. Using the Napster model, the Internet becomes a widely distributed server farm.

Since wireless devices are more pervasive than desktop PCs, the Napster model can have huge implications on the wireless Internet market.

Wireless Internet as an Interface to Technologies

Technologies such as WAP, voice recognition, mobile agents, and position location are bringing huge benefits to the way we do business and orchestrate our personal lives. However, it's the integration of these disparate technologies that makes the use of technology more compelling to the everyday user. Consider the following scenario.

You step off a plane in New York City and turn on your personal communicator. The device is an electronic organizer with an integrated wireless modem and a phone. Here's what you receive via a wireless network, based on your personal profile:

➢ Email that you've designated for wireless transmission from your corporate server or Internet service provider

➤ A list of half-price front-row NBA tickets for a New York Knicks and Los Angeles Lakers game and the ability to immediately purchase tickets wirelessly

➤ The current value of your stocks and bonds, with the ability to transfer funds, purchase stocks, and pay bills wirelessly

➤ A map of midtown Manhattan, with your bank's ATMs pinpointed and, based on your calendar information, the location of your hotel and the meeting place

➤ The headlines and first paragraphs of very specific news articles

➤ The five-day weather forecast for New York

➤ Today-only discount coupons for shopping at Macy's, Border's books, and several favorite computer stores; discounts are personalized based on your past shopping experience and history

Then you switch to phone mode and speak to your mobile agent to find out whether or not your colleague who was coming in from Europe has landed and where is he staying so that you can contact him to get together for a dinner meeting. Your mobile agent then goes and negotiates with your colleague's mobile agent to set up an appointment at a restaurant of your mutual choice, which is not far from either of your hotels. Your mobile agent automatically books a cab for you. And all this activity happens in a mere few seconds!

In this futuristic but realistic scenario, multiple technologies interfaced and exchanged information with each other intelligently. In the future, wireless devices will become extensions of your personal and corporate network. Using these devices, you will be able to tap into the powerful resources of desktop PCs and supercomputers to do a majority of your "grunt work" and have information delivered to you via content (text, graphics, audio, video). It's the promise of integration that will provide enormous value to us all as consumers and corporate users.

In this chapter we looked at various futuristic technologies and concepts. In the next chapter we will conclude with some final thoughts.

CHAPTER 10

The Last Word

In the past nine chapters, we covered a lot of ground. We reviewed the growing trends in pervasive computing and its market drivers, the technologies that are making it possible, and the players that are providing solutions in this market space. We also looked at some of the applications that are already available. We also evaluated some of the product offerings based on the needs of an enterprise project. Chapter 8 laid out the critical success factors that managers of wireless Internet projects should consider while strategizing and implementing solutions; finally, we reviewed some future scenarios. In this chapter, we recap our discussions and point out some potential opportunity areas.

Wireless Internet technology is set to take off in a big way. The industry is still in its infancy, so its impact is not discernible to all. The industry is pretty much in the same state as the Internet about five or six years ago. Innovative startups such as Netscape and Yahoo! helped start the global Internet Revolution. Firms such as Dell figured out a way to directly sell products to consumers online, thus eliminating middlemen. Not only did the speed of innovation accelerate, but the rate of acceleration has been on the rise ever since.

People around the world are still trying to fathom the impact on human society of this thing called the Internet. Perhaps there is a Moore's Law for Internet growth. Global boundaries have started to shrink, and today's business scene is all about information and how well it's shared and leveraged. Although Internet penetration is over 50 percent in the United States, it won't reach such high rates in some geographic regions anytime soon. For some users in Japan, Europe, and Latin America, access to wireless Internet services has been their first taste of the phenomenon called the Internet. This means that if you are a business trying to reach these individuals, wireless Internet technology is the most powerful channel you can consider.

Just as it happened with the Internet, the focus of wireless Internet-based applications and services will move from B2C to B2B and B2E fairly quickly. Wireless data has been around for a while, but it was available over proprietary networks, was expensive, and was for specialized services. Now, it's possible to provide similar and more enhanced services over the Internet using wireless networks, devices, and existing back-end infrastructure.

This optimism doesn't mean that there aren't challenges ahead. Wireless Internet is probably the most hyped technology in recent times. Every ebusiness is rushing to proclaim presence in this arena. Wireless infrastructure and network providers have consistently over-promised and under-delivered. However, with competition heating up and opportunities surfing up rapidly, it's increasingly evident that a new model of competitors working together to establish a market for the consumer good will win out. For instance, the push by Unwired Planet (now Phone.com) for HDML didn't take off until it partnered with Ericsson, Motorola, and Nokia to jointly work on a WAP standard. Historically, proprietary solutions almost never win in the end.

Ebusiness is all about establishing better and efficient relationships among consumers, producers, and partners. The transactions that make up ebusiness involve buying and selling goods among businesses (B2B—for example, Onvia.com), between businesses and consumers (B2C—for example, Amazon.com), and among consumers (C2C—for example, eBay). These transactions are forecast to deliver $3 trillion per year into the world economy by 2003 [source: *IEEE Communications Magazine*, September 1999]. The first generation of ebusiness services moved the traditional client/server applications to a Web-centric model, in which one could get connected to any networked computer using a simple Web interface that could reside on any computer. The powerful underlying principle of the next phase of ebusiness metamorphosis is *anytime, anywhere, any device, any information.*

Any technological revolution goes through its cycles of hype, disappointment, realism, growth, and "nirvana" (see Figure 10.1). Durlacher, a research driven investment and securities group focused on emerging technology and media, predicts mcommerce will take off in 2002, but with the current breathtaking pace of innovation, it won't be surprising if mcommerce becomes mainstream sooner than that. Some industries—finance, health care, telecommunications, field services, and retail—will be the early adopters of wireless Internet technology. Corporations will also start arming their road warriors with devices that help them connect with the corporate infrastructure from wherever they are to expedite information retrieval and decision making. We discuss some applications that corporations can start using almost immediately later in this chapter.

As we have been discussing all through this book, wireless Internet-based applications and services present enormous opportunities to almost every industry sector and ebusiness. So, if you haven't started thinking about wireless Internet, it should worry you. Your employees are already carrying multiple devices. Why not leverage that fact and make them more useful and powerful by connecting the devices directly to the enterprise? Wireless Internet has huge implications for the knowledge management programs within your company.

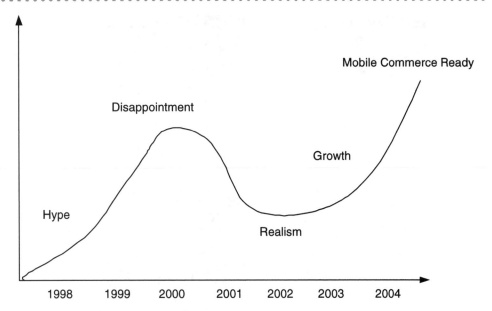

Figure 10.1   The mcommerce hype curve.
(Copyright © 2000, Durlacher)

Enterprise Applications

Let's review a few applications, some of which can be used by a majority of enterprises today.

Expense Reporting

Every company has its road warriors, especially the sales and business development folks. These people are constantly on the move. Sometimes it can be weeks before they are able to file their expense reports and get reimbursed for all the costs they incur while on the road. Sometimes these expenses are billable to the client. If employees were able to file reports quickly, approval and processing could be done quickly. The faster the processing, the earlier reimbursements and billing the client could be achieved.

Expense reporting can easily be integrated into a workflow application to make it more attractive and efficient. Figure 10.2 shows a sample expense reporting application built on the PalmOS that is integrated with back-end accounting databases and workflow applications. Users can file their expense reports from anywhere, anytime, and not wait until they return home from their trips.

Figure 10.2   Expense reporting application for PalmOS.

(Courtesy: Eswar Eluri, 2000)

Project Management

Good project management is key to successful project execution. Project managers often rely on tools such as Microsoft Project for organizing and assigning tasks, budgeting, and monitoring progress against time and budget. Natara has an application—Project@Hand that allows for Microsoft Project files to be converted for consumption on Palm devices. Figure 10.3 provides a sample of the versatility of such applications. Currently, you have to synchronize your Palm with your desktop, using the cradle to synchronize the project files. However, with technologies such as Bluetooth and SyncML on the horizon, this could easily be accomplished wirelessly.

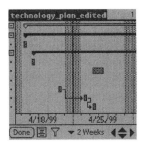

Figure 10.3   A Palm-based project management application.

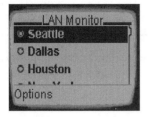  

Figure 10.4   An IT application for network monitoring on a WAP phone.

IT Network Alarm and Monitoring

If you have worked in IT supporting your corporate infrastructure, you will definitely identify with the desire to keep "taking the pulse" of your network, whether its performance of certain LAN segments or intrusion detection, alarms and alerts, or summary reports. Wouldn't it be nice if you could not only capture and extract information about your network but also execute certain commands remotely? Sometimes IT folks who are on 24 × 7 duty have to lug their laptops with them, boot their machines, and log in to diagnose and fix problems. If a majority of these tasks (which involve only a few keystrokes, not extensive debugging) could be accomplished remotely, the response time would increase and tangible cost savings could be realized. Figures 10.4 and 10.5 show sample IT applications.

For corporations, the cost savings lie in the following areas:

➢ Inventory reduction

➢ Lower overhead cost

➢ Disappearance of intermediary

➢ Lower procurement costs

➢ Shorter product cycles

Figure 10.5   Server response application on a Palm Pilot.

Vertical Industry Applications

This section reviews opportunities within various vertical industry segments and ways in which wireless Internet technologies can be leveraged for competitive advantage and productivity gains.

Health Care

Health care is an industry constantly in need of technology solutions to improve services. Doctors, nurses, and other medical staff are always seeking ways they can serve their patients quickly while maintaining quality of service. Applications such as the one shown in Figure 10.6 can be used intelligently to store and process patient information on the hospital floor using handhelds instead of paper. Similarly, medical guidelines can be accessed using wireless and handheld technology instead of browsing thick books. Wireless technologies can also help doctors prescribe medication and monitor patient conditions remotely, especially under severe and emergency circumstances. High-bandwidth networks not only can deliver medical diagnostic information but live-video feeds from ambulances or other locations as well.

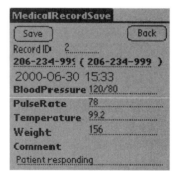

Figure 10.6   Health-care application on a Palm Pilot.

(Courtsey: Eswar Eluri, 2000)

Retail

The retail industry is fiercely competitive. With the advent of the World Wide Web, nontraditional companies such as Amazon.com emerged and forced bricks-and-mortar companies such as Barnes and Noble to rethink their strategies. Competition is also driving profit margins down. The success of a retailer depends on inventory management, cost control, and proactive customer service. To gain competitive advantage, more and more retailers are turning to wireless Internet applications to enhance worker productivity, operational efficiencies, and anytime, anywhere customer service. On the sales floor and in the warehouse, wireless solutions can help track materials and shipments from suppliers and distributors to customers, manage inventory, and support POS activities. Because a great deal of data can be collected in an automated fashion, it can be analyzed much faster and the results can be used to continuously improve operations and customer service.

Wireless Internet technology has allowed retailers to break their dependence on landline infrastructure for credit card processing. Wireless Internet applications are the next evolutionary step for retailers currently capturing data via batch data devices and fixed terminals. This technology is also a next step for arming mobile workers—from store managers to analysts—with information. This empowerment will lead to enhanced customer buying experiences, which is what every retailer craves.

Transportation

The freight and trucking industry has been using wireless data applications for quite some time. Courier companies such as FedEx and UPS have established pretty sophisticated wireless data networks that yield productivity gains and increased customer service, which are worth well over billions of dollars. However, with wireless Internet solutions becoming more pervasive, it's no longer necessary to deploy expensive and proprietary wireless data networks to gain competitive advantage. Applications can easily be built using the wireless Internet infrastructure to provide real-time communications. From point of dispatch to final destination, wireless Internet technology can be used to provide job status, dispatch information, proof of delivery, exception information, emergency notification, and other critical data. Wireless asset tracking can enable managers to more accurately coordinate pickups and deliveries and gain a good sense of their assets at any given instant. Wireless Internet technology offers solutions for companies involved with aviation, courier delivery, freight trains, intelligent transportation systems, LTL trucking, maritime shipping, asset tracking, and urban transport.

Field Services

Every day, thousands of field service technicians and workers are dispatched to investigate and fix problems and collect data in the field. For these workers, the majority of the workday is spent traveling from one location to another. Often, they must process lengthy forms, which is a detriment to productivity and efficiency. Customers don't like to fill out laborious sheets of paper over and over again, either. This is where wireless Internet technology is a boon to field services organizations. Not only can it help in automating data entry, it can also expedite routing and dispatching and status reporting and provide efficient access to corporate databases, customer billing, and vehicle location.

The field services market crosses multiple industries and vertical segments—manufacturing companies, third-party maintenance organizations, city governments, dealers and distributors. For effective services, field service personnel need real-time access to customer information, trouble tickets, product information, parts lists, schematics, dispatch schedules, maps and directions, weather conditions, and restaurants. With wireless Internet applications and services, all of these tasks can be accomplished. Because data entry is automated in most instances, time to resolve issues and to analyze and process data is drastically reduced, thus improving overall productivity and customer service. Due to efficient job scheduling and prioritization, billing cycles can be automated, thus reducing operating costs and increasing revenues.

Field service operations thrive on communication. With wireless Internet technology, cheap, reliable, and secure solutions can be quickly built and can help realize immediate gains.

Financial Services

The finance industry was among the first segments that recognized the value and need for wireless Internet applications and services. Today, it's no longer a competitive advantage to have wireless applications—it's a competitive disadvantage if you don't, since a majority of the companies already have wireless solutions or are planning to offer them in the near future.

Financial information, especially dealing with the stock market, is often time and location–sensitive, and wireless Internet technology provides an ideal medium in which to deliver such information to its destination. Through push and pull information architectures, users can be armed with powerful tools that enable them to make smart, informed financial decisions. Thanks to innovative services such as wireless ATMs and micropayment technologies, the convenience of financial services can be further extended.

Utilities

Since the deregulation of the utility industry, the business environment in this sector has changed dramatically. Utility companies need to be better informed and able to monitor their resources to stay competitive. Wireless-based applications are helping make the leap by providing highly efficient, reliable data and information in real time at low cost. Remote meters in the field can be monitored and controlled from a central location, allowing utilities to detect problems (sometimes before they happen) remotely and assign maintenance crews more efficiently. Wireless Internet technology will continue to play an increasingly important role in the development of this industry.

Conclusion

As discussed in this and preceding chapters, almost all industry sectors have plenty of opportunities to benefit from the wireless Internet revolution. The key challenges that application developers will face can be summarized as follows:

➤ Complexity of systems integration

➤ Low priority of wireless Internet projects in the total IT projects mix

➤ Lack of resources

➤ Rapidly changing market

➤ Multiple standards and interoperability

➤ Lack of robust development tools

A challenge to one player is an opportunity for another. Innovative solution providers look to aggressively develop and deploy useful solutions. The fundamentals for wireless Internet solutions for business process reengineering and augmentation are incredibly strong. The technology and solutions infrastructure is either available or going to be available shortly. It's not wise to sit on the sidelines until all the bugs are worked out and solutions harden. The time for launching wireless Internet initiatives is *now*.

This doesn't mean that any and all applications and services make sense. Each project needs to be evaluated on its own business-case merits. If the business case is strong but you don't want to commit too many resources, it's worth considering planning and launching the project in a phased approach. Use your early experiences to enhance your corporation's awareness of other possible mobile solutions.

As discussed in earlier chapters, it's critical to have a sound technology foundation for your pervasive computing projects so that you can leverage your investment on a continuing basis. So, always design and implement solutions with the future in mind. Things are changing very rapidly. Select technology components carefully. There are far too many solution providers today, and not all provide robust and interoperable solutions. So, ensure that the solution set you pick is based on open standards and has a future road map that meets industry needs and demands. Finally, usability and functionality of an application define its success. Keeping in mind the critical success factors mentioned in Chapter 8 will help ensure successful completion of your wireless Internet initiatives today and tomorrow.

Despite the challenges, mobile ebusiness solutions will inevitably evolve. New applications will be invented, and more wireless Internet content and design will be created over the next few years. Players in all industries will have to find a way to leverage the wireless Internet phenomenon to reinvent themselves and extend their reach to customers, partners, and opportunities. Those that don't risk being obliterated.

Although existing applications in the wireless Internet marketplace are compelling, upcoming advances and trends—including mobile agents, mobile enterprise applications, biometrics, smart cards, voice recognition, position location, personalization, wireless networks and devices, and others—will further define the vibrant economy and, in turn, our society.

The wireless Internet presents ample opportunities for almost every business sector. Success in the new business landscape requires careful consideration of technology capabilities and limitations and preparing for both. The critical success factors of strategy, competitive analysis, internationalization, personalization, security, standards, interoperability, billing, partnerships, usability, and aggregation of content must all be considered in the creation of device-independent services and applications.

Companies will increasingly target campaigns and online efforts to be compatible with both the wired and wireless worlds. It used to be that the "coolness factor" of the Internet was its accessibility anytime, anywhere—that is, anywhere that has a wired connection. With the wireless revolution, anytime and anywhere will be a reality. You will reach customers, partners, employees, suppliers, and other intended audiences , anytime, anywhere.

The world is ready to leap into the next information age. *Are you?*

Useful URLs

BIOMETRICS	
Authentec	www.authentec.com
Biometrics Consortium	www.biometrics.org
Identix	www.identix.com
International Biometrics Industry Association	www.ibia.org
Thomson-CSF	www.tcs.thomson-csf.com
Verdicom	www.verdicom.com
BLUETOOTH	
Bluetooth Consortium	www.bluetooth.com
Bluetooth Resource Center	www.palopt.com.au/bluetooth
Ericsson	http://bluetooth.ericsson.se
Extended Systems	www.extendedsystems.com
Lucent	www.lucent.com/micro/bluetooth
Motorola	www.motorola.com/bluetooth
Nokia	www.nokia.com/bluetooth/index.html
IPV6	
6bone	www.6bone.net
6ren	www.6ren.net
ARIN	www.arin.net
Internet2	www.internet2.edu
IPv6 Forum	www.ipv6forum.com

JINI	
Benefits of Jini	www.billday.com/Work/Jini
Jini Community Resource	www.jini.org
Jini FAQ	www.artima.com/jini/faq.html
Jini Tutorial	http://pandonia.canberra.edu.au/java/jini/tutorial/Jini.xml
SUN	http://developer.java.sun.com/developer/products/jini

MAGAZINES	
America's Network	www.americasnetwork.com
Communication Systems Design	www.csdmag.com
Ericsson Review	www.ericsson.com/review
Global Telephony	www.globaltelephony.com
MCI	www.mobilecomms.com
Network Magazine	www.network-mag.com
NewWaves	www.newwaves.com
RCR	www.rcr.com
Wireless Integration	www.wireless-integration.com
Wireless International Magazine	www.wireless.com.tw
Wireless Asia	www.telecomasia.net/wirelessasia/wa_new.html
Wireless Business & Technology	www.wirelesstoday.com
Wireless Design & Development	www.wirelessdesignmag.com
Wireless Systems Design	www.wsdmag.com
Wireless Week	www.wirelessweek.com

MICROPAYMENTS	
IBM	www.hrl.il.ibm.com/mpay/demo/forsale/lecture.htm
Micropayments Resource	www.globeset.com/Commerce/Technology/Micropayments/index.shtml
W3C Micropayments	www.w3.org/TR/WD-Micropayment-Markup

MOBILE AGENTS	
Ambit	www.luca.demon.co.uk/Ambit/Ambit.html
Ara	www.uni-kl-de/AG-Nehmer/index_e.html
D'Agents	http://agents.cs.dartmouth.edu
Frictionless Commerce	www.frictionless.com

MOBILE AGENTS *(Continued)*	
General Magic	www.genmagic.com
IBM Aglets	www.trl.ibm.co.jp/aglets
MARS	http://sirio.dsi.unimo.it/MOON
Mole	http://mole.informatik.uni-stuttgart.de
MySimon	www.mySimon.com
PageSpace	http://flp.cs.tu-berlin.de/pagespc
TuCSoN	www.-lia.deis.unibo.it/Research/TuCSoN
MPEG	
MPEG	www.mpeg.org
MPEG Home	http://drogo.cselt.stet.it/mpeg
NEWSLETTERS	
All Net Devices	http://devices.internet.com
Anywhereyougo.com	www.anywhereyougo.com
ePaynews.com	www.epaynews.com/index.cgi
Fierce Wireless	www.fiercewireless.com
Pervasive Weekly	www.pervasiveweekly.com
Strategic News Service	www.tapsns.com
The Rapidly Changing Face of Computing Journal	www.compaq.com/rcfoc
Wireless NewsFactor	wireless.newsfactor.com
ORGANIZATIONS	
Advanced Television Systems Committee	www.atsc.org
ATM Forum	www.atmforum.com
Bluetooth	www.bluetooth.com
CDMA Development Group	www.cdg.org
CDPD Forum	www.cdpd.org
Cellular Telecommunications Industry Association	www.wow-com.com
Digital Display Group	www.ddwg.com
European Telecommunications Standards Institute	www.etsi.org
GSM World	www.gsmworld.com
Home RF/SWAP	www.homerf.org
Institute of Electrical and Electronics Engineers	www.ieee.org

Continues

ORGANIZATIONS *(Continued)*	
International Union-Telecommunications-Standardization	www.itu.ch
Internet Engineering Task Force	www.ietf.org
Network Management Forum	www.nmf.org
SyncML Forum	www.syncml.org
UMTS Forum	www.umts-forum.org
UWCC	www.uwcc.org
VoiceXML Forum	www.vxmlforum.com
WAP Forum	www.wapforum.com
Wireless Ethernet Site	www.wirelessethernet.org
World Wide Web Consortium (W3C)	www.w3c.org
PALM	
Common Palm User Problems	www.nearlymobile.com/commonproblems
Handago.com	www.handago.com
Palm Developer's Developers Zone	www.palm.com/devzone
Palm Source	www.palmsource.com
PERVASIVE COMPUTING	
eBiquity.org	http://ebiquity.org
IBM Pervasive Computing	www.ibm.com/pvc
Pervasive Computing SIG	http://gentoo.cs.umbc.edu/pcsig/about.shtml
POSITION LOCATION	
Cambridge Positioning Partner	www.cursor-system.com
Cell-Loc, Inc.	www.cell-loc.com
Locus Corp.	www.locus.ne.jp
NENA	www.nena9-1-1.org
SiRF	www.sirf.com
SnapTrack	www.snaptrack.com
Trueposition	www.trueposition.com
US Wireless	www.uswcorp.com
Virginia Polytechnic's Polytechnic's Mobile and Portable Research Group	www.mprg.ee.vt.edu/home.html

SMART ANTENNAS	
ArrayComm	www.arraycomm.com/Technology/Technology.html
MetaWave	www.metawave.com
Virginia Polytechnic's Polytechnic's Mobile and Portable Research Group	www.mprg.ee.vt.edu/home.html

SMIL	
JustSmil	www.justsmil.com
SMIL Home Page	www.w3.org/SMIL

3G	
Ericsson	www.ericsson.com/3g/default.shtml
Mobile Applications Initiative	www.mobileapplicationsinitiative.com
Mobile Wireless Internet Forum	www.mwif.com
M-PEG TV	www.mpegtv.com
Nokia	www.nokia.com/3g/index.html
Wireless Multimedia Forum	www.wmmforum.com

USABILITY	
Human-Computer Interaction Virtual Library	http://web.cs.bgsu.edu/hcivl
Usability Group	www.usability.com
Use It	www.useit.com
User Interface Engineering	http://world.std.com/~uieweb/biblio.htm

VOICEXML	
IBM VoiceXML	www.alphaworks.ibm.com/tech/voicexml
Tellme	http://studio.tellme.com
VxML Forum	www.vxmlforum.org

WAP	
Ericsson	www.ericsson.com/WAP
Motorola	http://mix.motorola.com/audiences developers/dev_main.asp
Nokia	www.nokia.com/networks/17/wdss.html
Phone.com	www.phone.com/developers
WAP FAQ	http://wap.colorline.no/wap-faq
WAP Sight	www.wapsight.com
WAP's WAP Developer's Repository	http://wapulous.com

WEBTV	
Sony WebTV	www.sel.sony.com/SEL/consumer/webtv/products/main.html
WebTV Developers Zone	http://developer.webtv.net
WebTV Tools and Resources	www.geocities.com/Yosemite/Trails/4666/tools.html
MISCELLANEOUS	
ACM Sigmobile	www.acm.org/sigmobile
ACTS	www.uk.infowin.org/ACTS
Bell Labs Technology Journal	www.lucent.com/minds/techjournal/findex.html
Cap Gemini Ernst & Young Center of Business Innovation	www.businessinnovation.ey.com
Commercial Speech Recognition	www.tiac.net/users/rwilcox/speech.html
Compaq Research	www.research.compaq.com
HP e-services	http://e-services.hp.com
Microsoft Research	http://research.microsoft.com
Microsoft Wireless	www.microsoft.com/wireless
Mobile Review Communications Revieww	www.acm.org/sigmobile/MC2R
Network Query Language	www.networkquerylanguage.com/manual.asp
The Mobile Data Initiative	www.gsmdata.com www.pcsdata.com
TradeSpeak	www.tradespeak.com
UMTS Market Forecast Study	www.analysys.co.uk/news/umts/default.htm
Web ProForum	www.webproforum.com
Wireless and WAP	www.itworks.be/WAP
Wireless ASP Directory	www.wirelessweek.com/industry/ASPdir.htm
Wireless Developers Network	www.wirelessdevnet.com
Wireless Week E911 articles	www.wirelessweek.com/issues/E911/wwlinks.htm www.wirelessweek.com/issues/safety/e911wwlinks.htm

URLs of the Companies Mentioned in This Book

COMPANY NAME	URL	
724Solutions	www.724solutions.com	
ABC	www.abc.com	
Accucom	www.accucomw.com	
Accuweather	www.accuweather.com	
Aether Software	www.aethersoftware.com	
Airflash	www.airflash.com	
Airtel	www.airtel.es	
Akamai	www.akamai.com	
Alcatel	www.alcatel.com	
Amazon.com	www.amazon.com	
American Airlines	www.aa.com	
Ameritrade	www.ameritrade.com	
Andersen Consulting	www.ac.com	
AnswerLogic	www.answerlogic.com	
AOL	www.aol.com	
Arraycomm	www.arraycomm.com	
Ardis	www.motient.com	
Art Technology Group	www.atg.com	
Aspective	www.aspective.com	
AT&T	www.att.com	
AvantGo	www.avantgo.com	
Bank of America	www.bankofamerica.com	
Bank of Montreal	www.bmo.com	
Barnes and Noble	www.bn.com	
BBC	www.bbc.co.uk	
BellSouth	www.bellsouth.com	
BeVocal	www.bevocal.com	
Biztravel.com	www.biztravel.com	
Blaze Software	www.blazesoftware.com	
Bloomberg	www.bloomberg.com	*Continues*

COMPANY NAME	URL
BOE Securities	www.boegroup.com
Brightware	www.brightware.com
Brio	www.brio.com
Broadvision	www.broadvision.com
Business Objects	www.businessobjects.com
Cahners InStat Group	www.cahners.com
Cambridge Positioning Systems	www.cursor-system.co.uk
Casio	www.casio.com
Cat-Street	www.cat-street.com
Categoric	www.categoric.com
Cell-Loc	www.cell-loc.com
Certicom	www.certicom.com
Citibank	www.citibank.com
Citikey	www.citikey.co.uk
Clarion	www.autopc.com
ClarityBank	www.claritybank.com
CMG	www.cmg.com
CNN	www.cnn.com
Cognos	www.cognos.com
Compaq	www.compaq.com
Comverse	www.comverse.com
Continental Airlines	www.continental.com
Conversa	www.conversa.com
Corsair	www.corsair.com
Cybersource	www.cybersource.com
Cycorp	www.cyc.com
Databites	www.databites.com
Data Critical	www.datacritical.com
DDI	www.ddi.co.jp
Delta Air Lines	www.delta.com
DigitalCity	www.digitalcity.com
DLJDirect	www.dljdirect.com
Dragon Systems	www.dragonsystems.com
Dr. Materna	www.materna.de

COMPANY NAME	URL	
EasyAsk	www.easyask.com	
eBay	www.ebay.com	
eFax	www.efax.com	
eGain	www.egain.com	
EInk	www.eink.com	
Eircell	www.eircell.ie	
Eloan	www.eloan.com	
Elocal.com	www.elocal.com	
E-Plus	www.eplus-online.de	
Ernst & Young	www.ey.com	
Ericsson	www.ericsson.com	
Esat Digifone	www.esat.ie	
ESPN	www.espn.com	
Europolitan	www.europolitan.se	
Everypath	www.everypath.com	
Excite	www.excite.com	
Extended Systems	www.extendedsystems.com	
Ezoner.com	www.ezoner.com	
Forrester Research	www.forrester.com	
Fidelity	www.fidelity.com	
Foodline	www.foodline.com	
FSECURE	www.fsecure.com	
FusionOne	www.fusionone.com	
Gameplay	www.gameplay.com	
GartnerGroup	www.gartner.com	
GemPlus	www.gemplus.com	
General Magic	www.genmagic.com	
Genie Internet	www.genie.co.uk	
Geoworks	www.geoworks	
Globalstar	www.globalstar.com	
Grayson Wireless	www.grayson.com	
Handspring	www.handspring.com	
Harris Communications	www.harris.com	
HP	www.hp.com	*Continues*

COMPANY NAME	URL
Hutchinson	www.hutchnet.com.hk
IBM	www.ibm.com
ICL	www.iclhandheld.com
ICO	www.ico.com
IDC	www.idc.com
IDO	www.ido.co.jp
Integrated Data Communications	www.placethecall.com
Infinite Mobility	www.infinitemobility.com
Infinite Technologies	www.infinite.com
Infomove	www.infomove.com
Infospace	www.infospace.com
Inktomi	www.inktomi.com
InterAuct	www.interauct.com
IoBox.com	www.iobox.com
Iown.com	www.iown.com
Isovia	www.isovia.com
Itineris	www.itineris.com
Kana	www.kana.com
Keynote	www.keynote.com
Killen & Associates	www.killen.com
KPN Telecom	www.kpn.com
Kyocera	www.kyocera.com
Learnout & Houspie	www.lhsl.com
Libertel	www.libertel.nl
Lightbridge	www.lightbridge.com
Lockheed Sanders	www.sanders.com
Locus Corporation	www.locus.ne.jp
Lucent Technologies	www.lucent.com
Luminant Worldwide	www.luminant.com
Lycos	www.lycos.com
Mannessmann	www.mannesmann.com
Mapquest	www.mapquest.com
MasterCard	www.mastercard.com

COMPANY NAME	URL	
Merrill Lynch	www.ml.com	
Metricom	www.metricom.com	
Microsoft	www.microsoft.com	
Microsoft Network	www.msn.com	
Microstrategy	www.microstrategy.com	
Mindwave Research	www.mindwaveresearch.com	
Mitsubishi	www.mitsubishi.com	
Mobile One	www.m1.com.sg	
MobileID.com	www.mobileid.com	
Mondex	www.mondex.com	
Morgan Stanley Dean Witter	www.msdw.com	
Motorola	www.motorola.com	
Mysimon.com	www.mysimon.com	
Napster	www.napster.com	
Natara	www.natara.com	
National Discount Brokers	www.ndb.com	
NeoPoint	www.neopoint.com	
Net Perceptions	www.netperceptions.com	
Netpliance	www.netpliance.com	
Netscape (AOL)	www.netscape.com	
Newsvendor	www.newsvendor.com	
Nokia	www.nokia.com	
Nortel	www.nortel.com	
NTT DoCoMo	www.nttdocomo.com	
Nuance	www.nuance.com	
Oanda	www.oanda.com	
OmniSky	www.omnisky.com	
OneBox	www.onebox.com	
One 2 One	www.one2one.co.uk	
Onhand	www.onhandpc.com	
Oracle	www.oracle.com	
OracleMobile	www.oraclemobile.com	
Orange	www.orange.co.uk	
Oskar Mobil	www.oskarmobil.com	*Continues*

COMPANY NAME	URL
Oz	www.oz.com
Palm	www.palm.com
Passcall	www.passcall.com
Peoples Phone	www.peoplesphone.com.uk
Peter D. Hart Research Associates	www.hartresearch.com
Philips	www.philips.com
Phone.com	www.phone.com
PhoneRun	www.phonerun.com
Pinpoint	www.pinpoint.com
PopEx	www.popex.com
Psion	www.psion.com
PricewaterhouseCoopers	www.pwc.com
Prudential	www.prudential.com
Puma Tech	www.pumatech.com
QUALCOMM	www.qualcomm.com
Quote.com	www.quote.com
Qwest	www.qwest.com
Radiolinja	www.radiolinja.com
Radix Technologies	www.radixtek.com
RAM Mobile Data	www.ram-wireless.com
Razorfish	www.razorfish.com
Rediff	www.rediff.com
Research in Motion (RIM)	www.rim.com
Reuters	www.reuters.com
Roku	www.roku.com
Room33	www.room33.com
RTT Systems	www.rttsys.com
Sanyo	www.sanyo.com
Saraide	www.saraide.com
Schlumberger	www.schlumberger.com
Schwab	www.schwab.com
Senada.com	www.senada.com
SFR	www.sfr.com

COMPANY NAME	URL	
Sharp	www.sharp.com	
Shinsegi Telecom	www.shinsegi.co.kr	
Siebel Systems	www.siebel.com	
Siemens	www.siemens.com	
SigmaOne	www.sigma-1.com	
Signalsoft	www.signasoft.com	
SiRF	www.sirf.com	
Smar Tone	www.smartone.com.hk	
SmartServ Online	www.smartserv.com	
SmartTrek	www.smarttrek.org	
Smart Communications	www.smart.com.ph	
SnapTrack	www.snaptrack.com	
Sonera	www.sonera.com	
Speedwise	www.speedwise.com	
Sportal	www.sportal.com	
Spring Toys	www.springtoys.com	
Sprint	www.sprint.com	
Starbucks	www.starbucks.com	
Starfish	www.starfish.com	
Strategic News Service	www.stratnews.com	
Strategis Group	www.strategis.com	
Strategy Analytics	www.strategyanalytics.com	
Sun Microsystems	www.sun.com	
Suretrade	www.suretrade.com	
Surfnotes	www.surfnotes.com	
Sybase	www.sybase.com	
Symbian	www.symbian.com	
Symbol	www.symbol.com	
Synchrologic	www.synchrologic.com	
Synctalk	www.synctalk.com	
Taiwan Cellular	www.twngsm.com.tw	
Tegic Communications	www.tegic.com	
Telecel	www.telecel.pt	
Telecom Italia	www.telecomitalia.it	*Continues*

COMPANY NAME	URL
Telefonica	www.telefonica.es
Telnor	www.telenor.nor
Telia	www.telia.com
Telia Mobile	www.teliamobile.se
Tellme	www.tellme.com
TelSuf Networks	www.888telsurf.com
Telstra	www.telstra.com
Texas Instruments	www.ti.com
Text 100	www.text100.com
The Standard	www.thestandard.com
TicketMaster	www.ticketmaster.com
Traffictouch.com	www.traffictouch.com
Travelocity	www.travelocity.com
Trimble Corporation	www.trimble.com
Trueposition	www.trueposition.com
UcallNet	www.ucallnet.com
Unimobile	www.unimobile.com
United Airlines	www.united.com or www.ual.com
Universal Interface Technologies	www.universalit.com
Usability Group	www.usability.com
US Wireless	www.uswcorp.com
VeriSign	www.verisign.com
Verizon	www.verizon.com
Viag InterKom	www.viaginterkom.de
Vicinity Brandfinder	www.vicinity.com
Vindigo	www.vindigo.com
Visa	www.visa.com
Vodafone	www.vodafone.com
Weather.com	www.weather.com
WeatherNet	www.weathernet.com
Webley	www.webley.com
Webraska	www.webraska.com
WebTV	www.webtv.com

COMPANY NAME	URL
Wells Fargo	www.wellsfargo.com
WhoWhere.com	www.whowhere.com
Wireless MD	www.wirelessmd.com
Wirelessgames	www.wirelessgames.com
Wireless Knowledge	www.wirelessknowledge.com
W-trade	www.w-trade.com
Wysdom Inc.	www.wysdom.com
Xypoint.com	www.xypoint.com
Yahoo!	www.yahoo.com
Yankee Group	www.yankee.com
Yodlee	www.yodlee.com

APPENDIX B

Acronyms

3G	Third generation
AFIS	Automated fingerprint identification system
AI	Artificial intelligence
AIDC	Automatic Identification and Data Capture
AIM	Aether Intelligent Messaging
AMPS	Advanced Mobile Phone System
AOA	Angle of arrival
AOL	America Online
ARPU	Average revenue per user
ASP	Application service provider
ATG	Art Group Technology
ATM	Automated teller machine
ATVEF	Advanced Television Enhancement Format
AuC	Authentication center
B2B	Business-to-business
B2C	Business-to-consumer

B2E	Business-to-employee
BAPI	Biometric API
BER	Bit error rate
BI	Business intelligence
BSC	Base station controller
CCPP	Composite capability and preference profiles
CDMA	Code Division Multiple Access
CDPD	Cellular Data Packet Data
ChemML	Chemical Markup Language
CHTML	Compact HTML
Codec	Compression/decompression
COM	Component Object Model
CORBA	Common Object Request Broker Architecture
CRM	Customer relationship management
DES	Data Encryption Standard
DTD	Document type definition
DTMF	Dual-tone multifrequency
E911	Enhanced 911
ECMA	European Computer Manufacturers Association
EDACS	Enhanced Digital Access Communication Systems
EDGE	Enhanced Data Rates for Global Evolution
EIR	Equipment Identity Register
EJB	Enterprise JavaBeans
EOTD	Enhanced Observed Time Difference of Arrival
ESN	Electronic serial number
ETSI	European Telecommunications Standards Institute
FAR	False acceptance rate
FCC	Federal Communications Commission

FoIP	Fax over IP
FRR	False rejection rate
FLT	Forward Link Triangulation
GEO	Geostationary Earth orbit
GIF	Graphics Interchange Format
GPRS	General Packet Radio Service
GPS	Global positioning system
GSM	Global System for Mobile Communications
HDML	Handheld Device Markup Language
HDTV	High-definition TV
HLR	Home location register
HomeRF	Home radio frequency
HSCSD	High-Speed Circuit-Switched Data
HTML	HyperText Markup Language
HTTP	HyperText Transfer Protocol
HTTP-NG	HTTP Next Generation
HTTPS	HTTP Secure
iDEN	Integrated Digital Enhanced Network
IEEE	Institute of Electrical and Electronics Engineers
IETF	Internet Engineering Task Force
IMT2000	International Mobile Telecommunications 2000
IP	Internet Protocol
IPsec	Internet Protocol Security
IPv6	IP Version 6
ITU	International Telecommunications Union
ISO	International Standards Organization
ITRS	International Technology Roadmap for Semiconductors
ITV	Interactive TV

ITV	Interactive TV
IVR	Interactive voice response
JPEG	Joint Photographic Experts Group
JVM	Java Virtual Machine
LAN	Local area network
LDAP	Lightweight Directory Access Protocol
LEO	Low Earth Orbit
MathML	Mathematical Markup Language
MBS	Mobile Broadband Systems
MEO	Medium Earth orbit
MIN	Mobile identity number
MIPS	Millions of instructions per second
MIX	Mobile Internet Exchange
ML	Markup language
MPEG	Motion Picture Experts Group
MSC	Mobile switching center
MSN	Microsoft Network
MT	Machine translation
NLP	Natural language processing
NMT	Nordic Mobile Telephone
OMC	Operations and maintenance center
OMG	Object Management Group
OS	Operating system
OSI	Open Systems Interconnection
OTA	Observed time of arrival
OTD	Observed time difference of arrival

PAN	Personal area network
PCS	Personal Communication Service
PDA	Personal digital assistant
PDC	Personal Digital Cellular
PGML	Precision Graphics Markup Language
PGP	Pretty Good Privacy
PHS	Personal Handy Phone System
PIM	Personal information management
PIN	Personal identification number
PNG	Portable Network Graphics
POS	Point-of-sale
PPP	Point-to-Point Protocol
PQA	Palm Query Applications
PSTN	Public Switched Telephone Network
QA	Quality assurance
QoS	Quality of service
RF	Radio frequency
RFID	Radio Frequency ID
ROI	Return on investment
RTOS	Real-time operating system
SDK	Software Development Kit
SLA	Service level agreement
SLP	Service Location Protocol
SMIL	Synchronized Multimedia Markup Language
SMS	Short Message Service
SNR	Signal-to-noise ratio
SQL	Structured Query Language

SSL	Secure Socket Layer
SWAP	Shared Wireless Application Protocol
SyncML	Synchronization Markup Language
TACS	Total Access Communications System
TCP/IP	Transmission Control Protocol/Internet Protocol
TDMA	Time Division Multiple Access
TDOA	Time difference of arrival
TETRA	Terrestrial Trunked Radio
TIA	Telecommunications Industry Association
TLS	Transport Security Layer
TTS	Text to speech
UDP	User Datagram Protocol
UI	User interface
UIML	User Interface Markup Language
UMTS	Universal Mobile Telecommunications System
URL	Uniform resource locator
VLR	Visitor Location Register
VML	Vector Markup Language
VoIP	Voice over IP
VXML	Voice-Extensible Markup Language
W3C	World Wide Web Consortium
WAE	Wireless Application Environment
WAG	Wireless Assisted GPS
WAN	Wide area network
WAP	Wireless Application Protocol
WASP	Wireless Application Service Provider
WATM	Wireless Asynchronous Transfer Mode
WBMF	Wireless Bitmap Format

WCDMA	Wideband CDMA
WDP	Wireless Datagram Protocol
WIEA	Wireless Internet enterprise applications
WLAN	Wireless Local Area Network
WML	Wireless Markup Language
WSP	Wireless Session Protocol
WTA	Wireless Telephony Applications
WTLS	Wireless Transport Security Layer
WTP	Wireless Transactional Protocol
XHTML	Extensible HyperText Markup Language
XML	Extensible Markup Language
XSL	Extensible Style Language

References and Recommended Readings

Books

Balston, D. M. and Macario, R.C.V. 1993. *Cellular Radio Systems*. Norwood, MA: Artech House Publishers. Mobile Communications Series.

Bergman, E. 2000. *Information Appliances and Beyond. Interaction Design for Consumer Products*. San Diego, CA: Academic Press.

Bigun, J., Chollet, G., and Borgefors, G. 1997. *Audio- and Video-based Biometric Person Authentication. First International Conference, AVBPA '97 Crans-Montana, Switzerland, March 1997 Proceedings*. Berlin, Germany: Springer.

Cochrane, P. 1998. *108 Tips for Time Travelers*. London: Orion.

DeRose, J. 1995. *The Wireless Data Handbook, Fourth Edition*. New York, NY: John Wiley & Sons.

Dhawan, C. 1997. *Mobile Computing: A Systems Integrator's Handbook*. New York, NY: McGraw-Hill. Series on Computer Communications.

Doraswamy, N. and Harkins, D. 1999. *IPSec: The New Security Standard for the Internet, Intranets, and Virtual Private Networks*. Upper Saddle River, NJ: Prentice-Hall. Internet Infrastructure Series.

Duato, J., Yalmanchili, S., and Ni, L. 1997. *Interconnection Networks: An Engineering Approach*. Los Alamitas, CA: IEEE Computer Society Press.

Edwards, W. K. 1999. *Core JINI*. Upper Saddle River, NJ: Prentice Hall.

Faruque, S. 1996. *Cellular Mobile Systems Engineering*. Norwood, MA: Artech House Publishers. Mobile Communications Series.

Feinleib, D. 1999. *The Inside Story of Interactive TV and Microsoft WebTV for Windows*. San Francisco, CA: Morgan Kaufmann.

Fouke, J. 1999. *Engineering Tomorrow: Today's Technology Experts Envision the Next Century*. Piscataway, NJ: IEEE Press.

Gallagher, M. and Snyder, R. 1997. *Mobile Telecommunications Networking with IS-41*. New York, NY: McGraw-Hill. Series on Telecommunications.

Garg, V. K., Smolik, K., and Wilkes, J.1997. *Applications of CDMA in Wireless/Personal Communications*. Upper Saddle River, NJ: Prentice Hall. Wireless & Digital Communications Series.

Gershenfeld, N. 1999. *When Things Start to Think*. New York, NY: Henry Holt and Company, LLC.

Giguere, E. 1999. *Palm Database Programming - The Complete Developer's Guide*. New York, NY: John Wiley & Sons.

Glisic, S. G. and Leppanen, P. A. 1997. *Wireless Communications TDMA versus CDMA*. Amsterdam, Netherlands: Kluwer Academic Publishing.

Helal, A., Haskell, B. Carter, J., Brice, R., Woelk D., and Rusinkiewicz, M. 1999. *Anytime, Anywhere Computing Mobile Computing Concepts and Technology*. Norwell, MA: Kluwer Academic Publishing.

Heldman, R. 1995. *Telecommunications Information Millennium*. New York, NY: McGraw-Hill.

Hendtry, M. 1997. *Smart Card Security and Applications*. Norwood, MA: Artech House Publishers.

Hjelm, J. 2000. *Designing Wireless Information Services*. New York, NY: John Wiley & Sons.

IBM Systems Journal. 1999. *Human Interaction with Pervasive Computing. Volume 38, Number 4, 501-698*. USA.

Klusch, M. 1999. *Intelligent Information Agents Agent-based Information Discovery and Management on the Internet*. Berlin, Germany: Springer-Verlag

Kurzweil, R. 1999. *When Computers Exceed Human Intelligence—The Age of Spiritual Machines*. New York, NY: Penguin Books.

Macario, R.C.V. 1993. *Cellular Radio Principles and Design*. New York, NY: McGraw-Hill Communications.

Mann, S. 2000. *Programming Applications with the Wireless Application Protocol—The Complete Developer's Guide*. New York, NY: John Wiley & Sons.

McGrath, S. 1998. *XML by Example: Building E-Commerce Applications*. Upper Saddle River, NJ: Prentice Hall.

Milojicic, D., Douglis, F., and Wheeler R. 1999. *Mobility Processes, Computers, and Agents*. USA: ACM Press.

Nielsen, J. 2000. *Designing Web Usability*. Boston, MA: New Riders Publishing.

PriceWaterHouseCoopers Technology Forecast. 2000. *From Atoms to Systems: A Perspective on Technology*. 2000. USA.

Rankl, W. and Effing, W. 1997. *Smartcard Handbook*. Chichester, England: John Wiley & Sons.

Rappaport, T. 1996. *Cellular Radio & Personal Communications Advanced Selected Readings Vol 2*. Piscataway, NJ: The Institute of Electrical and Electronics Engineers, Inc. (IEEE).

Redl, S., Weber, M. K., and Oliphant, M. W. 1998. *GSM and Personal Communications Handbook*. Norwood, MA: Artech House Publishers. Mobile Communications Series.

Rischpater, R. 2000. *Wireless Web Development*. Berkeley, CA: Apress.

Tanenbaum, A. S. 1996. *Computer Networks, Third Edition*. Upper Saddle River, NJ: Prentice Hall.

The Operator Guide to WAP. 2000. UK. Mobile Communications International.

Wireless Application Protocol Forum, Ltd. 1999. *Official Wireless Application Protocol*. New York, NY: John Wiley & Sons.

Wong, P. and Britland, D. 1995. *Mobile Data Communications and Systems*. Norwood, MA: Artech House Publishers. Mobile Communications Series.

Wyzalek, J. 2000. *Enterprise Systems Integration*. Boca Raton, FL: CRC Press. The Auerbach Best Practices Series.

Yacoub, M.D. 1993. *Foundations of Mobile Radio Engineering*. Boca Raton, FL: CRC Press, Inc.

Magazine Articles and Whitepapers

Adrian, M., Zetie, C., and Rasmus, D. June 1999. *Connections Are Everything. Intelligent Enterprise*.

Anderson, M. 1999–2000. *Strategic News Service*.

Binding, C., Hild, S., and O'Connor, L. 1999. *Research Report. E-Cash Withdrawal Using Mobile Telephony*. IBM Research Division.

Biometric Industry Products Buyer's Guide. International Computer Security Association (ICSA).

BiStatix Whitepaper Version 4.1. www.motorola.com/LMPS/Indala/bistatix.htm.

Blackwell, E. and Fitchard, K. 2000. *M-Commerce: The New Face of Fraud*. TelecomClick.

Bourrie, S. R. June 5, 2000. *Fraud Is Down, But Not Out*. Wireless Week. 44–46.

Cabri, G., Leonardi, L., and Zambonelli, F. February 2000. *Mobile Agent Coordination Models for Internet Applications*. IEEE Spectrum. 82–89.

Collins, J. June 5, 2000. *Barbed Wireless*. Tele.com.

Developer's Guide. *Nokia Mobile Entertainment Service*. Nokia.

Developer's Guide. *Web Clipping*. Palm Computing.

FAQ about MPEG-7. www.darmstadt.gmd.de/mobile/MPEG7/FAQ.html.

Fitchard, K. 2000. *Subscription Fraud: The Battle Continues*. TelecomClick.

Harrow, J. F. 2000. April 10, 2000. *The Rapidly Changing Face of Computing (RCFoC)—Reaching Out and Touching*. www.compaq.com/rcfoc/20000410.html.

Hendricks, C. 2000. *Website Architectures for a Wireless World: Designing Internet Accessibility for Multiple Non-PC Devices*.

Joy, B. April 2000. *Why the Future Doesn't Need Us*. Wired Magazine. 238–262.

Jurvis, J. April 2000. *Choosing a Handheld Is a Matter of Trade-Offs*. Enterprise Development.

Jurvis, J. and Grehan, R. August 1999. *Reach Out with Handheld Apps*. Enterprise Development. 16–31.

Kaku, M. June 19, 2000. *What Will Replace Silicon?* Time Magazine Visions 21 Special Issue—The Future of Technology. 98–99.

Koshima, H. and Hoshen, J. February 2000. *Personal Locator Services Emerge*. IEEE Spectrum. 41–48.

Krub C. 2000. *Wireless and Usability*. Luminant Worldwide Corporation. www.luminant.com

Lindhe, L. May 29, 2000. *Waiting for Wireless*. The Industry Standard. 228–233.

Mann, C. C. May/June 2000. *The End of Moore's Law?* MIT's Magazine of Innovation, Technology Review. 42–48.

Mattis, M. and Daly, J. December 1999. *Web Visions: Shaping Tomorrow*. Wired Magazine. 162–177.

Miller, B. A. February 2000. *Bluetooth Applications in Pervasive Computing—An IBM Pervasive Computing White Paper*. IBM.

Mobile e-business. *Extending SAP Systems to Pervasive Computing devices*. IBM. www-3.ibm.com/pvc/mobile/sap.shtml.

Mobile Internet: Content, Commerce and Applications. April 10 2000. Mobile Communications.

MPEG-7 Applications Document. July 1999. International Organisation for Standardisation. www.darmstadt.gmd.de/mobile/MPEG7/Documents/W2860.htm.

Newmarch, J. 2000. *Jan Newmarch's Guide to JINI* http://pandonia.canberra.edu.au/java/jini/tutorial/Jini.xml

Pankanti, S., Bolle, R., and Jain, R. February 2000. *Biometrics: The Future of Identification*. Computer, Volume 33, No 2.

Pappo, N. May 2000. *Middleware Bridges Internet, Wireless*. Telecommunications Magazine.

Passani, L. March 2000. *Building WAP Services—XML and ASP Will Set You Free*. WebTechniques.

Pehrson, S. 2000. *WAP—The Catalyst of the Mobile Internet*. Ericsson Review No. 1 2000.

Phillips, M. *Technology Backgrounder Whitepaper*. SpeechWorks.

Sharma, C. 2000. *Wireless Internet Applications*. Luminant Worldwide Corporation. www.luminant.com/

Sherman, L. December 1999. *The Knowledge Worker Unplugged. New Systems for Wireless Information Extend the Knowledge Chain to Mobile Devices*. Knowledge Management. 46–53.

Smith, J. February 2000. *The WAP Vision*. Webreview.com.

Smith, J. R., Mohan, R., and Li, C.S. May 1998. *Transcoding Internet Content for Heterogeneous Client Devices*. IBM T.J. Watson Research Center. Proceedings IEEE International Conference on Circuits and Systems.

Special Report on Biometrics. Feb 2000. IEEE Computer Magazine.

Special Report on the Future of Translation. May 2000. Wired Magazine.

Special Report. Mobile Wireless in Europe—The New Wireless Internet Services in Europe, and What They Mean for the United States. April 2000. Red Herring. 167–258.

Sundstrom N. May 2000. *Soren WAPs the Water Works*. www.ericsson.com/infocenter/publications/contact/Infoville_Vara_.html

UIML 2.0a Language Reference. January 2000. Universal Interface Technologies, Inc.

Voice eXtensible Markup Language (VoiceXML) Version 1.00. March 2000. VoiceXML Forum.

Welcome to 2010—Special Report. March 6, 2000. Business Week. www.businessweek.com/reprints/00-10/design9.htm

What Distribution Scalability Means for Internet Business. A KPMG and Inktomi White Paper.

White Paper. 2000. *Building an Industry-Wide Mobile Data Synchronization Protocol*. SyncML Forum. www.syncML.org.

White Paper. 2000. *Enabling the Wireless Internet*. Phone.com.

White Paper. 2000. *Pervasive Management: Expanding the Reach of IT Management to Pervasive Devices*. Tivoli.

White Paper. 2000. *The Future of Enterprise Mobile Computing*. Synchrologic, Inc.

White Paper. SpeechSite: *Bringing the Web Model of Self-Service to the Telephone*. SpeechWorks.

White Paper. *The UIML Vision*. February 2000. Universal Interface Technologies, Inc. www.universalit.com.

Wired Magazine. Jan 2000. *The Future Gets Fun Again*. Special Anniversary Issue.

Wireless in Cyberspace—Special Report. May 29, 2000. Business Week—International Edition. www.businessweek.com/datedtoc/2000/0022.htm

Wireless Net: Not Yet. May 22, 2000. The Standard. www.thestandard.com/research/metrics/display/0,2799,15258,00.html

Reports

Business-to-Business E-Commerce. Investment Perspective. 2000. Durlacher Research Ltd.

Dalton, J. P. April 2000. *The Web's Speech Impediments.* The Forrester Report.

Godell, L. March 2000. *Mobile's High-Speed Hurdles.* The Forrester Report.

Going Mobile—A Cookbook of Wireless Data Solutions. 1999. Wireless Data Forum.

Kasrel, B. June 2000. *Many Devices, One Consumer.* The Forrester Report.

Mobile Commerce Report. 2000. Durlacher Research Ltd.

Perspectives on Business Innovation. Issue 3. Electronic Commerce. The Ernst & Young Center for Business Innovation.

Rhinelander, T. July 1999. *The Information-Rich Consumer.* The Forrester Report.

Technology and Telecommunications Quarterly. February 2000. Salomon Smith Barney.

The Wireless Marketplace in 2000. February 2000. Peter D. Hart Research Associates.

Wireless Data—Issues & Outlook 2000. 2000. Goldman Sachs Global Investment Research.

Zohar, M. October 1999. *The Dawn of Mobile E-Commerce.* The Forrester Report.

Conferences

RTT Programmes, Ltd. The US Programme Technology Track. February 1998. Atlanta.

Wireless Application Protocol (WAP) Developer's Symposium, June 1999, San Francisco, USA.

GartnerGroup Conference Presentations. Fall 1999. GartnerGroup.

Wireless Application Protocol (WAP) Developer's Symposium and WAP Congress, November 1999, Barcelona, Spain.

RTT Programmes, Ltd. The US Programme Technology Track. March 2000. New Orleans.

Wireless Application Protocol (WAP) Developer's Symposium, June 2000, Los Angeles.

Index